THE GIRL IN THE WARDROBE

Jennifer Farrell

ORIGINAL WRITING

978-1-907179-32-7

A CIP catalogue for this book is available from the National Library.

Published by Original Writing Ltd., Dublin, 2010.

Printed by Cahill Printers Limited, Dublin

For Maura and Jennifer

Acknowledgements

Many thanks to the late Nuala O'Faolain for her support and encouragement. To the hard working committee of Listowel Writers' Week. To all the staff at Original Writing Publishers who are the sponsors of the Inaugural Memoir competition. I thank them for being so patient with me. To Anthony King for his help with proofreading. To the National Library of Ireland who gave permission to reproduce the cover photograph. To the staff in the reading room at the National Photographic Archive in Temple Bar who were always helpful. To my family for their constant support. My sons Vincent and Ian were very helpful with computer and technical problems. To Maura, who always used to say she could write a book. "I could write a book." That was one of her sayings. Maybe somewhere in her head there was a book, because like her mother before her, Granny Connor, she's a terrific storyteller. I hope this book tells something of her story as well as mine.

Some of the names in *The Girl in the Wardrobe* have been changed.

FOREWORD

It all started in a café in Dungarvan. I started to write what I thought was a short story. Something sparked the memory of the boiled sausages and the dreaded coddle, a dish I'd always hated. I was gathering stories; the year before I'd won the Hennessy Writer of the Year award, with my short story Beached that was published in the Sunday Tribune. I wanted to make a collection and maybe have them published. In the café, over a huge pot of tea, the story of the sausages unravelled and the memories of that day came flooding in. I was right back there, in the dark scullery of our old corporation flat, with Ma beside me gripping the sweeping brush handle, and the girl in the café tipped me on the shoulder and said they were closing. The story continued, one scene following another, down long tunnels of memory, leading me back to where it all began. The smells and the sounds, the faces and the voices. The living and the dead. All the time I could see Ma's pale face, and it struck me how full of expression that face was and how she might've been a good actress in another life. I wasn't sure. Something was telling me it was too long for a short story, but I kept writing and the dead came back to life. The Granda's and Grannies, the Aunties and Uncles. The babbies. Da. It was like they all wanted to tell their story. Then the Listowel Writers' Week brochure arrived through my letterbox and I knew what it was I was writing. A new competition, the Inaugural Memoir award was listed to be judged by Nuala O'Faolain.

I sent in an extract and forget about it. The white envelope when it arrived looked suspicious. I'd had a test done at the hospital and I suspected bad news. On the label it said: Winner: Original Writing Memoir Competition, but it didn't make sense somehow. I tore it open. It said: I am delighted to inform you that your entry entitled "The Girl in the Wardrobe" has won first prize. As I read the first line, my knees buckled and I slumped into the armchair. It was like winning the lottery.

Meeting Nuala at Listowel was the highlight. It was the first and last time I saw her in the flesh. I will always remember her, lit from behind by a pool of sunlight in the foyer of the Listowel Arms Hotel. She looked radiant in a white cotton dress. Clutching a large handbag full of notes in one hand and a mobile phone in the other.

She'd just finished a workshop on the memoir and was rushing across the road to a reading. She greeted me with a warm smile. Touched my arm gently, like she knew me all her life. She loved the story, it gave her hours of pleasure, she said.

"Can you work this?" she said when the mobile phone rang? It was a new phone and she hadn't got used to it yet. We fumbled with the buttons and the phone stopped ringing and we kept talking and then she had to run to the reading.

I never did get to send her the letter I wrote her after she announced she had a terminal illness. I finished it the night she died, sat up late into the night, intending to post it the next morning. I listened to her last broadcast with Marian Finucane on a pod cast in front of my computer screen and promised myself I would finish the book. It took longer than expected. Ma got diagnosed with Alzheimer's and things started to fall apart in the family. There were times I was finding it hard to write about her when she was young. Some of the memories were so painful. Back then the women were burdened down with large families and terrible living conditions. In many cases, the men were heavy drinkers. One of my first memories is that tenement I call The Drunken House. It wasn't fit for human habitation and that's why it was classified a condemned building and demolished. Back then if you lived in a condemned building your chances of being re housed in a corporation flat were improved. It was a rat-infested hellhole and we had to use a bucket or else go to the pub on the corner to use the toilet. Sometimes I was staying with my granny, but I came and went between the three flats north and south of the Liffey.

Ma looks back at those times with mixed feelings. She doesn't deny tenement life was hard. Sometimes she refers to her own childhood in the tenements before her mother got the corporation flat in Cooke Street and it seems similar to what I experienced in the Drunken House. Her long-term memory is still very good and she's defying the medics in the nursing home where she's now a resident. She has good memories and bad. Her best years were probably in her fifties and sixties, when she was at last freed of the burden of child bearing. She broke out and did her own thing, going to bingo and the local pubs for a glass of Guinness with her friends. I know if there's a Heaven, that's what it would be for her. A nice pint of Guinness in a nice little snug, maybe a fire going and a bit of a singsong. She's never had a holiday and I don't think she missed it. Maybe it's true that what you never had you don't miss, but she likes to hear of the places we've travelled to. She's proud of our travels and tells people we travel all over the world even if we only go to the Canaries on holiday.

From the safe distance of half a century the memory can be selective. I've written this story the way it came, from the pictures and flash backs of memory about the time and place where I grew up. It was a different century, the swinging sixties they called it, but there wasn't much that was swinging about it. Yet there was laughter and song and music, the ghost stories and the jokes. A complication of hard times and funny times and interesting times all mashed up.

I found out my real name was Jennifer in 1991, when I had to get a birth certificate when starting college at the NUI as a mature student. It was strange because I called my daughter who was born in 1981 Jennifer.

PART 1

I

A DRUNKEN HOUSE

The Flats where Patti lives are like two capital Ls, lying down on their sides, facing each other backwards with a road in-between. There's a drunken smell of whiskey and a rotten smell of fish and a nice fruity smell from the market. When the tide goes out, there's another horrible smell like rotten eggs from the Liffey. During the summer, she has to hold her nose if all the smells mix together. It catches her in her throat when she breathes in through her mouth. Sometimes she feels a bit dizzy. She likes that; the woozy feeling in her head, like if you do a spin on your tippy-toes with your arms out, or drink a sup of Buckfast Abbey tonic-wine when no one is looking.

There's the Four Courts and the Bridewell and churches and markets. The markets sell fish, fruit and vegetables, delf, second hand clothes. The match factory has another smell. It goes up her nose and gets stuck there. It's sulphur, her Da says.

The girls in her flats work in Patterson's match factory and Carton's chicken factory and William's & Wood's jam and beet-root factory. There's Mike Nolan's sweet shop and a wallpaper shop and Boland's bakery and Stein's pork shop in Capel Street. In the wallpaper shop the nice woman with the greyish red hair, lets her look at the wallpaper books, all the lovely colours and shapes, all the new velvety ones they call Flock. There's Japanese red wallpaper with gold lanterns and girls in long kimonos with buns in their hair and pins sticking out. She'd love a bit of that, she says to the wallpaper woman, to cover her English reader. So she cuts a bit off a roll-end and a few other bits too from job lots that no one will buy. She smiles and says: "Your welcome pet." Patti says: "Thanks very much." No one ever called her that before. She makes a picture out of all the pieces of odd wall-paper, sticks them together, with gum to a board. Now it's a red Japanese garden, with Irish yellow daisies and black winter trees. There's a mauve flowery sky and grey wavy mountains.

Next-door is the bakery. The bakery smells gorgeous; it makes all the yukky smells disappear. All the lovely cakes in the window, doughnuts and scones, iced fairies and custard slices. There's trays of cream buns on the counter, when she goes in to buy the brown soda for her granny. She sneaks a dollop of cream with her finger when the woman with the green smock is out the back at the ovens.

Mike Nolan is humpy; he has a girly voice and a baldy head; he wears a raggy tweed coat. Her Da says he has a camels back because he has two humps. He looks out over the counter at her and she can see up his nose. There's little spiky hairs up there and she hates them. He leans over and looks down at her. He wants her to put her money up on the counter first in case she runs off with the sweets without paying.

"Put your money up," he goes in his girly voice, "so I can see it."

She stretches up her arm.

All the sweet-jars are on the counter; Pink- Mice, Carmels, Bulls-Eyes, Silk-Cushions and Bon-Bons. He hands her down the white bag of Carmels. She knows they're bad for her teeth, but she likes the toffee taste, the way you chew and chew until the toffee is small enough to swallow.

If she hasn't got the babby, or the other kids, she skips along. She does a hop, then a skip. Hop skip, hop skip. She bangs a stick in between the railings. It makes a metal sound: Alung alung aling. She does twirls. One twirl. Two twirls. Loads of twirls until she gets dizzy. Skips and twirls.Twirls and skips. Hops, skips, twirls. The sky twirly wirly. Blue shapes and white shapes. Mashed-up clouds like mashed potatoes. They call her different names. Sometimes they call her Pat, or Patti or Paddi. Da calls her Pashy and Ma calls her Pahi. In school it's Padrigín and she thinks that's a right little culchie name. Posh people call her Patricia and that's even worse. If they call her Patsy it sounds like a Patsy ice-pop. She knows she has another name, a special girl's name that's written on her birth certificate. Her Ma gave it to her when she was born, but then they took it back. She wrote it out on the form. She gave it to the matron in the Rotunda.

That's how come you get registered. Ma can only remember, it starts with a J, it's either Jeannette or Janet, or something like that, she's not sure. Ma thinks it suits her better, it goes better with her face. The Connors call her Jennette sometimes and granny Connor told her never to forget her own name, the one on her birth certificate. Especially when she grows up. And never to forget where she came from either.

They all wanted a boy but she's dead glad she's not a boy. Imagine! Everything you wear is grey or brown. Imagine, wearing them horrible short trousers that boys wear and the itchy grey socks with the bony knees, imagine the crew cuts and the pointy ears and the hair-oil. Imagine your confo and all you can wear is a grey suit or a brown suit or a black suit. Imagine! It must be terrible to be a boy.

She can remember when they moved from the big old-fashioned drunken house, because it was getting knocked down. The bulldozers were coming to flatten the place. It was a *Condemned* building, her Da said; that's how they got this place in the flats. It had a big black door with a broken knocker, a dirty hall where spunkers slept in a big heap on top of one another and you had to step over them and her Ma had to drag the pram across the hill of smelly spunkers. You could feel their prickly bones and their spongy bodies and they'd go Ahhh and Uhhh! in drunken babble. Sometimes, an arm would try to catch her leg and sometimes she'd give the arm a good kick with her rock-in-roll boot. Ma kicked them too, if they tried to catch her leg, especially if she had on high heels. She'd bate them good lookin' she said. She'd swing for them.

"Geraway yiz dirty filthy things," she'd shout and then she'd drag the pram up the stairs, saying she was cursed the day she set foot in this rat-ridden hellhole. Patti hated that drunken house, not just because of the spunkers. Not just because of the dirty walls and rotten floorboards and the smelly toilets. There were rats, big huge brown rats. Every night her Da had to turn into a rat-catcher. In their room, he lifted the boards to put down the poison and traps. First, he rolled up his sleeves, then he knelt down and lit the candle. If he found a dead rat down there, he'd pick it up by the tail, swing it round and throw it in the bucket-bin. Ma always stood, against the door with the sweeping brush up and her hand over her face. Patti looked down into the dark underneath and she could hear scratchy noises and voices.

"Da, whadown there?"

"Nick, the devil. That's where hell is. That's where you go if you're bold and cheeky," he goes, straight into her face. She was only a toddler at the time. She didn't know what hell was, but she does now.

Out in the yard it was all weedy, huge stalks like green monsters up against the wall. There were rusty cans and pram-frames and bikes. The toilet was the worst part; all shitty and greeny and slimy, a smell that made Patti want to get sick. You'd catch Polio if you sat on that toilet pot, Ma said, and it wasn't fit for human habitation. There were yard-rats out there; she could see them from the hall-window, their big long tails, and their pointy faces. They'd sneak along by the wall with their fat wobbly bodies. They lived on the top floor; a room with noisy floorboards, two long windows, with smaller squares, a sink at the side, a bed at one end, a fireplace at the other. The people in the house had hoolies. They'd be up all night singing and dancing. Underneath them, the fat woman who sells flowers had a piano and underneath her, there was this man who played a fiddle. And the house kind of shakes and wobbles.

They sang songs.

They danced.

It got bright through the long windows.

In their room, there were big cracks in the walls and the ceilings. Down on her hunkers, she saw the holes under the sink. Da was filling them in with pink gooey stuff on a wallpaper scraper. He made the holes go away. He said no rats could get in through there anyway. It was winter. She could hear the rain on the roof, see it dribble down the windows, all skinny bandy lines. She loved to be at the window. She kneeled on the bed and looked out through one of the small squares. She saw loads of roofs and chimney pots. The chimney-smoke joined up with the clouds. The clouds moved across the houses and made animal-shapes in the sky. She saw giant dogs and fishes and elephants. One day, she saw a bull on the loose. It was galloping down Parnell Street. Out in the middle of the road. All these men after it with their sleeves rolled up, waving sticks in the air, a big gang of them with red faces. The bull turned and ran into her street. She saw it under the window. It was trying to get away from the men. It bashed itself up against the wall. It turned and kicked its legs. She was afraid it would come up the stairs. She called her Ma. Ma was washing clothes in the zinc bath, a cloud of steam around her. She blessed herself when she saw the bull. She started to root in the drawer for the Our Lady holy water bottle.

Here's Ma praying: "God protect us and spare us and Sacred Heart have mercy." She's splashing holy water all over the place and Patti gets soaked. She bolted the door and put the brush up against it.

People had to keep their doors shut. Everyone was at their windows. The bull ran through the hall into the backyard. It was trapped in a corner, near the smelly toilets. It had pointy horns. It was brown with roundy square shoulders. All the men had walking sticks and some had ropes. They were shouting stuff at the bull in culchie voices. They told it to stay where it was, that it needn't think it was going nowhere. The bull had its head down and its horns out. It made bull noises at them. They cursed; they made a big circle and surrounded the bull. The bull tried to make a run for it, but they lassoed it like cowboys, until its head was caught. At last, they had it trapped, so it couldn't escape. The women were shouting from the windows to get it t'hell out of their house. Her Ma was at the open window, the holy water bottle in her hand.

"Is it gone yet? " she kept saying.

Then the whole street was out. Cheers and whistles and claps. They led the bull outside, the men with the walking sticks, the poor bull caught up in the gillions of ropes. Afterwards, a trailer truck from the Cattle Market comes and the bull is taken away. Ma told Da they had a narrow escape and Da said he heard it in work. It was in the Herald the next day. The headline said:

5

BULL ESCAPES IN CITY CENTRE

There's a picture of their street and all. A picture of their house with the bull with the men behind it. Her Da said it's a big story all over town and everyone is talking. It's like their street was famous for one day. It's like the bull came and made them all famous as well. Ma said it was just as well she had that holy water and only for Our Blessed Lady we might all be stone dead. Everyone was reading the Herald, leaning out windows, talking up and down to one another. Saying they were blessed the bull didn't kill someone in the house, saying God spared them.

She's glad she's not living there now. She hates the smelly yard with the yard-rats and the drunken spunkers and the creaky floorboards. She hates the rusty pipes that make ghosty noises in the night. When they go past, Patti sees their old room, with the green flowery wallpaper and the black fireplace at the end-wall. All the fireplaces on top of one another, all different flowery wallpapers. Hickey, now they look. Dead hickey and old-fashioned. The floors are all gone now, the place underneath their room, where hell was. An iron rusty thing is standing up against the house. Her Ma says it's a girder, the Corporation put up to stop the rest of it falling down. She stands back. She's glad to be out of it, she says, even though the place they're in is not exactly a palace; it's a king to that heap of rubble. Patti sees the stalky weeds poking through the ground, the rusty cans and bikes. She wonders are the rats still there out in the yard. Do the spunkers still sleep there in a tangle of hilly coats? She says nothing, but maybe her Ma reads her mind. She gives a kind of shiver and walks on. They go home the same way as the day they moved.

They came up from Wolfe Tone Street this day; they crossed roads and turned corners, they cut through cobblestone alleyways.

"Not a bad day out," her Ma said.

Most of their stuff they had on the pram when they moved, except for their big furniture like the bed. Patti was carrying a bucket; someone else was carrying a basin. The babby was hidden in behind the brush and mop. Ma looked lovely in her good three quarter length leopard skin coat; the one with the swingy back. There they were walking beside the pram and the noise of all their stuff: Clatter Clatter Clang! A jingle jangle of pots. There's things under the pram and things over the pram and things hanging from the pram-handles. Her Ma kicks the pram-wheel as she goes along.

"That bloody wheel, that, bokety good for nothin' pram-wheel."

She says the axle came loose and Da was supposed to fix it.

"We need a new pram for that babby as well as everything else for the new flat."

The sky was full of squealing seagulls. On the ground, more seagulls pulling at a fish-head in the middle of the road.

"Ma, the smell. It's yukki," Patti said.

"Yiz'll have to get used to it."

They were all holding their noses.

Up a bit, around this corner they saw the bowsies, a bunch of them at the gate in leather jackets.

"Keep walkin'," Ma goes, fixing her scarf knot into a bigger knot.

They kept going.

She makes a big turn with the pram into their new flats.

"Don't go near them. Keep well away. They'd slice you to pieces as quick as they'd look at you."

The bowsies kept gawking with their mean faces, their shoulders all huddled together, smoke coming out of their mouths. They heard them snickering and grinning.

"Don't look at them,"

Ma's whispery voice.

"Are they baddies?" Patti asked.

"You better believe it," Her Ma said under her breath.

The bowsies won't move out of the way. They try to block them with their shoulders. Then her Ma straightens her own shoulders and gives the pram a good hard push.

"Mind outa the way," she says. "Give us an inch for Godsake."

She breaks them up with her pram and walks right through them. They huddle into smaller bunches. They look dead dopey. They give her looks. They blow smoke in her face. The leader nods his head like a doll and grins on one side of his face. They think they're great, but Ma is not afraid of them. She'll take none of their guff, she says, when she gets well past them.

"Only little good-for-nothings, holdin' up walls and gates. Oughta be ashamed, should be out working instead of tormentin' people."

Patti looks back. She sees them combing their hair back real slow in long slimy lines off their foreheads.

She saw the bowsies before. There's gangs of them around town. You see them swaggering along with the leader up front, the others trying to keep up in a straggly line behind. They walk with their shoulders swinging side to side, a bit like the way her Da walks. The leader has a big stupid lump of greasy hair at the front like a beehive and her Ma says he washes his hair in sugar and water.

Da says they're not as tough as they look, but still in all, Ma says, you'd have to be careful. They carry steel combs down their stockings. They wear pointy boots and chain-belts. When they're fighting, they swing the chain-belt in the air like a lasso. They heard stories about the big fights downtown between different gangs. The gang-fights were wicked, Ma said. She remembers one fight in particular between the Animal Gang and another gang and she called that a Blood Bath. There were pools of blood everywhere. The blood flowed into shores and gullies like rain water. Throats were slashed. Fingers were cut off. It's not something she could ever forget in a hurry. The police were afraid of them, because they knew they carried weapons. Ma says the Animal Gang was notorious.

She turned her head back around. They were inside the flats. They were all holding their noses. They saw the long bumpy grey wall with the barbed wire on top, the clotheslines full of washing. They saw the three balconies with all the heads and shoulders hanging over.

"Nosey parkers, " Ma said in a low voice. A butt lands in front of them. Ma stops and looks up at all the heads. Some have hairnets and some have scarves. An old woman with grey hair says: "Nice mornin' Misses," and her Ma nods up at her and smiles. Then they see it, their new place with the boards up to the windows. It's on the ground floor and Ma is delighted. She opens her purse, takes out her new shiny Corporation-key and holds it up. She twiddles the key in the lock. She gives the door a good push with her shoulder. It makes a creaky sound. There's a musty smell from the hall.

She pulls the pram up the steps into the hall. She switches on the hall-light.

"Oh thank God. Good job there's electric," she says.

She lifts the babby out.

"Isn't that some coal hole," she says, opening a door and they all look into this black empty place beside the toilet.

"Daahky," the babby says in Ma's arms.

"Begod, that's no ordinary coal-hole, you'd want a coal mine to fill that place up." She lights a match and you can see the black coal dust on the floor. Ma's white face in the match-light.

"No fear of them leavin' any coal behind," she says stepping back out.

"Ma, it's dead spooky in here. I think it's a haunted house," Patti says.

"No it's not."

She closes the door.

"The boogy man, the boogy man," one of the kids says.

"The boogyman will take anyone that's bold."

"Oogyman Oogyman," the babby says.

Ma closes the door. She says she'll have to get that doorknob fixed. It'd be terrible to get locked in that coal-hole.

"Ma it's cold. I'm foreezin'," Patti says.

"Shut your mouth for Godsake, it's not that cold."

But it was; it was cold and musty and spooky.

Into the toilet quick because Patti was bursting. She pushes the door back. It creaks. A bit smelly in there. She presses the roundy black light-switch. Oh fizz it, the light doesn't go on. Her Ma says there's enough light from the hall and a bit from the window and you'd only be wasting good bulbs in a toilet. Then she makes an inspection.

9

"It's not too bad. Needs a bit of Jeys Fluid. Plenty of elbow grease. That's all."

You can see the pull-chain and the cistern and the little window with the tin boards outside. Good job there's cracks in the tin, with bits of stripey light showing. It's brown and stripey in the toilet-pot, a black stone floor, and dark-green walls with a red crooked stripe across the middle. There's a brass latch and a doorknob. The chain makes a funny roaring noise when her Ma pulls it.

They might have to get that fixed as well, she says. The kids are running around the empty rooms **like** mad things. It's dead empty with no furniture in yet, but Ma says, "All in good time."

All the other walls are bare and pinky, except for a few holes where the curtain- wires were. There's dirty marks where the holy pictures must've hung. The bath is in the scullery next to the draining board, it's black on the outside, with rusty stains on the inside, it has a wood bath board over the top you can leave closed or open. Everyone likes the bath board, especially Ma. She tests it out. She gives Patti the babby to hold and climbs up. She holds onto Patti's shoulder with one hand.

"I'll go skatin'," she says. "It's nice up here. That'll be grand, for seeing out, when the Corporation take them feckin boards down."

She jumps back down with a THU-UMP!

"All that bath needs is a good scrub and that bath board'll come in handy too."

The kids climb into the bath. They pretend they're in a boat. They sing: *Row Row Row Your Boat.*

That's when Ma takes out the holy water bottle from under the babby's pram-cover. She bites the crown off the Our Lady bottle. Shakes the holy water round the rooms, in the toilet and the coal-hole. All the corners. All the doors. Around the frames, around the windows. Drowns the place!

"Ma, the place'll be drownded, " Patti says, but she doesn't care. She shakes and splashes, shakes and splashes, like she was a priest giving a blessing. She says she hopes they'll have good luck in this place. She blesses herself then and says a quick prayer for new places. Another one to all their guardian angels. The plastic virgin bottle is nearly empty.

"That blessed water came all the way from Lourdes," she says.

"Here you might as well finish it off."

She hands it to Patti. Patti takes a small sup. It tastes warm and stale and holy. It's supposed to be good for keeping away the devil, for bad kidneys and sore throats, for chest infections and fevers, for indigestion, for Polio, for scurvy, for chilblains, for . . .

"That's better than any tonic," Ma says, fixing the blue crown back on.

Afterwards, in the kitchen, she stands back.

"It'll be lovely," she says. "With them boards down, with the curtains up."

It wasn't lovely. The dark. The cold rooms. The creepy-crawlies. But it wasn't as bad as the other place. No creaky stairs. No drunken spunkers. And no rats. Ma says you'd never see a rat around here because of all the cats in the fish market, so they needn't worry. They didn't see them that first time. It was after they moved all their stuff in. In the back bedroom, they were playing on the floorboards. That's when they saw the creepy-crawley's, shiny silvery things crawling up the floorboards behind the bedroom door. A wriggly line of them, near the skirting board.

"Silverfish," her Da said. "Must be the damp."

Da was scratching his head, like he was planning his next move with Ma beside him holding the babby. Her Ma said they're for good luck and you shouldn't kill innocent creatures, but Anna wanted to catch them and Jimmy wanted to race them and the babby wanted to eat them. They were all down on their hunkers watching the silverfish.

"Why are they called silverfish?" Patti asked.

"Because, they just are."

"They don't look like fish. Don't fish swim and not crawl? "

"These ones are different."

"Would they swim if we put them in the sink?" Jimmy says.

"No! Now that's enough questions," Ma said.

The next day, Da spread the powdery stuff around that he got from the apothecary and the silverfish disappeared. He used his wrench to take the boards off the windows. Her Ma put newspapers up before she cleaned them on the inside and out. A crowd of kids came to gawk at their furniture when it arrived. Ma says this place is full of nosey parkers.

Patti can remember that first day, like a picture in her head. The big bumpy grey wall of the flats, a horrible fishy smell from the fish market, the tangly barbed wire on top of the wall and her Ma said you'd think it was a prison camp. It was all grey in the flats, the walls and the balconies, the ground and the sky. She watched the sky for bits of blue. In the far block, a gang of young fellas were throwing a white kitten against the wall. They were swinging it round by the tail and she heard it crying like a baby and she nearly died with the fright.

"Villain's," her granny said. "Villain's and bowsies."

Around the fish market, there's millions of cats; black ones and orange ones and white ones. A white cat is for bad luck, a black cat is for good luck. If you see a white cat you close your eyes at once and try not to see it. If you see a black cat you make a wish as quick as you can, only you can't wish for money. An orange cat is very vicious and you should keep well away. They can hear the cats in the night fighting and crying like the banshee. It's a spooky place where they live. Before the flats, it used to be a graveyard. There's the bodies of monks and nuns from centuries back buried under the concrete. Their flat is probably built right on top of one. No one can read the two stone plaques on the fish market wall, because they're written in Latin.

On the stairs they tell ghost stories. A young one in the flats told them there was a ghost in their flat. This old woman who lived there died in her bed and her ghost walks around every night in her blue Child of Mary habit. Sometimes they hear noises in the night, but they never saw the ghost thank God. And Patti hopes they won't either. There's ghosts everywhere, they told her. They're on the stairs at night, the ghosts of the monks and nuns, who rise up out of their graves and walk around in their black shrouds. Across the street near the whiskey distillery, there's a haunted place called Hangman's House. A man hanged himself years ago and he comes back every night to hang himself again and again because he doesn't know he's dead. There's a headless coachman who drives a horse-drawn coach past their flats, at midnight, dressed in a red army uniform. The four white horses can almost fly. If you listen real hard, you're supposed to hear the sound of galloping hoofs. At night, Patti covers her head with the sheet, so as not to hear. Her Ma says that oul coachman couldn't do you any harm if he's headless.

They were a couple of weeks in the new flat, when her Da brought home a bundle of wallpaper with a border to match; what he calls a Joblot. A joblot is cheaper, because they're the end of stock lines in Wigadors. Some of the rolls are opened and some shades don't match exactly, but they're close enough so you wouldn't notice the difference. Da rolls up his sleeves. He unrolls the roll of wallpaper out on the table. Then the border. He holds the border up against it. They all have a look. The wallpaper is grey, like a rainy sky, with black trees with no leaves. The border is nicer, it's red flowers with gold leaves in a squiggly line. Da says it's a contrast, the red and the grey and it'll set off the wallpaper lovely, but Ma keeps looking at the black trees, like she can't make up her mind.

She say's: "It's nice," but when Da goes out she has another look. She holds it up to the wall. She says that wallpaper'd put years on ya and she never saw black trees in her life.

"It's too dark, like a bloody morgue. I'd've liked somethin' summery to brighten up the place. But it'll be grand when it's up, with the border to set it off. Better than bare walls, I suppose."

The pattern is a bit plain all right. The trees all the same, next to each other and on top of one another and it must be winter, that's why there's no leaves.

"It's supposed to be winter Ma," Patti says.

"Yes, I s'pose so, but it'd be nicer if it was summer."

"Maybe it's winter in a snowy country."

"It must be Siberia then. You don't see black trees like that in the Phoenix Park or Stephen's Green? "

The smell of wallpaper paste is everywhere. Her Da uses the bath board to paste and a bokety green chair to stand on. He gets breathless hanging the wallpaper. His face goes shiny and pink. The kids have him tormented, dipping fingers in the paste, and knocking over his bucket and pulling at the new wallpaper. After a couple of days, the kitchen becomes a winter garden and they're all surrounded by black trees. He stands back and looks. He says there's enough wallpaper left over for the bedroom if he does a bit of patchwork. Ma is raging, she was hoping for something with bright flowers for the bedroom, but she says nothing. She nods her head, like everything is grand. When her Da runs out of matching strips, he cuts and pastes and patches. Some of the trees are lying sideways and upside down, but it won't matter because you can't see it properly, behind the bed, Da says. As long as the wall is covered. As long as there's no missing bits.

At night the trees look spooky. Patti covers her head with the sheet and tries to fall asleep with the kids beside her. They're little kickers; they kick and dig and scrob in their sleep. Her Ma says they're peevish. In the dark room of black trees, they twist and twine like skipping-ropes, everyone gets tangled up, arms and feet and legs. That's why she sleeps on the edge. It's better on the edge, except if you get pushed out onto the cold floor. If one moves, then the other one moves, then the other one. She wouldn't sleep at the wall. You get pushed up against the cold Siberian wall, your head and your knees and your elbows, all the bony parts of you into the winter garden with the sideways trees. You hear the voices in the wall and you have to climb over everyone to go to the toilet. Worst place is in the middle, in-between them all; a knotty lump of petticoats and arms and cold feet.

It's pitch dark in the hall. There's only two light bulbs, one in the scullery and one in the kitchen. Da says you'd know all about it, when the ESB bill comes, if you put on all the lights. They have to touch their way through the pitch-dark hall into the pitch-dark toilet and it's dead ghosty. She puts out her arms and feels her way along the cold green wall. She closes her eyes.

In case. She doesn't want to see Misses Reilly's ghost, or any other ghost.

Sometimes, they hear the lonely sea-sound of the foghorn and it makes her think of the Titanic and the poor people lost at sea, the giant underwater iceberg and the lifeboats and the drowning children, floating forever in the black icy water. The Titanic was the biggest ship ever built, her uncle told her. The Titanic was supposed to be unsinkable.

Her Ma says: "The foghorn has a peculiar lonely sound that sends shivers through you, a sound that makes you appreciate your life, no matter what. There's always those worse off than yourself and there's many a man at sea who might need a prayer in a hurry."

So she whispers a quick prayer for the seafarers, that they'll find shelter from the storm. Patti listens to the prayer and the different breathing sounds around her, soft, wheezy, crackly, snory. Near morning, the black trees start to shiver and shake in the grey light. The winter garden wakes. All the morning sounds mix together in the sleepy room. The seagulls wake everyone with their squealing over the fish market. The market- bell rings and the men start to auction in their singsongy voices.

2

PLAY PLACES

Around where they live, there's gillions of places to play. Father Matthew Square, the handball-alley, the Ice-Lane. They found the Ice-Lane easy. It's behind Coalman's sack and rope weavers. It joins up with the fish market and the flats in an L shape. Up there, they make ice to keep the fish fresh. It smells real bad in summer, when the ice machine breaks and the fish goes rotten. There's this little shelter with railings around it and that's where they go if they're doing a concert. Patti likes concerts with princes and princesses, queens and kings, robbers and pirates. Sometimes they have a concert on the stairs, but the cranky oulones give out for making noise. They collect old clothes around the doors or in the Daisy market, the raggy old-fashioned clothes no one will buy; curtains and scarves, hats and high heels. They dress up. The boys won't dress up, so she has to dress a girl up for a boy part. She makes a moustache and beard with a piece of coal. She wets a red smartie, rubs it over her lips to make lipstick. The same for face rouge. She does eyebrows, with a brown smartie. Sometimes she robs clothes out of their wardrobe and her Ma gives out.

"Get outa that wardrobe. Shooo! This is not a playhouse! "

The courthouse is another place to have concerts. Outside, in front of the blue door there's steps up the middle and two flat wide pillars, like stages on each side. After it closes, they have concerts there. They might buy the sweet cigarettes and pretend to be grown ups. There's a bit of red at the tip and you'd swear it was a lit cigarette. On the courthouse stage, Patti inhales, like her Ma, blows out the pretend smoke with her lips curled. Her Ma says she'll be a grown- up soon enough.

In the flats they play rounders, O'Grady says, piggy beds, skipping rope. There's the trolley season and the boxcar season and the marble season and the roller-skate season. Girls don't usually play with boys, except for kiss chasing. It's disgusting.

It's yuk! If a young fella catches you, you have to kiss him so Patti doesn't play. Instead, she watches them playing. Some of the girls run too slow around the yard. They do this loop thing, pretending they don't want to get caught, but you'd know they did.

Another good place to play is beside the Liffey. It's only around the corner, across from the Four Courts. When she was a babby, her Da used to sit her on the high bridge at Church Street and she could see straight down into the water. On Sunday's after mass, they fed the swans and ducks with stale bread. They saw the Liffey Swim, the green water full of swimming hats and moving arms, crowds of people cheering and clapping along the wall. They'd go for long walks down the quays. She was afraid crossing the Halfpenny Bridge. The wood boards shifted and creaked under their feet. She watched through the slits, slices of green scummy water below and she wanted to run away. She held Da's hand very tight and they kind of floated on the wood boards. Her Da thought it was funny, but she didn't. He used to rummage through the book- stalls on the southside and sometimes he bought a book. He told her they were lucky to be able to cross that bridge for nothing, because you had to pay a halfpenny toll to cross in the olden days, that's why its called the Halfpenny Bridge. The fruit seller with the red cheeks knows her granny. She always gives them two Beauty of Bath, apples for nothing, even though they're five for a shilling. She shines them with her flowery apron.

She says: "Enjoy that now."

Da says: "Thanks very much."

The woman says her and her granny go back years. Her Da smiles at her and waves goodbye. He used to sit her on his shoulder on the way home and pretend to throw her over the wall. He doesn't bring her for walks anymore. She's too big and in-anyway, she wouldn't go with him.

They're not supposed to play near the Liffey wall, even though they cross the bridge all the time to granny's place. She likes the Liffey. When it's full and glassy and you can see the sky upside-down. And the trees kind of shiver and shake. And the clouds wiggle and it's like a big wiggly photograph. Sometimes, they hang around the Liffey wall and they have to hold their noses, when the tide is out. With the tide out, you can see rusty prams and bikes and bed-frames all stuck in the green slimy sand. Down on the end step, they sit and dip their feet in. This day, her foot got stuck in the slime and her sandal was full of mucky gunge. They can't swim yet but they're learning, in Tara Street Baths. She wouldn't swim in the Liffey, because of the water rats; the big black yokes that come up from the sewers underneath the city. You can get diseases from the Liffey: Typhoid and Polio and another disease from river rats.

The boys don't care; they see them diving in in their shorts. They do a doggy- paddle across to the other side and run back up the steps with the water dripping off them. During the eel season, they have eel competitions, between the northsiders and the southsiders. There's always fights about who has the biggest eel; someone says the northside eels are fatter and someone else says the southside eels are longer so there's murder. Eels are horrible slimy yokes that look like black snakes. They take them out of the buckets to measure them out on the ground. They chase the girls around the flats with the wriggly eels. They shove them in letterboxes to frighten the oulones. A woman saw this eel wriggling up her hall and she nearly had a heart attack. Eels are supposed to be able to crawl on land as well as swim.

3
LAMPY AS ANYTHING

She has spaces between her front teeth and her Ma says she'll be a good singer some day and maybe she'll be on the radio.

"You know, some of them opera singers have splits between their teeth."

"Why?"

"That's the why. That's the way God made them."

Then her Ma puts her finger up to her teeth.

"That space there, that makes the sound of the song travel further. True as God, wait till ye see."

She doesn't want to see. Maybe it's true, but she doesn't like gappy teeth and she's not gone about being an opera singer in-anyway, like the ones on the radio. Everyone'd jeer her if she sang like that. Someday she'll get them splits filled in. When she grows up and makes stacks of wages. Her Ma says you shouldn't fly in the face of God. You should be happy with the way he made you. It's one of her sayings. She always says: "You have your arms and legs, your eyes and ears, a brain in your scull! What more would you want?"

Well, maybe eyes that see properly, Patti thinks. Eyes that see the blackboard, eyes that see the steps before you trip over them, eyes that don't make you bang into things, like Mister Magoo! She had to get specky four-eye glasses. She couldn't see the blackboard properly in school. She got these hickey pink frames with pointy corners. Her Granny called them *stylish!* She says "They're the very latest in spectacle fashion," but they are in their eye.

"Look at them stylish frames, and the price of them if you had to pay for them out of your pocket."

Her granda says she looks like a little scholar. Granny nods her head and says: "Scholar is right."

Her aunty Jinny holds them up to her face and looks through them. She blesses herself and says: "Blessus and save us, but how can you see through them? It's all blurry, I can't see a thing."

Granny Connor says: "They're very unusual all right," and goes into knots. Aunt Dinah says they suit her down to the ground and they go nice with her German plaits. Everyone else says they're like milk bottle ends.

They're not Corporation glasses, thank God, the roundy wirey ones that make you look dead dopey. But still in all, her eyes are like brown conkers when she looks in the mirror. It's like looking out through big windows, where everything is gynormous and wavy. Out the sides everything is small again. Down on the ground is miles away. Her eyelashes rub up against the lenses and she has to push them down on her nose. There's deep red lines on the sides of her nose, when she takes the glasses off.

It's called lampy, when you can't see properly. The oulones call her lampy and the young ones call her specky four eyes. Her Ma says they're all just jealous.

In the Richmond hospital, the doctor put in yellow eye drops. She had to read the eye chart. It starts off ok on the first line. Anyone could read that, she thinks. It's grand on the second line too. She has to squint a bit after the next line. Then it goes hazy and blurry, when she tries to read the lower lines. The letters all join together and go dizzy. The doctor makes her sit down in a leather seat beside a desk. He opens up a brown case. There's a set of roundy lenses. He tries them out holding them up to her eyes with a kind of iron pinchers with a handle. She has to read the eye chart again, through the lenses. He asks her which is the best lens to see through. He does the right eye first.

"This one or that one?"

"That one or this one?"

"This?"

"Or that?"

"That?"

"Or this?"

It takes ages, but then she knows. Then it's the same with the left eye. Then it's the two eyes together. He keeps rushing back to his desk and writing in his notebook.

All of a sudden, he puts out the lights. What's he doing? She can't see a thing. Then he opens a curtain and hey presto! On the wall, there's a green and a red light, like traffic lights. The Richmond doctor asks her which is the clearest light.

"The red or the green?"

"The green or the red?"

It's hard at first, but after ages she knows. He does more writing. He says she's long-sighted. It sounds nice: long-sighted. She thinks that's grand; at least she's not short- sighted in-any-way. It must mean she can see long distances. He asks her can she see the numbers on buses and she tells him she never had to get a bus, but she'd like to. She tells him she only lives down the road, beside the Four Courts and she doesn't need to get buses, because her school is across the road up a hill. She tells him how many sisters she has and how many brothers. That her Ma couldn't come with her because she has to mind the babby and that her Da is in work. The eye doctor goes back behind his desk, writes stuff down fast and says her new spectacles will be ready in two weeks.

Then her brother has to get glasses as well. They're brown frames that make him look posh and granda say's he's like a little professor. The lenses are not as thick as hers. She tried on his and he tried on hers. They couldn't see a thing; it was like blind man's buff, when they cover your eyes with a scarf and your walking around the room with your hands out in front of you.

She hates her glasses.

HATES!

Everything is too big: noses and eyes and ears, like when you look into the spooky mirror in the ghost train in Bray. They're supposed to wear them all the time, not just in school. Patti hides hers in her gymslip pocket, before school and after school. Especially when she's in the flats. She wouldn't wear them in the flats.

Specky specky specky. Specky specky four- eyes, they shout after her.

Granny says: "There's nothing wrong with being a bit lampy. Wasn't the best of the scholars a bit lampy and look where it got them?"

"Yis. Wasn't the writer Sean O'Casey half blind? And don't forget James Joyce," granda says.

So they keep on about lampy people, about who was or who wasn't lampy. Then they're on about Mister Magoo.

"And look at Mister Magoo, he's happy go lucky," granny says.

Yes, Patti knows what she means. Mister Magoo is lampy as anything. Mister Magoo makes her laugh like she'll never stop. The first time she saw him on the telly, she was in stitches. Magoo is her favourite cartoon. Granny says he's some character all right. Here's Magoo with his baldy head and his squinty eyes; here he is, with his podgy, squashed up face. He won't admit he's lampy, or else he doesn't know he's lampy. He thinks a pole or a lamppost is a man or a woman.

He goes "Hello there! " and takes off his cap when he passes the pole. He has near disasters; he just barely misses falling into a river or a lake. He's dead funny, the way he toddles along, talking to himself, bumping into things and tripping over things and it doesn't bother him at all. At the end he goes:

"Oh Magoo you've done it again."

It's one of the programmes they wouldn't miss, if granny's telly is working.

4

THE WORM WOMAN

Her Ma makes them porridge for breakfast. It's called Flahavan's Progress Oatlets, grey bubbly stuff she soaks overnight and cooks on the gas stove the next morning. It's nice with the milk and sugar, but Ma prefers it with loads of salt. Ma likes everything salty. After porridge and tea, she blesses them in the hall from the holy water fount. She tells them not to forget to say their guardian angel prayer on the way to school. She waves them off at the door with the babby in her arms. She shakes the babby's hand to make him do a wave. "Day Day" she says for the babby. "Da Da," the babby says. They all go in a crooked line behind Patti. Outside the gate, they cross through the queues of horses and carts loaded up with pyramids of cabbage and turnips and cauliflowers and they step around the steamy smelly heaps of horse dung that are everywhere. There's always stuff on the ground. Sometimes a man will throw them an apple or an orange from the back of a lorry.

Porridge is supposed to be good for your insides. So are senna pods. Saturday is senna day. The senna pods float on top of the tea like long green islands. Every month they get senna pods. It's the yukkiest thing after castor oil.

"Why do we get senna Pods?" Patti asked one day.

"Because."

"Because what?"

"It's good for you and remember the worm woman?"

When she thinks of the worm woman, the senna pods are not that bad. It's because of the stupid worm woman; it's all her fault. A woman died because she had this gynormous worm inside her. It ate the inside out of her. After she died, they did an operation. They took out the worm. In the College of Surgeons, they kept it in this special tank to do experiments. Experts came over to Ireland from foreign medical schools to examine the specimen. The experiments showed it was the biggest worm they'd ever caught in a human being.

"Like a big long snake," her Ma says.

People were allowed to visit the College of Surgeons to view it; they had the worm on display in the tank. Her Da went to see it.

"It's not something you'd ever forget in a hurry," he says.

Reporters came to take photographs of the worm and the story made it into the newspapers. There was a photograph of the worm in the tank. So that's how come they have to get senna pods. It's all because of the woman with the worm in her belly.

It's always the same on Saturdays. Here they are, all around the table staring into their cups. They won't drink it. It makes the tea go green and slimey looking; it makes Patti feel sick. Her Ma says the senna pods keep you clean on the inside; her Da says they keep the worms away. The tea looks like Liffey water when the tide goes out and tastes like poison, but they can't move until they drink every drop. They'll get the bellyaches then and they'll have to queue for the toilet. The toilet will get blocked, with all the newspapers and the water will overflow. Ma will have to put her arm down to free it up. Then she'll be all day moping and scrubbing with disinfectant. It'd be better if she never gave them the senna pods in the first place.

The senna pods are bad enough, but the castor oil is worse. It has a horrible, rotten fish taste. First her Ma shakes the bottle. Next she gets a spoon. She pretends to drink it herself off the spoon.

"That's gorgeous," she says, lettin' on.

She holds your head back. She forces your mouth open. She sticks the spoon into your mouth and closes your mouth tight in case any spills out.

"Swally that," she says, so if you spit it out she does the same again so you might as well swallow it the first time. Patti pinches her nose tight so as not to smell the fishy smell. The kids hide under the table and behind the bed when they see her with the bottle. They like Syrup of Figs, the brown stuff in the square bottle. They drink that no bother, because it's nice and sweet, a bit like a toffee taste, mixed with a fruity taste, but you can't get that on the blue medical card in the dispensary. You have to buy that in the chemist. Ma says the blue card is a Godsend and she'd be lost without it for the medicine and the tonics and the free milk. She gets the free milk for the baby; the health nurse fills out the pink form every time she has a new baby. They listen out for the milkman. The milk gets robbed sometimes, if they don't take it in straight away. Or the seagulls stab the red silvery caps, with their beaks and drink the creamy head.

They have tonics. A raw egg makes you strong if you're run down. You have to swallow the yoke whole and not burst it. They watch your face to make sure. There's other kinds of tonics for grown-ups, like Buckfast and milk stout. You can take a course of Buckfast Abbey tonic wine after a nervous breakdown. It's only like medicine, they say. People take it for their nerves, or before or after an operation, for septic throats and bad kidneys. It's allowed. It's the second best tonic after milk stout. The monks make it from the Buckfast Abbey monastery, so it's not a sin; even people who took the pledge can drink it because it's a tonic. It's allowed for you to take three small glasses a day for good health and lively blood; that's what it said on the label. Her aunty Annie took a sup for her blood once, but she said it was shockin' sweet. Her aunt Rita tried it for her nerves, but it only gave her a splitting headache. Her other aunt who doesn't touch a drop had a small glass at Christmas to celebrate Jesus' birth. Her Ma says it's good for the blood, but it looks a bit like Red Biddy to her and she prefers a milk stout herself. Patti was allowed a small sup of Buckfast for her bad kidneys, one tablespoonful three times a day. They keep it in the cupboard in her granny's place. Sometimes, when no one is looking, she has a small tablespoon. It makes you strong and healthy. It's supposed to make you feel happy as well.

5

THE CHERRY ORCHARD

As well as Buckfast, Patti likes vinegar. It has a sour kind of taste but it's nice. They sell it in the pub and the druggist store. You bring your own bottle and they fill it up to the brim for sixpence. On the way home, she has a little drink. Only a small sup, so they won't notice.

"Vinegar is not for drinkin'. It's on'y for fish and chips," her Ma says.

It's supposed to be bad for you, because it thins out the blood. So maybe she drank too much vinegar this day, because she got the hot fever and she had to be shifted to Cherry Orchard. She remembers the grey itchy blanket wrapped around her, someone was carrying her, a nice ambulance- man with a soft voice.

"There, lovey dovey," he goes, "you'll be all right."

It's real bumpy on the stretcher, the wheels rolling backwards and forwards against the door. The ambulance goes fast over the roads. The nice nurse pats her forehead with a damp cloth. When she wakes she's in this room. A shiny blue floor with black dots. The windows half covered, so it's darkish. No one there only this little toddler in a nappy. He cries and cries in his cot for his Mama. He stands up and shakes the bars. Ma Ma Mama! Mama! He screams and bangs his head against the bars. Then he starts to sob with his whole body shaking. Then he looks over at Patti with his eyes full of tears. He sits down, like he's exhausted. He rolls over and falls asleep. He's about the same age as their own babby, with curly fair hair and a chubby little face. She felt dead sorry for him.

She remembered then, a little bit more. In her granny's, they heated water on the gas stove. They gave her a bath in the scullery. She was roasting with a mad hot fever. Then she was frozen. Then she was roasting again. Her legs were wobbly when she tried to stand. They said she was going to the Cherry Orchard.

"A lovely place, like a holiday camp, " they said. "A whole bed to yourself. Roast potatoes for your dinner. Jelly and ice cream for after. Bottles of lemonade."

What more could she want? It sounded lovely, when they said it like that, but it wasn't. Two tall towers outside the windows, a smell of hospitals everywhere, loads of babbies crying all day. Her petticoat was stuck to her back. She had a big sore lump in her throat, so she couldn't swallow. She must've fell asleep then. Next thing, a fat nurse with puffed armbands on her sleeves looked down at her. Her face was hazy and swimmy, like in a dream. She gave her a needle in the arm. There's this wide grey door with a little glass window. No one was allowed in, only the nurse or the doctor. She saw eyes through the glass window one day, a bit of a coloured scarf, like the one her Ma wears.

"Ma! Ma!" she called out, but no one answered. Maybe it wasn't her. She's not sure. The eyes and the scarf went away then. She started to cry. The tears tasted salty in her mouth.

They tried to give her baby food, horrible grey mushy stuff, like goody goody. She spit it out. Her throat was burning. All of her was. She got more injections. Then they moved her to another place. She said bye bye to the toddler. The toddler waved with his chubby little hand. They wheeled her bed along this long, long hall with a shiny floor and a glass case full of peculiar old fashioned stuff, like for operations. They stopped. They pulled in the bed. It's this skinny place, about the size of a toilet, with a skinny door in front of the bed. There's this window behind the bed, a green grassy field behind the window.

"You're in isolation love," the porter said. She didn't know what isolation was, but she said nothing. They kept taking her temperature and giving her more needles.

It must've been a few days after, when she looks out the window and sees them all coming across the grassy field. It's her Ma with the babby in her arms, the kids running along beside her. Patti waves so they can see her. Ma waves back. Then she's knocking on the window.

"Howea? Are ya nearly better?"

She puts the babby's face up to the glass.

"Say 'ello," she says, as if he could talk. The babby nearly jumps out of her arms. He smiles and starts to bang the glass with his little fists. She puts him down and lifts the other kids up, one after another, so that their faces are pressed against the glass and their noses go flat and squashy. They make funny faces in at her. Then it's time to go. She has sweets for her in a white bag, but she can't get the bloody window open. It's no use, because the window is locked, so they all say bye bye. They go back across the field towards the gate. They all wave and Ma takes the babby's hand and makes him do a wave too. She wanted to go with them. She banged on the window with her two hands. She couldn't stop crying. Then this cranky nurse with a fat face comes in and gives out hell to her. Tells her not to be a cry babby. Tells her to stop them silly baby tears.

It must've been weeks before she went home. A nurse dressed her and she had to wait outside the ward. They sat her on this chair in the corridor, but there's no sign of Ma. All morning, no sign. All day no sign. Her Ma was dead late; it was nearly night time when she came up the long hallway. Here she is with her heels clackity clack on the shiny floor. Here she is with her swingy leopard skin coat and her hair in clips under her scarf.

"Is she ready?" she says to the nurse.

"Patricia was ready at ten o'clock this morning," she goes, a bit cranky like.

Ma's nervy face. Then her other more cheeky face.

"Oh that's right. I forgot, but I'm here now, aren't I?"

They walk back down the long corridor, past the glass case with the old fashioned operating stuff, past the nurse's office. The nurse gives them a wave. Outside the gate, across the road, they have to wait ages for a bus. She's never going back to the Cherry Orchard, she tells her Ma on the bus. Never! Never! Never!

Her throat was still a bit sore. Granny had the blessed scapulars and the brown paper with the smelly ointment. She covered her chest and throat with the paper and put the scapulars around her neck. She sewed red flannel into the inside of her vest. A woman in the market rubbed her throat over with a relic from Saint Blase. Someone else had something belong to Saint Oliver Plunkett. She's able to play out again. She's able to swallow and sing hymns at mass. She likes *Star of the Sea* and *Salutaris Hostia*. They have singing concerts on the stairs. Her pal Vera sings a song about little boxes on a hillside, that are made of ticky tacky, in a small town, on a corner of Pittsburgh, Pennsylvania. She opens her mouth wide; she moves her head and her hands like a real opera singer. It's a stupid bloody song, Patti thinks.

6

A FAIRY IN A MATCHBOX

Not too far away from the Cherry Orchard, a fairy was found in a field in Ballyfermot. A group of mushroom pickers had it in a matchbox and everyone was rushing out there to see it.

"That fairy in the matchbox might be unlucky," her Ma says.

"That fairy in the matchbox is makin' someone a small fortune," her Da says, "It's a bloody hoax, chargin' people a shillin' to see a bloody fairy."

They take your money first, open the box faster than a blink and close it again, so you don't know what it was you saw. They say the fairy is too fast and could jump out of the matchbox, so they can't open it too far. A reporter from the Herald went out to take a photograph, but the photo never turned out properly, so he writes this article anyway, with a blurry picture of a half open matchbox. Patti wanted to see it for herself, but she's not allowed out to Ballyfermot. The field is near a place called the California Hills, miles out from the city in the sticks. Granny says, it's like the Wild West out there and there's plenty of cowboys and Indians, never mind fairies.

Her brother thinks there's no such a thing as a fairy, so she doesn't tell him. She'd never tell anyone in the flats either, but she saw a real fairy herself. A few times. In the old drunken house, before they moved. It was at the fireplace when the fire wasn't lighting, this little cobbler man, the colour of dirty silver mending a shoe. He has this hat on with a wide brim. He looks up at her. He says nothing. She's sitting on her Da's lap and he's falling asleep with his head nodding. There's a tap tap from the cobbler's hammer. It's always the same, him mending the shoe, tapity tap tap, near the grate, her looking down at him. Him looking up again and then he disappears back into the fireplace. Her Da didn't believe her, he said it's her childish bloody imagination again, but her Ma did. Her Ma believes in fairies; she says, there's a fairy world all right, underneath them, not too far down, under Dublin Town. What she calls an underworld. They're called "The Little People" and they were there long before us, but they can be dangerous. They can take you away, to their fairy kingdom. If they put their fairy eye on you.

Granny Connor told her children were taken away by the fairies years ago and were never heard of again. There were fairy forts where you couldn't venture. The fairies can enter our world through cracks in the ground. You might fall down through the cracks, so that's why it's dangerous to walk on lines. The paths around where they live are broken and bokety, so you have to watch your step all the time. You're supposed to say a quick prayer if you walk on a line by mistake. Patti prays to her guardian angel if she does.

In her place, there's good luck things and bad luck things. Her Ma is afraid of mirrors, she says mirrors are bad luck, so are umbrella's up inside the house, so are shoes on the table. Rainbows bring good luck. Her Ma likes rainbows; if there's a rainbow, she stares up at the sky through the lookout glass in the scullery. One day the rainbow was over the flats, and then it turned and moved a bit further away. Patti followed this rainbow out the gate, past Coalman's sack weavers, across the road, past the Four Courts. She skips along. The quays are full of traffic, cars beeping their horns and flashing their headlights, even though it's daytime. Up the steep hill, the ground is all wet and shiny. It seems to be near Christ Church, the nearer she gets, it moves a little bit further away.

Here's an oulfella running down the hill with a boxcar full of turf.

"Get outa the way young one!" He shouts.

She jumps back and gives him a look. She thinks it might be Ony Delony, the boxcar man from the flats. She's not sure; his cap is pulled down over his eyes, and his coat collar up over his ears so all you see is a red nose and mouth. He shouts again, in a dribbly voice. He goes in a zigzag with the boxcar all around her and runs towards the bridge. The hill is slippy and slidey, so her feet make squelchy sounds; plish plash, plosh, there's water coming out the sides of her sandals, but she doesn't care. She goes faster, the sky goes darker. Then she steps into this puddle in Bride Street and the rainbow is there in the oily water. She's outside Saint Patrick's proddy cathedral, and nearly blesses herself, but then she remembers, it's a sin to bless yourself outside a protestant chapel. The rainbow is between the steeple and the tall houses across the road. There's more clouds coming, big purply yokes, like bunches of black grapes.

Inside the gate, there's grass and flowerbeds you're not supposed to touch. There's all kinds of colours, but they look a bit shaggy after the rain. She stands in the porch out of the rain. She knows it's special, even though it's a proddy place. Dean Swift who wrote Gulliver's Travels was here, years and years ago. Some day she might read that famous book. It's supposed to be very good, with funny bits and all. Dean was a proddy, but he was a great scholar.

"Why, hello there young lady."

This man's yanky voice beside her.

"What has a little kiddo like you out in weather like this?"

He appeared out of nowhere. She feels a bit stupid, so she says she was just out for a walk. He has a beige cardigan pulled over his head, there's lumps of his hair hanging in wet streaks at his forehead.

"Your pretty hair and your feet are soaked," he goes in his yanky voice.

She doesn't answer. She's not supposed to talk to strangers.

"Your Mom not worried?"

It's stopped raining, but it might start again. She thinks she better go. She legs it out the gate. She doesn't look back. Down the hill, past Christ Church, left around the corner, all the way to the Forty Steps, where the Banshee lives. She walks past. She stops. She has a sneaky look. It's near her granny's flats, beside Saint Audoens Chapel. She can see the first few steps, shiny with rain. It looks spooky. She's all in black, the Banshee. They say she sits on one of those steps, combing her long white hair. She starts to keen when someone is dying. She keens and keens until they die. Then she keens more. Her Ma says it's a sure sign of a death, when you hear that keening.

She feels a bit hungry. She'd love a pear, a ripe William pear, with the brown patchy skin. She wouldn't mind a black spotty Jamaican banana, or a juicy slice of pineapple.

She sits on a bench a bit further up, near the bottom of the hill. You can make a wish on a rainbow, as long as you don't ask for money; it's the same as a star, or a black cat. She closes her eyes. She'd like a pet, a puppy or a budgie would do, a bed of her own, a house with a flower garden, a coffee table, a piano, a book shelf with stacks of books, a fancy white crib for the new babies, a bike, a red Triang with a basket at the front, Bunty's wardrobe of fab clothes. She'd like a radiogram, one of those swanky mohair swing coats for her Ma, a Da who got the Pledge, who lives in the house with the flower garden, with the baby crib, who buys Martinis for her Ma. It's like a lovely dream and she doesn't want to wake up. She blinks open her eyes. Thinks for a minute. She knows it's stupid. You're only supposed to wish for one thing at a time. She thinks again. She knows. She says it in her head. It's not really what she wants, it's what she doesn't want. I wish I wish. I wish that there were no more coddles. No more bloody coddles ever! No more boiled sausages!

7

SAUSAGES

Her Ma never sits down. She eats her dinner in the scullery, drinks her tea there too, at the gas stove, or at the bath board. She picks and pecks like a bird, with a fork. No one can eat before Da. He has to get his dinner first, even if he's dead late; that's the rule. It's the same with all the Da's; it's because they're out working. And because they're the most important people in the house. They always have coddles. Patti has to go to Steins for the sausages. She hates boiled sausages. Boiled sausages are disgusting. Boiled sausages in the coddle-pot always reminds her of drunken oulfellas, when they piss up against the wall, or the stairs or the gates.

Steins sausages are the best for coddling. Her Ma pricks them with a fork first, and puts them in the water. She uses sausages, collar rashers, carrots, a Spanish onion, two Oxo's, parsley and thyme and potatoes. The collar rashers have stringy bits of white fat down the sides. They float like rafts with the sausages on top of the soup, then they sink and you can only see a few carrots and onions, until she adds the potatoes. Granby sausages are the worst. Her Ma wouldn't buy them. She says they're atrocious, the worst sausages in Dublin. A woman they know used to work there. She said people don't know what they're eating and they put all sorts in the sausages for a joke.

"You should see what them Granby girls put in the sausage meat for the gas, when they're makin' them."

"What?" Ma says.

"You don't want to know," she says, but then she tells her anyway.

Rosie whispers the next bit and Ma says, "That's disgraceful."

"That's not the half of it. There's worse."

Ma says, "Little piggy's have big ears," so Patti pretends not to listen. It's all about what the Granby girls do with the sausages, when they go out on hen party nights. Rosie says they make this big huge sausage, the biggest, hugest, fattest sausage, when the supervisor is not looking. And then she digs her Ma's elbow and whispers something in her ear.

"You know where," she says and goes into knots.

"Go way outa that," Ma says. "You're only coddin' me."

"Sure as God. Next hen party, drop over and see for yourself."

"Do you think I've nothin' better to do, than gallivant in sausage factories all day?"

"It's only a bit of gas!" Rosie says.

"Mind your tongue in this house, there's children present," Ma gives out to her.

All of a sudden her Ma is a big goody goody.

They have coddles on Tuesdays; same every Tuesday, when she stays in her Ma's place.

"Run down to Steins and get me six sausages," she says.

"Ah Ma"

"Don't start Ah Ma! Ah Ma! Ask Misses Stein to show you them first. Don't let her wrap them up till you see them. Make sure they're not the skinny hungry ones when she cuts them. No meat in them. Go into nothin' in the pot. Be nice to her and she might throw in one for good measure."

"Ya know she won't."

"Here, come over here, 'till I fix that hair. And straighten them shoulders, d'ya hear me. Misses Stein has a soft spot for you. Try an smile, and clean them bloody glasses, they're filthy."

She grabs her glasses off her nose, breathes on them and rubs them with the corner of her smock.

"I don't know how you can see through them glasses, they're like dirty windows."

Feckin coddle it must be again, greasy white sausages, the fat squirting out into the brown gravy, the parsley and thyme like a tree floating in the middle.

"Fizz. Feck. Fuc . . ."

She says it under her breath. Fizz is all right, Feck is a bit worse, but that other word, where it's a U instead of the E, is a mortaler.

Ma reefs at her hair with a half toothless comb, pulls it tight off her scalp into an elastic band.

"Leave me alone. You're hurtin' me!"

"Stand still."

Here she goes.

"Those eyes are gettin' worse, you'll go blind, end up cross-eyed from all that book reading in that bloody library. I told your Da, I told him, 'she'll go stone blind, I said."

In her head she tells her Ma to shurrup.

To leave her hair alone.

Shurrup!

In her head.

She hates her hair in a ponytail. She only likes it down over her back, so she can put it under her bum when she sits down.

"Here take Franey witcha."

"Ah Ma, ya know Franey'll only run away, he always does."

"He won't!"

"He will!"

"D'ya want a box?"

"No."

"Then take him for God's sake."

She licks her finger, twirls Franey's hair it into a kiss curl at the front. She rubs his face over with the towel. She takes his hand, puts it into Patti's, folds her fingers around it.

"Hold his hand tight. And here, as you're at it, bring that babby as well."

She sucks the rubber soother, stuffs it into his mouth.

"That babby needs a bit of air too."

A half crown is pressed into her other hand.

"Mind that money, hold it tight and don't lose it."

Patti makes the face when she turns.

Her Ma washes the babby's bum under the tap, puts on the powder and the clean nappy. She has him lying on the bath board. He screams and kicks her in the belly, while she tries to close the safety pin.

"That babby is like a tiger," she says, rubbing her belly bump.

Ma's belly-bump is getting bigger. She says it's because she's eating too many sausages. But she always says that, the same thing every year. Sometimes she says it's the cabbage and potatoes that's making her fat, or the pigs' feet, or the ribs. And then she goes to the hospital with the baby gowns in her messagebag. Then she comes home with a brand new baby and hey presto! The belly-bump is gone. The new babies are fab; they all have black hair and they don't look like they're from a cabbage patch. There's no muck on them and they're always spotless clean. Goo Chaney kind of winks, when Patti asks her about the cabbage patch. She's not sure what the wink means.

Steins is packed. She pulls in the pram with one hand and Franey's arm with the other. Franey pulls away from her, so she has to drag him by the sleeve. Inside, he starts to mess around in the sawdust.

"How's your Ma?" An oulone at the counter says.

"Oh she's all right."

"Is your Ma still there?" this other one says.

"Still where?"

"Would youse leave that young one alone, for God's sake? She's only a kid," Misses Stein says, but they keep on.

"In the way again isn't she?"

"In whose way?"

"The family way. She must be near her time and she with the houseful already,"

one says to the other.

"She's a bit touched, that young one; blind as a bat too, see her glasses, like bottle ends."

The cheeky oulone in the check coat draws a big circle around her eyes with her finger.

In her head, Patti tells her to shurrup, to mind her own business, to feck off. She's one of the nosey parkers, that want to know all your business.

"Tell them nothin'," her Ma always says.

She has to queue behind all the backs: broad backs and skinny backs, long coats and three quarter length coats, check smocks, loads of scarves, perms and pony-tails, black hair and

37

white hair and grey hair, smoke coming out the sides of their mouths, like chimney-pots, so it's all mixed up in the air over the counter. She tries to squeeze in between them but they stick out their bony elbows. There's a row of prams and go-cars along the green tiled wall, kids throwing handfuls of sawdust at one another, like snowballs.

She has to watch Franey and keep an eye on the babby, who's strangling himself trying to take off his pram-straps. He kicks against the pram, twists himself into a knot. He pulls out his soother with his thumb, throws it across the floor. He thinks it's dead funny. It lands in the damp sawdust. Patti picks it up, wipes it off with her sleeve, and sticks it back into his mouth.

"Keep that in your gob! Ma'll have murder, if we lose that soother."

He knows he can't get out of the pram, so he lies back and starts to suck the soother. His eyes look sleepy all of a sudden. He rubs his nose and gives a big yawn. After a while, he's asleep. He's a bloody handful, Patti thinks.

She watches the strips of green grassy stuff up between the trays of meat in the window. There's pigs' cheek with one eye and a sideways grin, rows of hairy pigs' feet with pointy toes and nails, gristly white tripe, purple ox tongues.

"Piggy piggy," Franey says pointing at a pig's cheek. He tries to reach his hand into the window, but Patti catches a hold of him.

The smell in Steins is nice, a bit spicy and meaty. It's called a pork shop. It has green and white tiles on the walls, a long, long counter with a glass front. The sausages are hanging over the counter in big hanks and knots. Behind the glass counter, rings of black and white pudding, a tray of runny liver floating in a puddle of blood, chops, kidneys, cow heel, rashers. After hours standing there, she asks for the sausages. Misses Stein reaches up with her knife, gives it one good chop, and that's where she has to watch out for the skinny sausages.

"Ma says she only wants fat ones," Patti straight tells her.

The oulones start to titter. A row of titters and splutters that turns into one big convulsion.

"That young one is a ticket," one of them says.

"Your Ma'd want fat ones right enough," another one says.

She can see shoulders shaking along the counter.

"Tell your Mammy, these are nice and fat," Misses Stein says, wrapping the sausages up in white paper.

"Would she like a nice ring a white puddin' as well? Or maybe she'd prefer a black one."

That's the cheeky one in the check coat again.

"No. Only sausages," Patti says and hands over the half crown.

The sausage meat's nice. It tastes peppery and salty and mushy. Sometimes, on her way home, she squeezes a bit out of the skin, closes it back and makes a knot at the top. Maybe that's why the sausages are skinny sometimes, but she can't help it. It's Gorgeous! Near the market Franey tries to make a run for it. She has to leave the pram and gallop after him. She half carries, half drags him and it takes her ages to get home.

Her Da eats tripe and cowheel and pigs' feet and pigs' tails. She hates tails! Yuk! They have bits of pink meat where the pig's bum used to be. The tail feels rough like sandpaper; there's horrible spiky hairs as well. Her Ma picks up a tail and examines it for meat. She boils them in the pot with the ribs or pigs feet.

"There's plenty of meat on them," she says, pulling off a big slithery piece.

There is not. It's all wobbly fat hanging off the tail with hardly any meat.

They're horrible, she wouldn't eat them, or pigs feet either, or tripe or cowheel. Imagine eating a cow's heel, or its tongue? Ma says she's very particular indeed and maybe it's lamb-on-salmon she'd like instead. She's not sure what that is, but it sounds posh.

"Tails are only massive with the cabbage," her Ma says, but they are not.

Patti sees bits of fatty tail in among the cabbage on the plate. She keeps thinking of the pig, and what it did out from under the tail. She likes mashed potato and cabbage. She likes peas and meat with hardly any fat. She likes it when the sausages are all burnt in the pan, when they're black and crispy and smoky. Ox tongues are slimy purple yokes you have to boil for hours. Her Da likes them cold, with vinegar and salt and smothered in mustard. Patti thinks they're spooky as anything. Hearts are all right roasted, but they're fatty and bloody, with tunnels like underground pipes in the middle. Kidneys are not too bad, if they're fried in lard with a bit of onion and tomato. They're supposed to be very good for you with protein and iron and stuff. Her granda says they put hair on your chest, but she wouldn't want hair on her chest.

She pulls in the pram. Franey runs off into the bedroom. The bath in the scullery is full of clothes; there's jumpers and shirts and trousers and socks. It's like a big clothes-coddle. There's a smell of wet wool and nappies. She sees the bucket full up with nappies. Her Ma is bent over the washing board, her bumpy belly rubbing against the edge of the bath. Her cigarette is lighting, out on the edge of the draining board. She's singing along with the radio on: *If I Ruled the World,* in her funny tinny voice. If her Ma ruled the world, every day would be the first day of spring. The new washboard has glass bars like Venetian blinds between two wood handles. Her Da got it cheap in Norton's in Moore Street. She's rubbing trousers up against the glass bars, the handles sticking up past her shoulders.

"I need more Rinso," she says. "The feckin muck in these trousers won't budge."

She stands up straight, rubs her back first, then her belly. She lifts up her cigarette, taps ash onto the floor, takes a long, long drag. Then she scrapes the ash away with her slipper.

"Is the babby asleep?"

"Yeah, he nearly lost his soother in Steins."

"Didya get the sausages?"

"Yeah."

"Fat ones?"

"Yeah."

"No skinny ones I hope."

"Nope."

"I hope so."

"Did aul Stein give ya the extra one?"

"I don't think so."

"Right so, the hungry oul bitch. Leave them there on the drainin' board."

She takes a big deep breath through her nose, blows out her mouth, waits, takes another drag from her cigarette and blows a big swirl of smoke up to the ceiling.

"Jesus!" She goes, holding her belly.

"Bring the kids for a walk, wouldya?"

"No. I want t'go out and play."

"Ah go on."

"NO."

"D'ya want a clatter?"

"No"

"Well go on then."

"Where'll I go?"

"How do I know? Walk around the gates."

"And then wha'?"

"Around again. Oh Jesus!" she says, holding onto the wash-board handles. The butt is getting smaller now. She takes quick drags every few seconds until it's the size of a pea, a red lit-up pea. She has it between her thumb and her finger. She'll burn herself if she's not careful.

"Oh Mammy! Oh Christ t'night!"

She grabs hold of the sweeping-brush handle. Then she gets the tablets, from the press, shakes two from the bottle into her hand, puts her chin up and knocks them back with no water. They might be the blood tablets her Ma takes to put iron in her. Patti watches her. She sees the wiry blue veins are sticking out of her legs. They're a holy show. She thinks her Ma'd want to rub them over with lemon juice and olive oil.

"What's wrong with ya Ma?"

"Nothin'. I'll be all right in a minute."

"Run up an ask Rosy has she a smoke for your Ma."

"NO!"

"GO UP I SAID! "

"NO. She'll only say, 'Tell your Ma I've none for meself'."

"She WON'T; she only got paid yesterday."

Rosy will only send her on stupid messages all over the place, to the dairy and the chemist, to Boland's bakery for the turnovers, so instead she lets on to go up. She waits on the lobby for a few minutes, and then comes back.

"She's none."

"She has so."

"She HAZANT She said, she hasn't a light."

And that's when Patti sees it; there's water gushing out of her Ma, all down her legs, like a broken drainpipe. She leans over on the brush. She has a big pain on her face.

A BIG HUGE PAIN.

"Oh Ma! Go into the toilet quick."

She crosses over her legs. The water is all over the lino, a stream going out to the hall.

"Ask Goo Chaney to come in quick," she goes, all breathless.

Goo Chaney is deck-scrubbing the step next door; there's suds all over the place and a smell of Drummer pine.

"What's wrong with you? You're very pale."

"Nothin', Ma says you're to come in."

Goo puts on her cranky face.

"Did she now? Does your Ma think I've nothin' better to do, than yap all day?"

That's what Goo always says, but then she yaps all day anyway. She pours the basin of water over the step, stands the deckbrush upside down against the pole.

"Tell her I'll be there in a minute so."

It was the sausages gave her Ma the pains, Goo Chaney says, but Patti tells her she didn't eat them yet, she has to make the coddle first. The sausages are still on the draining board in the white wrapping-paper. She's in the bedroom. They're not allowed in. The mop and the deck brush are up against the door. The kids are trying to smash open the door, but it's well stuck. Anna keeps thumping with her shoulder and Franey is kicking like a mad thing and Bernie is at the keyhole. Goo is running around in her slippers and apron, collecting newspapers for the floor. She spreads piles of them out over the wet. She fills the ham pot full of water and puts it up on the gas stove.

"Is there any clean rags in this house?" She says with her hands on her hips.

"Hold on, I think there's some in the wardrobe," Patti says.

Her Ma keeps the old baby-vests and petticoats in there; she cuts up for dishcloths. Goo tears them up, and throws them into the pot. Then she says: "Shoo shoo out of the way the lot of youse." Patti says: "Shoo yourself," under her breath. Then they're all pushed out into the courtyard like a pack of wild geese.

"Take them kids out to play. Your Ma's not well."

"Not again. She's always not well. Is she lyin' down?"

"Never mind, now off with yiz like good children!"

Then they see the Coombe ambulance coming around the corner, the nurses, rushing past them with a smell of hospitals off them, their navy-blue gabardine coats and their culchie tan stockings. One is carrying a black leather bag. Goo says they can't come back in until the nurses are gone. Then all the flats' kids are around the door and you'd think someone was getting married.

8

THE NEW BABY

The new baby is lovely; she's nine-pound weight, with loads of black hair. She has a dimple in her chin and her Ma said she had "a caul for good luck."

"A sailor would pay pounds for that," Goo Chaney says.

"It was over her head in the cabbage patch," Ma say's.

"The stork left it for good luck," Da says, when he comes home.

The nurses didn't stay long. Goo tells someone at the door they were too late in-anyway.

There's new matinee coats and shawls and nappies. The matinee coats are turquoise and lemon for a boy or a girl. The baby has this gorgeous new baby smell, her skin is silkysoft. Goo says her eyelashes are like brushes and where did she get that mop of lovely black hair? The bit you can't touch on the top of her head, goes in out, in out, like her head is breathing. She doesn't have a name yet, but they might call her Olive Elizabeth. She's the image of Patti, everyone says, same nose and eyebrows and Patti is delighted. Her Ma is thin again, her slip hanging off her shoulders in the bed. She looks pale and tired with her hair hanging in damp streaks around her face.

"So perfect, a little beauty, one of God's creatures," she says with the baby in her arms. Patti is allowed to hold her then; she can feel her through the blanket, all soft and warm and cuddly. They're all climbing up the bed; they want to keep holding the baby and kissing her and feeling her. They're pulling at her toes and her fingers. They're touching her face and her head. They don't know her neck is delicate and could break easily.

"She's not a **rag doll,** you have to support her neck," her Ma says.

A few of the neighbours come to the door to ask about the new baby. One leaves ten Players, another one leaves a bottle of stout for the milk stout.

The next day, she's still in bed, but they're not allowed into the bedroom. There's no sound from the baby, so she must be asleep, Patti thinks. First, granny Connor comes with her messagebag, then her other granny after her with her messagebag, so there must be something wrong. They have on heavy dark coats. Granny Connor says to Patti, "It's wicked out there, that north wind'd skin a body alive, but it's as draughty as a morgue in this place."

Without talking to one another, the grannies start to tidy the place. They break sticks over their knees and light a big fire. They heat water on the gas stove. They put two chairs together near the fire and pour warm water into a basin. Granny Connor tests it with her elbow first, then one of them brings out the baby. They take off her clothes and wash her in the basin, even though she's clean already.

They're all around the baby. They say, she cried, but then she didn't cry. Her eyes are closed. She's all sudsy and floppy in the basin and her little hands kind of hang. Patti tries to give her her small finger to grip, but her little hand is wide open and cold, like a doll's hand. They wrap her in a towel and dry her. They shake on Johnston's baby powder, then they put on the clean nappy and baby-vest. All the time, they're dead quiet. Next it's the white lace christening-robe with the mother of pearl buttons. They fold over the crochet christening-shawl into a three corner shape and wrap her up real snug.

Why is she getting christened today? Patti wants to know. And how come her Ma was still in bed and how come it's not Sunday when babies usually get christened? The grannies say nothing, like they don't hear; they keep passing the baby backwards and forwards to one another like pass the parcel. Granny Connor first, then her other granny, then granny Connor again. It's like they don't want to let her go. She's gorgeous in all the white robes.

"Perfect, only her little lips are a bit blue." Granny Connor says.

They say prayers then. They kneel down in front of the chairs and make the kids kneel as well.

At the scullery window, they see the Coombe ambulance coming back, with the two cranky faced nurses with the blue berets plonked sideways on their heads. A crowd of kids are gathering near the door. One of them starts to climb up on the ambulance-bumper, then another one. Freezing out it is, with puddles of ice under the clothes- lines, young fellas digging them up with sticks. The nurses give two hard knocks, but this time they won't let them in. So they keep knocking.

"Nosey aul bitches," Granny Connor says, peeping through the letterbox.

She says they want to take the baby, but they won't let them, not until they're good and ready.

"Don't let them take Olive Elizabeth," Patti says.

They lie her down in the Moses basket. She's dead still, like the bride doll that's under granny's bed in the cardboard box. People come down from the balconies, with coats wrapped around their shoulders. They want to see the baby. Patti is allowed into the bedroom then. Her Ma is sitting up smoking in bed in her slip and cardigan, her eyes are half closed; they blink like a doll's eyes, down up, down again.

"Go way!" she says when Patti asks her does she want tea.

"Get outa that, shut that door."

It's the coldest saddest winter she can ever remember; there's ice on the windowpane and the trees in the winter garden look blacker and the grey looks greyer. The clothes are stiff on the wash-lines outside, trouser-legs and shirt- sleeves and collars all sticking out, like they were dancing and got stuck in the air. The water is stuck in the taps and the toilet.

She's stone cold now, her little face like the marble statues in the chapel, all wrapped up in the christening shawl in Da's arms on the steps. Da has to christen her himself, it's allowed, to stop her from going to limbo or purgatory. She won't have to go to Limbo or purgatory because she got the holy sacrament of baptism. It's like her Da is magiced into a priest, when he says the prayers and puts the holy water on the baby's head. *I baptise you in the name of the father and of the son and of the holy ghost.* All the neighbours say goodbye to Olive Elizabeth. She has to go in the ambulance then. Anna makes faces at the nurses behind their backs.

Snow falls then and the sky over the flats is all pinky, like the pink marshmallows in Mike Nolan's. The nurse has Olive Elizabeth in her arms in the ambulance with the window rolled down and you'd think she was her Ma.

"Say **goodbye** to your little sister," she goes, in her culchie voice. They're allowed to kiss her goodbye, just one kiss each. Patti goes first, she gives her a little kiss on the frozen cheek. It's like kissing her doll, Molly, only colder.

"Bye bye Olive Elizabeth. Bye bye."

The others kiss her then. Franey has his face through the ambulance window, his arms wrapped tight around the baby. He won't let her go, so the nurse has to pull him away. A crowd of kids are waiting to kiss her goodbye, but the nurse gives them a cranky look and closes up the window.

The grannies are standing on the steps, beside her Da. Her Ma is somewhere behind them in the hall, her face like a damp sheet. A small group of women around the door, praying and blessing themselves as the ambulance drives away. All granny's prayers and cures and blessed scapulars and poor Olive Elizabeth is still gone to heaven. They do more tidying, even though the place is tidy already and granny Connor breaks more sticks to keep the fire going.

"This place is frozen,"she says. "No wonder she got sick, the little angel. The Corporation should do somethin' about the damp of these places."

Their flat is always cold, when the fire goes out. There's draughts under the doors and damp under some of the windows. That's why the baby got sick. Granny pulls at her hair and gives out stink. She walks round and round the flat in little circles, like a mad woman.

"Her little heart wasn't strong enough," she says.

They all say it's Gods will and that's supposed to make it all right. They always say that when someone dies. Patti hides in the wardrobe and she cries and she cries until there's no more tears. She knows she'll never see her sister again. She's gone to Heaven and Heaven is full of angels who'll take care of her but still. She wishes she wasn't gone. The Holy Angels is where she's getting buried. They have another baby in there, a little baby boy called John Michael. They'll keep each other company in the Holy Angels, granny Connor says, so she won't be lonely.

Goo Chaney gives out custard creams at her door and there's a queue of kids waiting. The grannies stay and make a big coddle. Afterwards, they get the kids ready for bed. In the dark kitchen, they sit around the fire. They wipe their eyes and blow their noses into hankies. The flames make big shapes and shadows on the grey wallpaper and the trees seem to sway. Their faces look spooky in the firelight. Patti hopes they don't give out to one another, like they usually do. But they don't. Instead, the grannies give out stink about the Coombe nurses.

"Why didn't they take that baby back to the hospital if she was sick?"

"Why didn't they know she was sick?"

"Have they no brains, them country bitches?"

"Didn't she turn blue after they left?"

They should've done this or that or the other thing.

Why?

Why?

Why?

Her Ma is in the bedroom again, she won't drink tea or eat toast. They try to make her eat a boiled sausage in a bit of coddle, but she's not hungry; all she wants are cigarettes. Granny Connor says: "What else has she only the cigarettes?"

One says:

"She should've had more sense leaving it to the last minute."

The other says: "How was she to know it was the last minute?"

Goo says what's done is done and arguing won't bring the little one back. They bow their heads. They kneel down again and take out the rosary beads and it's a quickity quick decade of the Rosary, with them all racing along.

"HailMaryfullagrace thelordiswithee . . . holy Mary . . . mother a God."

Her Da goes out; maybe he has to work all night in Radio Cabs. Before bed, they get radiomulsion and castor oil and orange junior aspirins for their colds. Someone brings holy water and shakes it around the rooms. They make faces at the grannies behind their backs. Franey sticks out his tongue and does granny Connor's funny walk and Patti has to check him.

Her Ma can't go out until she gets churched. She always gets churched in a little font of holy water after the baby is christened. She's not strong before that and it's a sin in-anyway to go out until your churched. Granny reminds her, the next day:

"Make sure you get churched."

"I can't get churched with no baby," she shouts back.

"Don't stir out of this house until you do."

And then she closes the door and they can hear her angry brown boots tramping down the block. Patti thinks that's stupid, because her Ma has to go out to get churched, doesn't she? She can't get churched in the room can she? It's always the same, when a new baby comes. Her Ma never ventures out until she's churched. She has to stay indoors. She can't show her face in public. She feels horrible. She looks pale and sick. She doesn't smile. It's like she has this new-baby-sin on her soul and the priest has to pray it away with a special blessing and holy water. Her Ma says it's a bit like when you get confession and your soul feels clean again.

If someone in your family dies, people are nice to you, they give you sweets and rub your head.

"God love them," they keep saying.

Patti keeps thinking of Olive Elizabeth, out there in the cold wet graveyard, even though she's supposed to be in Heaven. Her white shawl, her cold little face, what kind of a box was she in?

"A shoe box," one of the targers said. But the baby wouldn't fit in a shoe box, she's too big and her Ma only says "Shurrup!" if she asks her questions.

"Shurrup, shurrup, shurrup."

She had to figure it out for herself. She's too big for a shoe box, so maybe they have baby coffins, she thinks, like with white silky bits to cover them, like the grown- ups have when they die. This targer said, they dump the babies into this big horrible hole in the Holy Angels, a bunch of dead babies at a time. She hopes that's not true. She hopes the coffins will all stick together down there, like next door neighbours. She hopes they'll keep each other warm. All the babies in the Holy Angels are dead lucky, because it's holy ground up there, in a blessed graveyard. Before the Holy Angels, the Limbo babies without baptism had to get buried outside the graveyard, in the ditches and the hedgerows. That's what her granny said.

Everyone says, we all have to keep praying for poor Olive Elizabeth, that she has the safe journey to Heaven. And we have to pray for Ma, that she'll pull herself together. Maybe they're right, when they say it's God's will and he has a special plan worked out.

"Only very special babies go to Heaven," Ma says, "the ones God wants."

"Why does he want them?"

"Because."

"Because what?"

"Just because . . . He makes them into angels."

"Then why did they come here in the first place?"

"Just because. Now shurrup, you'd give a saint a headache with your forty questions."

Her Ma is narky and nervy and lonely. She's skinny as anything, her grey blouse hanging off her shoulders. She never goes out, even though she got churched and it's allowed. The aunties say she'll waste away. One of her friends says, it might be a good idea to visit the Holy Angels' grave. It might do her good.

9

THE HOLY ANGELS

So they all went to the Holy Angels one Sunday. They walked from town, a big big long walk up the Broadstone Hill, past the pointy stony wall with the plants and purple flowers growing sideways. The big breeze blows them all up the street.

They picked a few daffs in Mary Street Park when the gardener wasn't there. One daff each for Olive Elizabeth and John Michael, one for her Ma and a few for the kids. Miles and miles they walked, past the bus station, the babby bawling his eyes out in the pram. Franey sat down on the path and started to take off his shoes. Then he starts to run away in his socks.

"Get a hold of him!" her Ma goes, and Patti has to chase after him.

Anna and Bernie were digging and kicking as usual, tearing each others daff's and calling each other names.

Jimmy was fed up.

"Oh Ma, I'm jaded, I can't walk all this way," he says.

"Oh Ma! Oh Ma! Oh Ma is up there in proddyland, with Ah Ma. Walk! Your not feeble! You have legs!"

It looks dark all of a sudden.

"Looka that sky, were in for it all right with more bloody rain on the way."

Her Ma starts to walk faster. A big truck goes by and splashes them. Patti wipes her glasses on her sleeve and sneaks them into her pocket. They have to go miles in from the graveyard gate, past the big posh graves, with the holy statues and the big mouldy crosses and it's real creepy and spooky. There's holes in some of the old graves, where you can see down.

"Some of those graves are over one hundred years old," her Ma says.

It lashed then when they got to The Holy Angels. Out of the heavens! A big black sky over their heads, with masses of moving clouds. Then they hear the banging noise of thunder and her

Ma is afraid of her life of thunder. Patti didn't see this big dirty puddle, so she steps right into it. Water comes out of the sides of her shoes and makes a sucky sound.

"Look where you're goin' and put them glasses back on for Godsake."

Her Ma's voice sounds shaky. They're all drenched. Their feet as well: Jimmy's bopper boots, Franey's rock-in- roll boots, Anna's and Bernie's good T strap shoes. There's this rubbery smell of wet socks. Patti's socks are sopping. Her Ma's slip-on shoes are like accordion pleats, the way they slip down at the back. Her scarf is stuck to her head. She has hair-clips in. With the hairnet over the clips, and the scarf over the net, she looks funny, like one of the factory girls. They all start to shiver. They want to go home. They hate this place. It's spooky as anything.

They all spread out around the big fat grave, but it doesn't look like a proper grave at all, it's just like a big hill of mucky ground. Behind an iron bar, there's rows of dirty teddy bears, golliwogs and rag dolls, plastic flowers in glass roundy cages. There must be hundreds of babies down there, teeny weeny new born ones like her sister, and bigger ones that could crawl and bigger ones again, that could toddle and talk when they died.

"Where's Olive Elizabeth?" Patti says and she tries to see her under the ground. She thinks she must be near the top part, under the hill, with all the other new dead babies.

Her Ma looks sad.

"They're all angels now," she says, trying to light her cigarette.

"All holy angels and all together up in Heaven."

"If they're angels," Anna says, "how come they're down there in the muck?"

Her Ma tries to explain.

"They're not really in there. Their souls kinda fly up ta Heaven; it's like they get their wings. It's only their bodies stay here."

Anna keeps staring at the grave. She doesn't understand.

Her Ma's face is a bit puzzled looking.

Franey is climbing up a mouldy cross, with green velvety scabs stuck to it. It's a Celtic cross. Patti is learning all about the Celts in school. There was the Iron Age and the Bronze Age. They made lovely jewellery with tools they made themselves.

"Get him down quick, before we're put out," her Ma says.

Patti pulls him down. He kicks her in the legs, tries to bite her wrist. Her Ma says she'll tell their Da when they go home, but they know she's only messing. A man with a navy coat with silver buttons gives out to them for messing. He's collecting rubbish into a plastic bag. He has on green rubber gloves.

"Hey Missus, control them kids," he shouts over.

Her Ma's starey face looks over at him, but says nothing.

It's too wet to kneel down properly so they kind of half kneel, the way men do in chapel. They say prayers for their brother and sister and their granny's dead babies and all the other babies and a special prayer for any that got stuck in Limbo or purgatory.

"May they rest in peace," her Ma says, but Patti knows they won't, if they weren't christened. Purgatory is a horrible place that you might never get out of, but it's not as bad as hell. There's tons of babies in purgatory, they're called the Holy Souls. They always pray for the Holy Souls at Halloween. She's glad her sister and brother aren't stuck there. Patti knows they're up in Heaven and not really in the ground. They were magic'd up as soon as they got christened and away they flew, like lovely birds through the fluffy clouds. She thinks she sees them in little white cribs with frilly covers, in the christening robes, the two of them cooing and gurgling to one another. The Holy Angels up in Heaven are taking care of them. A nice little place they have up there, with their granda Connor and their cousins and God. Maybe they had a welcome party.

They leave the daffs down on the muck inside the bar; they're a bit shaggy from all the rain. Bernie's and Anna's are pulled to smithereens, but Ma says that's all right, because the baby won't mind. She fixes them nice and straight. A yellow row of shaggy daffs then, near the teddies and the golliwogs. Then she has the waterworks, little tiny tears she wipes with the corner of her scarf. They all have the waterworks, even the babby.

"We'll all be together some day up in Heaven," she says, blessing herself.

Patti wonders will the babies be grown up by then or still be babies. Can you grow up in Heaven or do you stay a baby forever?

A woman beside them says to her Ma, she has six in that grave. Ma says:

"Lorda Mercy," and blesses herself again."I'll say a prayer for the poor creatures, but sure they're in Heaven to be sure."

The woman nods and wipes her eyes. She has the waterworks too, big streaky lines down her face. She's kneeling down in the muck, she has on a black coat and Patti sees holes in the soles of her shoes, her stockings in wrinkles around her ankles. She wants to go then. The woman might bring her Ma to the pub. Yes. And she'll have to wait outside the pub with all the kids, so she pulls at her Ma's coat.

"C'mon Ma."

She knows she wants a little glass of stout for her nerves. She knows by the look on her face, sort of sad, sort of lonely and a little bit nervy.

"Ma it's gettin' late and were all drownded and Franey is messin' and the babby and. . . . ."

"Shurrup for Godsake. You're as bad as a husband, always watchin' everything."

Her Ma looks up at the sky, a heavy shower of rain hits her in the face. She closes her eyes for a minute and the rain makes stripes on her face. A loud bang of thunder then. She covers her face with her hands.

"God between us and all harm." She blesses herself.

"It doesn't look much like Heaven up there this day," she says in a low voice.

The woman in the black coat asks her where do they live. Ma tells her they live in town near the markets. The woman's eyebrows go up. She says, she only lives a stones throw away in Stonybatter herself.

"Go way outa that, now there's a coincidence. I'm delighted to meet ya," her Ma says.

They start to yap as they walk towards the gate. They go left and walk back down the long graveyard road, past the railings and the high wall. After ages they turn at a busy corner. Then it's another long road that takes them onto the Broadstone and Constitution Hill. It's a long, long walk and everyone is fed up. They all have the waterworks on the way home. Another truck goes by and splatters them again. A big huge wave of dirty water, but her Ma roars at the driver this time.

"Ya bloody eejit ya!"

Then the woman in the black coat waves her fist at him, but the driver just grins and spits sideways out the open window, like he doesn't care. The babby in the pram is drownded, his face and his hair.

"Never mind that cheeky bugger, I have the price of a glass, Missus," the woman says. "I'm gaspin' with the drought."

Oh O! Patti thinks. Her Ma's face lights up. She says she's parching herself and they'd better take shelter in-anyway out of this woeful weather. They stop at a pub in Stonybatter. It's the woman's local, a grand little place, she says, with a snug and a fire and a nice glass of stout. Outside the pub they gather into the porch. They won't be ten minutes, they say. The two of them sit down near the door in the snug. It's empty in there, so they have the whole place to themselves. The woman brings out a packet of Tayto to share out with the kids. Patti shakes the little bag of salt into the crisps and the hands start to grab. Then her Ma brings out another packet. Good job the pub has a porch or they'd all be drownded. After a good while, they come back out.

The woman says: "Bye bye and God bless."

She grabs their faces and gives them big messy porter kisses on the cheeks. Anna wipes hers off with the back of her hand. Franey says:Yuk yuk and does spits. Bernie makes a face. Ma is only a bit tiddly, because Ma's are not allowed to get sozzled.

In Nelly's, they get the bag of broken biscuits and maybe they're having a going- away party for Olive Elizabeth. Nelly comes out from under the counter to get the biscuits out of the glass box. She has to bend down and they can see her fat flowery bum and her big iron shoe. One of her legs is shorter than the other, so Nelly has a halt. There's a smell of Lifebuoy soap and ham and sweets. Nelly is nice and friendly. She fills a white bag to the top and throws in a couple of chocolate gold grain.

"Oh thanks very much Nelly." Her Ma hands over the money. Patti sees her Ma is happy then. For a minute. Then she looks sad again.

Outside, near the flats' gate, she says she might be going to England and they'll all have to go into a home. Patti heard her say that before. Sometimes when she's sad or fed up, she says that.

"Yiz'll all be put away." And she has this queer dreamy look.

"We're not goin', " Patti says.

"Yiz are."

"No we're not! We'll go to our granny's."

"Yiz'd be better off in a home."

"No we wouldn't!"

Granny says Ma'll be all right in a few months time, when she gets another new baby. It's because of Olive Elizabeth, she's so sad. Patti thinks she won't be all right. She hears her crying in the night, she sees her sad red eyes.

On the southside, everyone is praying a big mountain of prayers. In her lace Black mantilla, with her beads hanging and her head down, Aunt Jinny says a whole rosary in Adam an Eve's chapel. In John's Lane, uncle Fran kneels in the end pew and you can hear his whispery prayers around the walls. In Saint Audoen's, Aunt Annie lights candles to the Sacred Heart and the Blessed Virgin and Saint Francis. All the prayers offered up for Olive Elizabeth's soul. She must've got her angel wings by now. Her soul must be spotless clean, like a dusted blackboard. Patti thinks of the prayers and the baptism making her pure.

10

NO BED OF ROSES

It's like a line out of a song. Whenever her Ma says it, it's usually the start of a crappy day.

"It's no bed of roses." She says.

It's not just her Ma, it's other Ma's too. Especially if they're broke and in bad humour.

"It's no bed of roses, "they say, if they're out yapping at the doors.

At first, she thought it was something to do with flowers. But it's only one of their sayings. They mean, it's no bed of roses after you get married, it's more like a bed of spiky thorns. You have a husband; that's maybe the worst bit. It gets hard. You have babies, maybe one every year, maybe two in the same year. All of a sudden, you have a new baby and a babby and a toddler at the same time. You have tons of dirty nappies to wash. You have mouths to feed and bills to pay and sometimes you can't manage. It's like they're trying to tell you something, in code language, about what it might be like, when you grow up. They're trying to give you a warning. Her Ma always looks sad and miserable when she says it, especially if the wages are all spent, or if her Da is like a bear with a sore head.

"It's no bed of roses."

"God is good," that's another one of her sayings.

"It's no bed of roses, but sure God is good."

That's ok, if she says it that way.

Her Ma is very quiet and moody. Since the new baby went to Heaven. She lies down a lot. Sometimes she just sits there, staring at the floor. She smokes and smokes rings around her. She closes the curtains to keep out the light. The bath fills up with dirty clothes. Sometimes, the babby's face is not washed.

"Ma." Patti says.

"Wha'?"

"Do ya believe in Heaven?"

"Course I do."

"Are ya sure, on'y . . . ?"

"On'y what?"

"On'y . . . Nothin'."

Her voice is deep and choky. She stares at the floor. She blows smoke downwards. It goes in under the table, swirls round there near her feet She's not wearing stockings. Her legs are very white. There's no veins there now, only white skin and a few abc marks. All her clothes are loose. It's a grey blouse she's wearing now, not a loose smock, like she usually wears. She starts to look at the backs of her hands. She turns out the palms like she's looking for something. Her hands are red and cracked, the fingers swollen, like fat sausages. It's all the hard work, Patti supposes, the washing and wringing out, the heavy messages she carries from the shops. The babbies. Her fingers and nails are yellow. She says it's from the cigarettes, all the Players Navy Cut she smokes. She doesn't use hand-cream. It's like she doesn't care. The aunties use Nulon hand cream and Nivea cream on their faces. Why doesn't her Ma? Patti wonders.

"Ma."

"Wha'?"

"Aunt Dinah uses Nulon. "

"So?"

"So? Your hands! Lookit! They're all red and sore. Nulon makes your hands soft. Aunt Dinah rubs it in every night. It has a lovely lemony smell. She says lemons are good for your skin."

"Does she?"

"Good for veins and abc's as well."

"Is that so?"

It's no use talking to her. Sometimes, it's like she's gone away with Olive Elizabeth. Or with the fairies or the gypsies. Sometimes, it's like she's never coming back. Her face is different. She has a faraway look. She won't wash her face. Or rub the bit of Vaseline into her eyebrows, like she used to, or wear the bit of rouge to give her face a colour. They don't go out anymore. Ever! They used to go out for a drink to Boland's bar. Her Ma and her Da. Very seldom. An odd time. It was dead mad, when Aunt Dinah came to baby sit, with bagfuls of yummy stuff for the babysitting party: ice-cream and Taylor Keith's orange, peanuts and popcorn and they'd have this brillo time while they were out. But that was ages ago, before Olive Elizabeth came. In the bedroom, at the mirror, Aunt Dinah used to make up her Ma's face. Out comes the rouge, lipstick and pancake makeup from under the clothes in the wardrobe. On goes Ma's happy going out face.

"On'y a little bit. He'll have a canary," she used to say and Dinah used to say, "Let him have two canaries," even though she's Da's sister. Her Da thinks rouge and makeup are common and vulgar, but her Ma always looked nice, with her face done up.

"Ma."

"Wha'?"

"D'ya think the baby can see us? From Heaven I mean?"

All her Ma does, is hunch her shoulders.

"Ma."

"Wha'?"

"There's washin', in the bath, woolens and socks and . . ."

"Yeah, I know. Now drink your tea and stop annoyin' me."

Granny Connor comes over to give a hand with the washing, but her back is not up to it. She's no good at wringing out and she won't use the washing-board.

"Move that contraption outa the way," she says.

She kicks it out of her way. Patti tries to help. The clothes are dripping over the bath, water pouring down like a waterfall. Granny says she's not as young as she used to be. She rubs her back in the middle part.

"All them clothes! How does your Ma manage atall? How is her back not broke from washin'?"

She wipes her forehead with the back of her hand.

"Your Ma's in smithereens. She'll end up in the Gormon if this keeps up," she says.

"She will not," Patti straight tells her.

In the bedroom, granny tells her Ma to pull herself together, to buck up or else. But she doesn't seem to hear. She's too faraway, hiding in under a big cloud of cigarette smoke.

Granny looks angry. She puts one hand up to her head, she presses the part between her eyebrows. Then she starts to tidy up the place. She makes a fresh pot of tea. She empties nearly half the packet of mauve label into the pot, after she wets it. Then she pours water from the kettle and puts the gas on a glimmer.

"She won't refuse a cuppa tae. Now bring them childer for a walk, like a good girl."

"All she wants are her Players and tea," Patti says.

"Don't I know, she drinks oceans and you'd want a tea plantation as well as a tobacco plantation for that one."

It's like her Ma is thinking all the time. Maybe like Patti, she's wondering what would Olive Elizabeth be like if she grew into a kid; a little messer, like Franey, a little rise-a-row, like Anna, a bloody dribbler, like the babby, or dead quiet, like Bernie. Would she like Liga biscuits or Farley's rusks, Goody Goody or mashed potato? Would she be a bawler or a whinger? Would she like elocution? Would she like chapel? Be lampy like Patti, have a split in her teeth, be short and chubby, or skinny and lanky? Would she read library books? Would she like Macaroon bars or Trigger bars? They'll never know, so it's stupid wondering. Aunt Dinah says it's only natural and any mother who lost a child would be the same. This day, to cheer her up, she buys her ten Players and four jam doughnuts. Ma's face is like a lit up statue, when she sees Dinah with the smokes, so in she toddles pronto to the scullery to make tea. Dinah cuts up the cakes into slices and they have a little party. And it's like the old babysitting times. Everyone has jammy faces. Everyone is happy again.

11

THE SCHOOL ON THE HILL

School is crap. The nuns and the stupid navy gymslip. The yukki horrible smell of chalk and cabbage and cauliflower.

The margarine lunches!

The dunce's corner!

Drill!

The scratchy blackboard!

Needlework! Especially needlework.

She remembers her first day at school, she was only three and a bit, but they took her because she was big for her age. Her Ma left her at the class room door. Patti had shivery waves and knotty bits in her belly. She wanted to cry but she didn't want to be a crybabby.

Ma goes: "Go on now, be a good girl for teacher and no messin'. Hear me?"

Then she gives her a little push in through the door. She saw her rushing down the hallway then, her check coat swinging, her black hair bouncing. Then she was gone.

The room is huge with big glass walls; there's rows of kids with their arms folded.

Teacher sits her up at the front because she's new. All the kids gawk at her. Brown eyes and blue eyes. Big eyes and small eyes. After a bit, she bawls her eyes out and teacher gives her this pink tin elephant to keep her quiet. She squeezed the elephant too hard and it cracked into smithereens. She wasn't allowed to go to the toilet until the bell rings. She had a pain in her belly. The wet went down her leg into her stockings. There was a trickly line of pooly under the desk. She could feel it, all squelchy in her boots. Warm at first, then cold. So teacher sent her home with one of the big girls.

When she was four, she went to the convent on the hill. Everyone is afraid of the nuns with the long black habits and veils. You can only see their faces and hands. They wear a white cardboard thing, like a baby's dribbler, across their chests, black lace-up shoes with blocky heels. They carry big sticks to bash you with.

Her Ma says: "You wouldn't mess with the likes of them nuns."

They're supposed to put manners on you and make you holy and brainy. Her first teacher in the convent wasn't a nun. She was a skinny woman with a tweed skirt and brown curly hair. She had red lipstick lips that go in a straight line, like they're stuck shut. Everyone was right when they said she's hard and cross. She walks backwards and forwards across the blackboard, with her ruler held up and her heels bang hard against the floorboards. Miss Moriarity talks in Irish and English at the same time. She mixes the words up in a sentence, so you don't know what she's talking about.

That was called low babies, they had slates and chalk and sticky grey marla. Patti made a roundy shape for a man. Roundy shape for a woman. Roundy shape for a cat. She stuck on arms and legs and paws. She made holes for eyes with her pencil. They learned the abc rhyme, the A for apple, B for ball stuff. They counted coloured beads across a yellow bead frame. Patti falls asleep on the desk sometimes and teacher shakes her awake. Then she might have to stand out at the wall up behind the blackboard, near the dunce's corner. That's when her knees get tired and she has to move from one foot to the other, like she's doing a dance.

You have to ask to go to the toilet in Irish. You put up your hand. You wave it around in the air. You wait. It's hard to say it in Irish, a big long word. Willcadagumdulamach . . . something like that. Teacher gives you a look that says, no you cannot. Patti crosses her knees and waits until small break. She listens to the sounds outside, people calling other people in the market, the brass bell ringing, the singsongy voices of the auctioneers: *bybiddybybiddyby*. Through the high windows, the cloud shapes move across the sky and turn into animals: a white poodle, a grey elephant, a blue fish with a big fluffy tail. She thought of her Ma, at home with the babby. She thought of Russian slices and Trigger bars and pink mice in Mike Nolan's window. She made a run for it then, out the door into the back yard to the toilet. She nearly bursted.

***

Nuns are baldy as anything under the black veils. They have to cut off all their hair when they marry God. They take vows and oaths. They eat tons of cabbage. A big girl in the flats told her, they're supposed to have blue pooly instead of yellow.

"Nuns have blue piss, cause they're pure as anything, " she whispered.

"Whacha mean?" Patti said.

"It's like holy water, only it's blue."

"Are ya sure? There's these kidney tablets that makes it go blue as well. Granny has them. I think they're called Dewitt's kidney pills."

"No. It's not tablets. It's holy piss. I swear."

They see their clothes hanging on the lines in the convent-garden. The nice nun with the tied up apron and the lovely face hangs out washing every day. Huge black bloomers, black stockings, black vests, black petticoats, black other things, she doesn't know the name of. They can't go near them. One day, they got into serious trouble. It was only for the laugh, after big break when everyone was gone back in. They kept looking at the clothes flapping in the wind. Vera takes down the bloomers and puts them up to her. Then Patti feels one of the stockings.

"Go on take it down, I double dare ya," Vera goes.

"I will not. It's horrible."

The bloomers are gynormous! Nearly up to Vera's shoulders.

Vera puts her legs through the elastic holes, holds them up and runs around the convent garden like a mad thing. Then they see her, Staniclaws with her bendy back coming from the convent chapel. Vera kicks off the bloomers and leaves them on the grass. They leg it quick, but it's too late. She saw them. With a big face on her, she comes rushing over and drags them up the stairs by the cardigan sleeves to Reverend Mother's of-fice. She whispers something into her ear. Then she looks at them out over her silver glasses. Reverend Mother is the oldest nun in Ireland; maybe she's the oldest nun in the whole world. She starts to get up, with her walking stick. Then she flops back down with a thump. She looks across her desk at them with her bulgy eyes. She talks in a shaky voice.

"What kind of behaviour is this? What would our foundress have thought of this disgraceful carrying-on?"

She looks past them at the two pictures on the wall; Nano Nagle and Maria Teresa Mulally, with a bonnet tied under her chin.

"Well? Speak up I said."

"I don't know mother," Patti says. She looks over at Vera then. Vera says: "Neither do I mother," and starts to splutter. Reverend Mother's face goes red then, a big stain all the way up to her eyebrows. She shakes her head from side to side, like this new walkie talkie doll that's out. For their punishment they get two hard slaps each, loads of extra eccer, and they have to stay back all week after school, to dust the statues and holy pictures in the convent hall. It's like someone lit a fire in the soft part of her hand. It's like her heart moved down her arm and into her hand; it throbs and beats the same way. She has to run it under the tap to cool it down.

The next day, they have to sit at the back of the class with the slow girls. There's the girl that keeps twisting her head and laughing for nothing. There's one with a bad stutter, who can't hear properly. They all mess down there with the ink wells, or stick pencils in their ears, or pinch one another under the desks. One of them makes funny babby faces and has dribbles down her chin. Poor Kathleen can't even hold her pencil properly and maybe she might be an orphan from Dominick Street orphanage. There's a few orphans in their school, with no Ma's or Da's. There's the very poor girls, who wear long flowery dresses, called Hand-me-downs. There's a small stocky girl, with hunched shoulders and her head twisted to one side all the time. There's a girl on crutches with steel braces on her legs. She leaves her crutches at the wall and takes big giant side-steps to her desk. She doesn't want help, even though her legs are twisted. They heard you can get polio from a dirty toilet seat; that's why Patti has to crouch and not sit on public toilets. One of the girls with no gymslip has a lazy eye. She looks at you with one eye and the other eye looks somewhere else. There's a few like that with bad eyes: lazy eyes and cross eyes, eyes that stare too long at you, eyes that roll for nothing.

Sometimes in class, they have to share books, one book between two girls, or two books between three girls. The girls with the Clarks shoes and the snow white socks always have all their books on the first of September. The rest of them pay something off their books every week.

***

Most of the girls in her class are ok. Some of them live in cottages, in Church Street and Beresford Street; a few still live in the old houses on the quays. Catherine lives in Finglas; she gets the number forty bus in every morning with her little sister. They have a pet hamster and a rabbit. She's a bit quiet, but she's nice. They share their books sometimes. They tell each other stuff about home, about Ma stuff and Da stuff, about drunken fights and new babies. Catherine is not posh, even though she lives in a house.

There's this lovely looking Indian girl called Gita with tan skin and black eyes. Her gymslip is brand new with all the box-pleats pressed dead neat into shape. Her crochet knee-socks are always snow white. Her hair shiny as anything in the long po-nytail with the flower toggle, a different colour every day. She wears Clarks leather shoes. She's a bit posh. When she stands up to read, everyone looks at her. First her face, then her shoes, then her face again. They must be rich, because her Da is going to be a doctor in the College of Surgeons and her Ma wears lovely clothes. She saw her Ma once at the school gate in a gorgeous long yellow dress with a shawl wrapped round her shoulders. Some of the girls are jealous, they say Gita is too full of herself. Maybe it's because she always has all her school books, in coloured plastic covers with her name on the front. Maybe it's because they have a lovely blue motor car. Maybe it's because she's nice looking. The posh girls don't mix with the flats' girls; that's the rule, so Gita would never be Patti's friend. She'd have to live in a house with a garden and flowers. Maybe her Da'd have to be a doctor or a policeman or a judge.

She has a hoarse, breathy voice, strange spots like chocky brownies on her face. One of the spots has a hair that sticks out near her bottom lip. Her permed hair is like rusty steel-wool; sometimes she wears a white hair-band to keep it back off her face. Twice a week they have drill in the drill-hall. Drill is supposed to wake them up, but it only makes them more tired. Their drill teacher, Miss Dredge, wears white ankle socks and Irish dancing pumps, with crossed straps up her ankles. They have to do stupid arm circles and march around the drill-hall like little soldiers. Then she makes them run as fast as they can, up and down, up and down, until they're out of breath.

"Girls Girls!" she goes, clapping her hands. She has a whistle on a string around her neck; she keeps blowing the whistle for nothing and grinding her teeth. Sometimes she leaves them on their own and lets them mess around. They do tumbles and cartwheels while she's outside. That's when Miss Dredge has a sneaky smoke outside the drill hall. She picks pieces of cigarette paper off her tongue with her nail. She puts out the cigarette if she hears one of the nuns coming down the stairs. She's teaching them a soft shoe reel, but it's not as easy as it looks. Miss Dredge says they all have elephant feet and they'd be more at home in a circus. They're supposed to have black leather dancing pumps, but only a few of them have. Dancing pumps cost a small fortune downtown. There's a couple of posh girls who go to Irish dancing lessons in the Father Matthew hall. They have all the stuff: pumps and hornpipe shoes and fancy embroidered dresses. They're always practicing for the Feis Ceoil and the Christmas concerts. Patti likes the hornpipe; it's the best Irish dance, well better than the soft shoe reel, she thinks.

In the canteen, there's black and white tiles in a diamond shape on the floor. They sit on long wood benches at long tables. It's always cold in there, even in summer. A draught comes over your shoulders, like a cold hand, no matter where you sit. They get a sandwich and a small bottle of milk for school lunch. The iron crates of milk are stacked up in the yard and sometimes, if it's sunny out, the bottles get warm. They drink the milk through the sticky cream at the top. The lunch woman hands out the soggy sandwiches from a huge basket. She wears a roundy black hat, like the one the Pope wears, on the back of her head, a white apron under her coat. It's always the same: tinned beef on Monday, gooey cheese on Tuesday, currant buns on Wednesday, fatty pink brawn on Thursday and jam on Friday. The bread is always damp and soggy, with lumpy bits of white margarine sticking through the holes. You'd know it wasn't real butter and it tastes horrible. Jam day's are the best, but it's not like real jam either, only a skinny scrape of red stuff with no blackcurrants or strawberries. The posh girls like Gita have their own made up lunches in greaseproof paper with small bottles of orange and cola. They have fancy looking three corner cut sandwiches, with real butter and ham paste and lettuce and cucumber. They wouldn't eat those free school lunches in a million years, they say, and Patti wouldn't blame them. Sometimes, they get a second bottle of milk, if there's some left over. The lunch woman hands them around the class. She shares out the leftover sandwiches and buns and some of the girls stuff them in their schoolbags.

At home, she practices her sewing on a square piece of cloth. It's supposed to be a seam, but it always goes crooked so she starts to mess. She has hard skin on her palms. She starts to make stitches there. The needle goes in easy. It doesn't hurt. She makes a pattern around the fat part of her palm. She joins up the tips of her fingers. That doesn't hurt either. It's dead neat, like a magic trick. They'll give out hell if they catch her, but what they don't know won't kill them.

Patti hates needlework.

Everyone says she's the hardest slapper in the whole school. She pulls ears and shakes shoulders, she gives them digs in the side of the head with her knotty knuckles, but, the worst thing about the needlework nun is the way she peers at you sideways from behind her silver glasses, then she puts down her head and looks at you over the top. It's a long icy-cold look. A look that says she hates you, a look that says, you're useless and you'll always be in her bad books. You try not to look at her pale watery eyes. You try to look at the sewing chart on the wall behind her, with the pictures of different stitches.

She calls her Staniclaws behind her back. Everyone is afraid of her. She has a bendy back, a red chinny face. She wears a black crochet shawl, fingerless wool gloves, so you can see all her fingers, with the thimbles like little silver lids. She marches around the class, with her shawl pulled tight around her shoulders. She moves kind of ghostly down between the desks, and you'd think she was on wheels. She holds up her slapper and watches for idlers down at the back of the class. Sometimes she taps the backs of their hands with the slapper to frighten them; it's a quick little tapety-tap, and they all have to stitch stitch, faster faster. All of a sudden, she might pull one of them from the desk and give her a good shaking to wake her up. Her face goes redder and she has to take off her glasses to clean them. She looks even crosser without her glasses.

Patti always has shaky hands in the needlework class. They practice hemming and tacking and running. First she has to thread her needle. She wets the thread in her mouth and holds the needle up to the light. Even with her glasses on, it's hard to see the eye. It takes her forever to thread the needle, with Stani watching over her shoulder. She taps her with her slapper on the knuckles and that's when they start to shake. Then everything goes wrong after that. Her line of stitches goes crooked, like bokety teeth. It's the same with knitting; she keeps dropping stitches and making holes, the holes get bigger and bigger, so what she's trying to knit looks like a fishnet instead of a neck scarf. Stani says she's a day dreamer. Stani says she's an idler.

They make faces behind her back, but they have to watch out, because she might have eyes in the back of her head. She might have eyes that see out through her head-veil. This day, she's walking up and down the class with her slapper held up, watching out for messers. Patti could feel her behind her. All of a sudden, she grabs her square of cloth and holds it up in front of everyone. The cloth is creased. The stitches are all crooked and bandy. Stani tells the class to pay attention. She goes to her sewing box on the desk, takes out a card of pins. She pins the cloth to Patti's school cardigan, like a horrible badge. It's a holy show. She sends her around the classes to show it off. It's to make a show of her; she saw her do that before to one of the slow girls. She's not a crybabby, but she cries outside the class door, the stupid tears sloshing down her face. She dries her eyes with her sleeve. Then she has to knock on all the class doors and walk up to the front like a thicko. Then they're all laughing and gawking at her and she feels dead dopey. Then it's Catherine's turn. Catherine cries bucketloads in the jacks at small break. She's leaving this school for deffo she says. She's going to a proper school out in Finglas where there's no horrible nuns.

***

In her new class, they started doing geography. It's all about their country. It's all about Ireland; the mountains and lakes and rivers. It's terrific! Nearly as good as history. Patti had to buy an atlas in Eason's and granny says she hopes it's worth it. First, she traces out the map of Ireland with tracing paper. Then she draws it free hand. They're learning the counties; they mark them into their maps with colouring pencils. The map shows the borderline dividing the north and the south. The six counties that got robbed from us have a red line marking them out. A big chunk of Ireland is up there behind the red line. Patti is glad she doesn't live up there, in the middle of the six counties. Sister shows them where they live on the map. She says they're very privileged to be city children, living in the heart of a capital city. Patti thinks it's terrific to be living on the very edge of Ireland. She likes the shape of Ireland, the way it's rugged around the edges; especially the leggy jagged parts down at the end, called peninsulas.

By the end of the year, they'll have learned the rivers, the lakes, and the mountains. Sister writes the names of the mountains on the blackboard: the Macgillacuddy Reeks, the Comeraghs, the Galties, the Black Stairs. She draws three hills beside the name to show it's a mountain range. They're learning about the sugar factories and Newbridge Cutlery and Waterford Crystal.

In the Atlas, Ireland looks very close to England. There isn't much sea between the two countries and you'd think they were great pals. Sister says we were done out of the six counties when certain politicians signed a certain treaty. She points them out on the big plastic map on the wall. They call it the north now, but you'd know the counties still belonged to Ireland, even though the border is marked out. They have to learn them off by heart as well as all the other counties.

"Padraig Pearse would never have agreed to that Treaty," Sister says, turning her eyes towards the window. Padraig Pearse is her hero. You'd know by the proud look on her face when she talks about him. She looks out, kind of dreamy through the window. She loves to tell them all about Padraig; there's Padraig the scholar, Padraig the poet, Padraig the teacher, but most important is Padraig the soldier at the GPO and how he sacrificed his young life for Ireland.

"To die for your country, it is a glorious thing," she says.

Patti already knew a bit about Padraig from her granny's 1916 stories. She knew he was very brave; she knew he had principles and he wasn't afraid to die for his country. She knew all about James Connolly and trade unions and workers rights, about strikes and lockouts. Umpteen times, she heard all about sacrifices and spilt blood and mean landlords.

She knows it's full of protestants, up there behind the red border line, there's orange men with sashes and bowler hats, and big drums they wear in front of them like belly bumps. She heard the arguments at the hoolies. The men always start. It's always about the north. Then the 1916 Rising. Then the bloody Treaty. They bang their fists on the table, Treaty this and Treaty that, about De Valera and the IRA, about civil wars and uncivil wars, between brothers in their own homes, about the Black and Tans driving up their streets in their tanks and aiming their big guns up at their windows. The women join in then. Her granny could tell them a thing or two, she says, because she was there herself in the flesh and sometimes she tells her own story.

It was stupid giving away the six counties for a stupid treaty, Patti thinks. If you draw the map without the six counties, it looks a holy show.

Her granda says: "It looks like someone knocked Irelands block off."

Her granny says: "Don't start."

"Why did they give the six counties away?" Patti asked granda.

All he says is: "Don't get me started. Our history is complicated, it goes back hundreds of years to the Battle of the Boyne and maybe even further."

It's better not to get him started, because then he'll be in bad humour and granny too and they might start on about De Valera and Michael Collins.

In class the 1916 proclamation hangs on the wall next to the map of Ireland. It's old with brown spots in the paper; it has a hard plastic cover to keep it clean. Sister reads out a few sentences at a time and they have to repeat it after her. She heard bits of that proclamation before as well. Sister holds up a spotty page from the Irish Times newspaper with pictures of the leaders that were executed. They have to learn them off by heart. They're learning songs about Ireland: All around my Hat and Kevin Barry and Boolavogue.

All around my hat I wear a tri colour ribbon- o.

It sounds a bit like a culchie song. Patti prefers Kevin Barry. Most of them know the chorus of Kevin Barry, because it's one of the hooley songs.

In Mountjoy jail one Monday morning,
High upon the Gallows tree,
Kevin Barry gave his young life,
for the cause of liberty.

The Market dealers like Kevin Barry too. There's photos of him in all the market pubs. He's nice looking with lovely bright eyes.

Boolavogue is about Father Murphy at another rebellion in County Wexford.

71

At Boolavogue as the sun was setting,

on the bright May meadow of Shelmalire,

A rebel hand set the heather blazing

and brought the neighbours from far and near.

***

Their new nun is mad about history. She mixes history in with geography; sometimes she starts off with geography and ends up with history. She tells them, Saint Michan's parish is full of history, that they should be very proud of their wonderful school, one of the best in Dublin. It was founded by Maria Teresa Mulally in 1766. It's famous because it was the first free school for catholic girls in the city. Before that, you had to have money and pay to go to school in someone's front parlour. Down the country, they called them hedge schools. No one can believe it. Everyone is flabbergasted. Imagine having to pay to go to school? They don't know how lucky they are, to have the free education. They're living in wonderful times with endless opportunities, Sister says.

She tells them their foundress was a pioneer, who was born just around the corner in Chancery Street. A milliner, who made hats and gloves for the well to do ladies of the parish. She won stacks of money in the lottery and spent every penny on building the school. But she had to be careful. It was the eighteenth century. The penal laws were very strict; it was against the law to teach catholic children. There were people called mass hunters and priest hunters who gave out summons's and fines. You could get sent to jail for breaking the law. People had to get mass in sheds and back yards. The protestants gave out free dinners and clothes and footwear in the charter schools to get them converted. Some of the poor people sent their kids for the free dinners and that's how they became proddies. So along came Maria Teresa who put a stop to their gallop with her brand new

school in the middle of the city. With the lottery money, she
bought an old glass factory. Then she hired a builder.

The streets were full of raggy beggars, so she made part of
the school into an orphanage for homeless kids. She taught
them how to make hats and gloves. Sister tells them, they don't
know how lucky they are these days, because these children
were in school at half past seven every morning and didn't finish until six when the angelus bell rang. They didn't get summer holidays, just a few day's off at Christmas. They sold the
hats and gloves to the rich ladies for when they'd be going to
garden parties and balls. The ladies gave donations towards
the school and left money in their wills. Maria Teresa kept all
her accounts in a brown book. She was good at sums. She had
lovely curly handwriting. After years, she wasn't well. She had
bad headaches and fits. Nano Nagle was her penfriend. Nano
had started her own catholic school in Cork. Maria Teresa went
to Cork to visit her in a stagecoach, because there weren't any
trains at the time.

Sister shows them a drawing of their foundress. It's the same
one that's in the Reverend Mother's office. An old fashioned
woman wearing an old fashioned bonnet. She's buried in a
crypt underneath the convent. It's beside the private chapel. It's
supposed to be haunted down there with nuns that walk around
when it gets dark.

12

A VERY SPOOKY PLACE

It's the spookiest place in Dublin. The oldest chapel on the northside. It's only around two corners from their school. They were all flabbergasted when Sister announced they were going on a history tour to Saint Michan's protestant chapel. It's a very historic chapel, hundreds of years old, she told them. They already knew it was famous, because of Dracula and the mummies and the Sheares brothers. They know it's haunted by Dracula, whose supposed to appear at the front gate, every night at twelve on the dot.

They're in a line outside the school yard. Sister counts their heads, two at a time with the handle of her umbrella. They start out down the hill. Around the corner, turn right, up Mary's Lane, turn left around another corner into Church Street. Sister is walking fast at the top of the line; her habit blows up in a gust of wind and you can see her black ankles. Then her veil blows up and she has to hold it down. They're all digging one another and watching out for bits of her neck, but there's nothing under the veil, only more black cloth. She checks the line again, before crossing Church Street. Out through the line of slow traffic, she holds up her black umbrella, so they all start to walk across. It's supposed to be a dead neat line, with no stragglers or messers. If a girl breaks the line, Sister pushes her back in with her umbrella. Someone beeps a horn. A man gives her a dirty look, but Sister ignores him and they all get across.

At Saint Michan's gate they stop. She counts their heads again, two at a time. She won't stand for any misbehaviour. She warns them, before they go in, about noisiness. About rudeness. About smirking. About talking out of turn and general misconduct. There will be consequences, she tells them, for any untoward or disruptive behaviour. She doesn't want any complaints from people afterwards. Outside the walls of their school, they are representatives of the Presentation Order and they must behave themselves at all times. She bangs her umbrella handle off the stone wall, to make them listen. She tells them, what they are about to witness is a miracle of science. They know already, it's about the mummies. The mummies that can walk, because they never really died, the mummies that still have skin on their bones after hundreds of years. The place is supposed to be walking alive at night with mummies, they're supposed to rise out of the coffins and mooch around near the church gates in their leathery skin. Patti has the shivers, so has Catherine and Vera. So has everyone.

All of a sudden, this humpy oulfella with white hair and a black suit appears at the gate. He's holding a huge set of keys on a ring. His hand has the shakes, so the keys kind of rattle.

He says: "Good morning Sister," and pretends to lift an invisible hat off his head. His jacket looks old fashioned and shiny and too short for him, like the porter's jacket in the Gresham Hotel. He holds back the gate and lets them come through. Then he bends down to unlock this trap-door. He pulls it up like a big lid. It creaks. They all look down into this black hole. There's steep steps to climb down. The oulfella goes first. He takes ages to get to the bottom. Sister goes next. It's tricky with her long habit. She has to bunch her skirt to one side and hold it in case she trips.

She says: "My goodness!" and her face goes red. With her other hand, she grips the rail and steps down very slowly. They all have to follow. Down they go, one at a time, behind her. There's a musty smell on the way down and Patty starts to cough. They're in this crypt with skeletons and mummies. Sister puts her finger to her lips to tell them to be quiet. She walks on. She stands back, so they can see. The walls are greenish under the light bulb. There's another smell of something yuk. Something like Daisy market clothes and something like rotten fruit mixed up. They follow behind Sister. Here they go. Along the side, they see them, the mummies in the open coffins, their ugly black faces, their leathery skin. Some still have teeth, brown rotten yokes that seem to be grinning. It feels cold and spooky, like in a graveyard.

"Holy nightmare!" Patti whispers. She feels sick, it's like that sicky feeling when someone dies and they make you kiss the face. She wants to go back up. She's not the only one. They're all holding their stomachs around the mummies. Catherine has the cramps and she'll probably have to run to the toilet in a minute. The oulfella waits. He gives them a minute to recover.

"It's perfectly all right, a normal reaction," he says.

He introduces them. He says the mummies have names.

"There's the Unknown, the Thief, the Nun, and the Crusader."

He says no one knows who the Unknown is, the Nun is just a nun, the Thief has one hand missing and the Crusader will bring you luck if you shake his hand. You have to give it a good hard shake. He points to the Crusader. He says the Crusader mummy is over eight hundred years old, he was too tall for the coffin when he died, so they had to cut off his legs at the knees. He shows them his bottom legs are crossed over his chest like a crucifix. He was like a giant in his day, at over six and a half feet tall. No one wants to shake the Crusader's hand, so they move away as quick as they can. Next he shows them the coffins of the Sheares Brothers. He starts to tell them how they were hung, drawn and quartered and Sister says they know that story already and it's a bit gruesome for this hour of the day.

She claps her hands to get their attention.

"Girls girls, come stand beside me and listen."

They gather around her in a bunch. She tells them the mummies are preserved by a scientific process; it's because of the lime walls and the constant dry temperature and a special underground gas called methane. It's as dry as dust down there, so nothing rots.

"It's a wonder of nature," she says, "and you'd have to go a long long way to see anything like it, yet here it is on our own doorstep. I want you girls to take notes, because there might be a test afterwards."

They start to write into their jotters.

Has lime walls. Has special gases. Has mummies. It's scientific. Sheares Brothers hung drawn and quartered, Patti writes.

Whitey head is standing there with his hands behind his back. He has another story he's dying to tell them. He looks at Sister. Sister nods an ok.

He says; "A very famous Dublin author, called Bram Stoker, visited Saint Michan's and got so inspired that he wrote a very famous book. Does anyone know the name of that book?"

No answer.

"That famous book was called Dracula."

"Dracala?" Someone says. "Oh Mammy!"

"Yes, the Prince of Darkness himself began right here on the very spot where your standing."

Everyone does a shiver, even Sister, who looks very pale all of a sudden. Everyone knows about Dracula, but no one ever heard of Bram Stoker. Maybe that's why people say the real Dracula appears here at midnight. Bram Stoker might be related to Misses Stoke who owns a shop in Mary Street, Patti thinks.

Sister says she thinks they've had enough stories to stir their fertile imaginations, but could they, by any chance, see that famous Handel organ in the chapel? Whitey head does a little bow and says: "Of course Sister. No trouble at all Sister."

He leads them back up through the trap door. It takes him forever to climb up and he nearly falls on the last step. Next is the chapel tour. He opens the chapel door with loads of different keys. Then another inside door. From the back of the church, they see the organ. It's gigantic! With long pipes up to the ceiling. It's dead plain in the chapel, not like a proper chapel at all; for starters, there's no statues or holy pictures or candles and Patti is glad she's not protestant. Everything is wood; the walls, the pulpit, the pews and the balcony. Whitey head walks real slow up the aisle, dragging his leg like a peg leg. He stops in front of the organ. He holds out his arm. Sister starts asking him tons of questions about the organ. He's on about the make and the shape and the date of the organ. Then he gets to the good part. He raises his voice so they can all hear.

"Your standing in a very historic place. This organ is the most famous organ in all of Ireland. This organ is known all over the world. It's hundreds of years old. It was played by . . .

wait for it. It was played by, none other than the famous composer Handel. Handel played the Messiah for the very first time on that organ."

He plays a long low note on the organ and the spooky sound goes everywhere; up to the ceiling, back down, around the walls, into your ears and down your throat. Then he smiles, a big wide grin with his big teeth. He plays a higher note and everything shakes. Then they're all allowed to play one note each. It takes ages to get through them all. Vera plays a high note and Catherine plays a low note and Patti plays a long shivery note. Then Sister has a go herself. She's able to play a bit of piano, but she says she's out of practice. It's time to go then.

At the gate, another tour is waiting, a bunch of people with umbrellas and coloured raincoats. On the way out, Vera says, the mummies were brill and the next time she'll shake the Crusaders hand no bother if Patti does too. They swear on the holy bible, they'll shake hands with the mummies, the next time.

Back in the classroom, Sister is all excited about the tour. They have a discussion about what they saw and then she writes out questions on the blackboard.

Who were the Sheares Brothers?

How are mummies preserved in Saint Michan's?

The first one is easy, but the second one is tricky. She knows, but she doesn't know. It's scientific. She knows it's scientific. Things that you can't explain are always scientific. Her Da said the hydrogen bomb was scientific and so was penicillin for infections and so was the sugar lump for polio.

She writes out the answers.

The Sheares Brothers were rebels who died for Ireland.

Then for the second question, she writes:

It's scientific how mummies are preserved. They don't rot, because of lime and gas and dust in the ground.

Then she draws the Crusader and the Thief, with their names in labels beside them. She has two coffins for the Sheares Brothers with an Irish flag in the middle. Vera has a drawing of the Handel organ and Catherine has Dracula with two fangs sticking out. There's a gold star for the best project.

13

A TEST IN YOUR VEST

They're getting a medical test and a needle. It's horrible. They got it once before in high babies. It's not really the needle that she hates. You have to take your clothes off. You have to stand there in your knickers and vest. In front of everyone. Upstairs, there's a nurse and a doctor, in white hospital coats. They have to queue in a line outside their classroom. The queue goes up the stairs and around the corner. Some of them have frilly knickers and fancy vests, the dealers' daughters, Gita the Indian girl and the ones that live in the houses.

Patti covers herself with her arms. She feels skinny. Then she feels like a little fatso. But no. It's not that. It's her vest. It's clean, but it looks a bit yellowy beside the snow white ones. So does her knickers; it's because of all the washing in Sunlight soap. She wouldn't mind the Arnott's ones with the bow and the pink frill, or the Frawley's cotton ones with the little holes in the material. They wait in line. One of the ones with the frilly knickers is showing off her scar, where she got an operation to take out her appendix. The queue breaks up and they're all having a gawk under her vest. She's even allowing them to feel the scar.

"Go on," fancy pants goes, "have a feel."

It's a small pinky line like the border on the map. You can see stitch-marks across it like little teeth.

"Ouch! It feels horrible," someone says.

"It was in the Richmond Hospital. I was rattlin'," fancy pants says, "I got the anstenetic an all, a huge big needle it was."

The nurse looks out with her roundy face.

"Next! Keep moving and no talking down there." She shouts down the stairs. Someone goes into the test room and the line moves up a step.

It's nearly Patti's turn then.

She's next. She's shivering. She's fizzen freezin'. The heaters mustn't be on. Sister told them to do drill on the stairs to keep warm. Gita is not shy; she's swinging her lovely brown arms in big circles behind her. She's doing marching steps like a little soldier.

In the test room, she has to lie on the couch bed. The doctor has a look down her throat with the thing like an ice-pop stick. It nearly chokes her.

"Say ahh," he says.

She says "Ahh!"

He feels her throat with his cold fingers. He pushes in hard and it hurts. He says her glands are a bit swollen. Oh brillo! She might get off school if she's sick. She hopes she is. He puts on this little torch-light. She has to take off her glasses. He has a quick look in her eyes. Then her ears. Up her nose. And at her sides he presses in hard. Her stomach then. Taps her knees with a little silver hammer. Her knee jumps on its own. Her whole leg. A queer wriggly feeling goes down her leg. The doctor says nothing, except:

"OK. NEXT!"

He puts his hammer in his pocket. He nods at the nurse.

She gets down off the couch.

There she is. Big roundy face, waiting at the top of the room. She wants to measure her first up against the wall. She tells her to stand dead straight and not fidget. On her head, she puts her hand down flat. She goes, "Umm." She marks out her height on a wall-chart. She sends her over to a trolly with a kidney dish and cotton-wool. She can see it, the big injection needle on its side in the dish. Yellow smelly stuff in a bowl. A smell of hospitals in the air. Now, she's beside her. She gets her arm. She holds it out in front of her. She dips cotton wool in the yellow smelly stuff. She wipes it across her arm. Then she gets the needle and holds it up. That's ok, she doesn't mind needles. Not really. She closes her eyes tight. The nurse sticks the needle in her arm and wipes it again with the cotton-wool. It wasn't that bad. Next she's gawking at her head. She looks in her hair; roots around in there like maybe she's looking for buried treasure.

She wishes she'd stop. She has a little lump at the back of her head, like a marrowfat pea, and a baldy patch near the top like a saucer. The nurse says nothing about the lump, but feels her baldy patch. She says: "That might be ringworm."

"Oh no!" She knows what ringworm is. Ringworm is a roundy worm, that eats your hair out and it might never grow back again. It can even eat its way down into your brain and make you go thicko.

"Now walk up and down like a good girl," the nurse says.

She walks up and down. She feels real stupid. Like a babby when its learning to walk.

"Turn."

She turns.

"Yes all right. Your feet are a bit turned out. Your shoes . . . yes, I think they might need a lift on one of the sides."

What's she on about? There's nothing wrong with her feet, Patti thinks. She's writing everything down on a pink chart. She looks at her hands then, her right hand first. Then her left hand. Good job, she hasn't got the chilblains; they're a holy show if they get inflamed. She goes between her fingers, she spreads them apart into a star-fish shape. She squints in close, feels the in- between parts with the tips of her fingers.

"That's fine," she says.

Then it's her shoulders. She feels the bones there and the other bone at the top of her back. She writes more in the chart. Then she tells her to go back to class and get dressed. Gita is next. She's like a model. She walks real straight with her head held up high. In class, Patti gets dressed. Afterwards, when all the tests are done, the nurse gives her a note for her Ma. It's a brown envelope, with a window at the front. On the way home, she tries to read it. She turns it sideways and upside down, but she can't see nothing through the window only white paper.

After she reads the letter, her Ma says: "They've an awful cheek, them country nurses. Nosey bloody parkers."

"What's it say?"

"Nothin', just you have a bit of a swollen gland."

"Nothin' else?"

"No. Not really."

So, it's into her smock-pocket with the letter.

"Nothin' about feet?"

"No"

"Or shoulders?"

"No. Amn't I always tellin' ya, to straighten them shoulders in-anyway? And there's nothin' wrong with your feet. They'd want to look at their own feet."

"Anthin' about hair or fingers?"

"No. For God's sake."

"She said I might have ringworm."

"Well, tell her I said you don't. It's only a bald patch, that's all and the hair'll grow back when it's good and ready. Didn't I rub in olive oil?"

"Yeah. But still . . ."

"It's only for the meantime, it's not for the duration."

"I don't want to go baldy and be called Baldy Brains."

"You won't. Sure you have oceans of hair."

In the bedroom, Patti feels the bald patch with her finger. It feels yuk. She hates it. It's a little island of hard skin, about the same size as a thropenny piece, on the left side of her head. She hopes she won't go baldy, like this poor girl in school who has to wear a pixie-hat all the time, because she's baldy as an egg underneath. She got a disease called alopecia and her hair never grew back.

In the wardrobe mirror, she looks at her feet. She stands back and points her foot at the mirror. A bit turned out, that nurse said. It looks like an ordinary foot: five toes, five toe-nails, a heel, a flat part in the middle. Sideways she looks again. One foot, then the other foot. She can't see any turned-out bits. The sole looks all right. What's she on about? Her Ma is right, them test nurses should mind their own business. No way is she wearing Corporation shoes, brown hickey old fashioned shoes with laces that make you look thicko. You get them in a dispensary in Lord Edward Street. They're supposed to stop you getting knock knees, but they only give you knock knees instead.

Inside the wardrobe, Patti covers herself with the old clothes. She rubs the part of her arm where the needle went in. It has a little bump like a pimple. It feels hot and sore at the same time.

14

THE WARDROBE

It's a quarter to one. It's time.

"Get in quick," her Ma says, "in case your Da comes home early."

She closes the wardrobe door. She puts on the latch. She bends up her legs and covers herself with the clothes.

"Are ya right ? Are ya in?"

"I'm ok"

"Right so, cover yourself and no fidgetin' or coughin', hear me?"

"Yeah."

Patti likes hiding in the wardrobe. It's well better than under the bed, or behind the curtains. Sometimes, if she doesn't go to school, she has to hide when her Da comes home for his dinner. He'd have blue murder. He'd have killin. He'd have twenty canaries. She's only allowed to miss school, if she's very sick, like with a fever or a bad infection. She always listens for his key in the door. Cranky footsteps up the hall, his wheezy cough, the kitchen door-knob turning. Then it closes and the coast is clear. She can lie back and wait until he's gone back to work.

The wardrobe is in the hall bedroom. It's at the end wall, between the window and the door. It's brown and grainy, with scratches on the outside and a long mirror on the inside. Her Ma says it's old-fashioned. It wobbles and shakes if you bang the door too hard. There's stuff on top of it and stuff behind it and stuff under it. It came from Ryan's auction rooms on the quays where they sell quality furniture.

Her Da says: "That wardrobe is in a class of its own, pure walnut with very unusual barrel doors, the type of thing you'd only see in well to do houses."

Her Ma says it's in a class of its own all right and it's seen better days and she'd prefer a modern wardrobe out of Cavendish's.

It's like her own private place in there. It's warm and quiet and dark. It's a nice mixture of smells: it's a clothesy smell and a wood smell, a smell of her Da's hair-oil and her Ma's 4 7 11 eau de cologne. There's a couple of good shirts and ties hanging on hangers. Ma's good slip and smock are folded real neat on the top shelf, with her panstick makeup and lipstick hid underneath. The other shelves are packed with the kids' clothes. On the bottom, there's a big pile of loose clothes she sits on. Her Da's old ties are tangled up, like wriggly snakes with her Ma's knotty nylons; there's a pair of pink and grey high heels, the good beige costume from years ago, a dusty pink sideways hat, dinged inside out and the worn wool jumpers she cuts the sleeves off for winter vests. She always says they're well warmer than cotton vests and they'd keep out a north-pole blizzard.

Patti makes a cushion for her head with the balled up jumpers, rests her feet along the side of the wardrobe and it's dead cosy. She can read in the wardrobe with a torch if she has one. Sometimes the wardrobe turns into a boat and she's below deck and she can hear the huge crash of the waves outside. Or it might be a woodcutters cottage in the forest, or she might be in a stagecoach, up a rocky mountain in a wagon train and there's Comanche's outside. Maybe she's Annie Oakley, ridin up ahead, watchin' out for Indians. She got an Annie Oakley cowgirl suit from Santy; it's a grey fringy skirt and waistcoat with a cowboy hat to match. It's dead neat.

Her Da'd go mad if he knew she was hiding in the wardrobe, but what he doesn't know won't kill him; her Ma always says that. What her Da thinks is, she's in school, learning to be a scholar. What her Da thinks is she's having her stupid little bottle of milk and her gooey cheese and margy pargy sandwich. Ma says it's no harm to stay home sometimes and she won't miss much in that convent and sure hasn't she enough brains already.

She likes the lonely warm feeling of being in the wardrobe. She likes it with just her and the clothes. All the outside sounds are muffled into a whisper, the traffic, the rubbish sliding down the chute, the seagulls squealing, the oulones giving out to one another over the balconies. It's like she's in her own little hidey-hole, like inside a storybook or a dream. She likes it at home when the others are at school. Maybe they're listening to the radio. Ma might sing, if she's in her singy mood. Patty helps her with the babby, or goes on messages or hangs up washing.

This day, she nearly got caught. She had to get out quick and under the bed pronto when her Da wanted his good Sunday suit in a hurry. She heard him coming in as usual for his dinner, so she tried not to cough or move. She heard his feet in the hall, then the doorknob turning. Then the door shutting. After a good while, he went into the toilet. Then all of a sudden, her Ma is there on her tipitoes. She drags her out of the wardrobe and pushes her under the bed.

"Stay there and don't move," she whispers.

Then the toilet flushes and she sees her Da's work shoes coming in through the door, then his grey socks when he takes off his shoes. He opens the wardrobe door. It creaks. Patti nearly coughs; she has to hold in the cough with her hand over her mouth. She has to suck in her jaws. It's very dusty under the bed. There might be spiders. There she is trying not to cough, with loads of odd shoes and Da's toolbox and hacksaw and his going away case. She nearly chokes. He's still in front of the wardrobe in his socks. Then he wants to know, where's his good Sunday suit gone? Then Ma shouts out from the kitchen.

"Wha- a'? Your wha'?

Then he shouts back.

"Me suit! Where's me bloody good suit for God's sake? "

Then Ma goes:

"Oh, it should be hangin' up where it was. It was there this mornin', I could've swore it was."

So Da starts to walk up and down the bedroom in his socks; he huffs and he puffs. Patti thinks he might blow the house down, like the wolf in the three piggies story. He thumps something then; she thinks it must be the side of the wardrobe. He bends down. Out from under the wardrobe, he pulls out his black mass shoes. He pushes his feet into them. He ties the laces real quick and rubs them over with the polishing brush. He must be combing his hair then in front of the mirror. Then it's his cranky footsteps out the door and down the hall. He bangs the hall door hard and the glass shakes, like it might break. It

goes real quiet then. For a minute. Then her Ma's slippers pad-
ding in the door.

"Come outa there quick! You only just escaped by the skin of
your teeth," she goes, pulling her out, like a sack of coal.

"What's up Ma?"

"He wants his Sunday suit. He has a funeral. That Mister
whatsisname upstairs died suddenly. Lorda mercy." She blesses
herself. "Good job it's children's allowance day and good job I
left his shoes there."

Her Ma's panicky face with the babby in her arms. Ma tying
her scarf knot and pulling on her coat.

"We'll have to hurry before he comes back or there'll be
slaughter in this place. Put on your shoes quick and wipe off
that dust."

Quickity quick, they're ready and then they're all rushing
through Smithfield.

"This is a surprise, " the pawn-man says, out through the
hatch.

"We don't usually have the pleasure of your company this
early in the week."

The place is packed with women. It must be because it's
children's allowance day. They're all getting out stuff early; the
wedding rings and Sunday suits and shoes.

On the kitchen table, they cut the twine and tear off the
brown paper. The suit's a bit creased, but the creases will fall
out, her Ma says, with the heat of Da's body. She hangs it up
in the wardrobe, brushes it over with the clothes brush. There's
a musty pawn smell, so she gives it a quick spray of 4 7 11 cologne.

"There, that's grand."

"Ma."

"What?"

"He'll know."

"Know what?"

"He'll know where it was."

"No he won't. He'll never be the wiser. Sure isn't it back
where it was. Everything is shipshape"

She's washing clothes in the bath, singing *Michael row the boat ashore,* when they hear Da's key turning. She stops singing.

"Say nothin'," she says.

They hear him rooting around in the bedroom. He looks in the wardrobe again. They hear the door creaking. In the kitchen, he says nothing about the suit. It's like the suit was never missing in the first place. It's like the suit was there all the time. Her Ma was right, everything *is* shipshape.

"Were you in school today?" he goes from behind the Herald.

"Yeah, course I was."

She'll have to tell it in confession, and she hopes it's not a mortaler.

"What did ya learn?"

"Oh em, about the sugar factories and the Easter Rising and tables."

"Name the sugar counties."

"Mallow, Carlow, Tuam and Thurles."

"That's very good. Now name three of the rebels from the Easter Rising."

"Em, Padraig Pearse and James Connolly and Thomas Mac Donagh."

"Right. Now, say your eleven times tables."

That's easy peasy and she's glad it wasn't the twelve times. He stops her at 99. He folds his Herald and stuffs it in his pocket.

She knows her Ma is listening from the scullery, she's standing on the bathboard, hanging up clothes. She has pegs sticking out of her mouth like buck teeth. She throws a jumper over the line, squeezes water from the arms.

Sometimes they don't talk and that's when Patti has to be piggy in the middle. She hates it.

Ask your Da for this and tell your Ma that.

"Ask you Da for the price of a smoke."

"Tell your Ma, I'm not made of money."

"Tell him we need coal and bread."

"Tell him yourself," she wants to say. Yes, tell him all the things he doesn't know, even if it kills him. Except for the wardrobe. Don't tell him about that.

All of a sudden, he gets up. He goes out and slams the hall door after him.

"Pity about him."

Her Ma jumping down off the bath board.

Patti was thinking, what if Ma hadn't come in and pulled her out of the wardrobe in time? The worst thing that could happen is, if scroungey Daddy Ryan, the school attendance inspector caught her. He might bash her first with his big stick, then send her to court in the Dublin Castle. He looks real mean. Has a shiny red face. Wears a brown crombie coat with a belt with a big buckle. He hasn't got much hair left. He does his rounds with the roll-book under one arm and a slapper stick in the other. They hear his hobnail boots, tramping through the courtyard. He bangs down the door, until he gets an answer. Her Ma peeps out the scullery window, behind the net curtain. There might be a rumour he was seen in the area. If people see him coming, they usually spread it around. It spreads from one flats to the next, from one block to another. It goes around the balconies, from the lower balconies up, or from the higher balconies down.

"Here's aul Ryan," her Ma whispers, if she knows he's coming. Then it's three hard knocks. They hear him lifting up the door-flap, then the letterbox. His thundery voice up the hall. Her Ma always has some excuse ready.

"Oh yes, she's very sick indeed. She's delirious with a sky-high temperature."

Sometimes he wants proof she's really sick, but she fobs him off, says she might be contagious as well as delirious. The nuns call him Mister Ryan, but everyone else calls him Daddy Ryan.

"He's some Daddy all right."

"Why is he called Daddy?"

"Oh, that's a very long story, but they don't call him Daddy for nothing. "

That's all she'll say about it. Then she has on her mystery face.

He comes into the classroom sometimes to check the roll book. He takes down the names of the marked absent girls. First, he goes around the doors. Then he goes after the mitcher's.

If he finds a mitcher, he drags her back to school by the scruff of the neck. Her Ma says he has powers beyond his station, so you have to be polite and talk nice to him, even if you can't bear to look at him. Kids can get sent to Letterfrack or Daingean or Artane if they end up in court. Everyone is afraid of him.

15

ELOCUTION

Everyone is saying she's very young for a teacher. Her name is
Miss Stritch; she's their new elocution teacher. Sister introduces
her to the class. She tells them Miss Stritch usually works in
private schools, so they were very lucky to get her. Miss Stritch
smiles and goes a bit red. She starts to hand out leaflets about
her new class. Sister says she has her work cut out for her. It's
a strange word; Elocution. None of them ever heard the word
before. It sounds like electrocution, but it's all about proper pronunciation; about learning to speak proper English and better-
ing yourself. The only thing is, it's not free, like the free education. Elocution costs throppence a lesson. Her granny thinks it's
disgraceful when she tells her. She gives out hell about the department of education and the politicians. She says: "So much
for the Free State and free education." Then she makes one of
her speeches. Is it not bad enough, they have to pay for school
books and jotters and pencils, in order to learn to read and
write? Is it not bad enough they have to buy gymslips and cardigans, sashes and white blouses? Next thing, they'll be charging for the ink in the inkwells. Next they'll be charging for the
chalk and the bottles of milk. Then she changes her mind all of
a sudden and gives her the throppence.

"It's dear enough, but maybe it'll be worth it in the long
run," she says.

"What's the world comin' to?" Her other granny says. There
was no such a thing as elocution in her day and there's nothing
wrong with the way *she* talks. Her Ma says:

"What next? Them nuns are always lookin' for money."

Miss Stritch is not a culchie, but they think from the way she
talks, she's from some posh place, like Harold's Cross or Terenure. Miss Stritch comes on Tuesday mornings. She sits on a high
stool at the top of the class with her legs crossed; she uncrosses
them if a nun comes in. She wears a white doctor's coat over her

skirt and blouse. She has a high pony tail, that topples sideways when she moves her head. There's stripy brown marks on her legs, so maybe she wears Tanfastic under her nylons.

At their first lesson, she starts with a warm up session of mouth exercises. First Miss Stritch makes her mouth into an O shape. It opens like a big polo-mint. She makes the O sound: OOO! They have to repeat it after her: OOO! Next, she stretches her lips sideways like a grin. Then she sticks out her long tongue. She does a demonstration. She wiggles her tongue in and out, and from side to side. Patti thinks of the purple ox tongues in Steins pork shop.

"The tongue," Miss Stritch says, "is a marvellous organ of speech. Without our tongues, we couldn't say one single word."

Then she's on about the roof of your mouth and your vocal chords and how sound travels. She wants them to become aware of their own tongues; to move them around, to feel the roof's of their mouths. She wants them to imagine what it would be like to be speechless. It's very hard. You have to try to remember before you could talk, or else, you have to imagine that your tongue was cut out. Vera makes a stupid babble sound, like the poor deaf and dumb girl they know in King Street. Miss Stritch gives her a dirty look. Next she wants to demonstrate the T H sound in the word the. She pulls back her lips like a horse. She sticks the tip of her tongue between her teeth. She wants them to do the same. They try to copy her. She says you have to push the tongue well out between the teeth to pronounce the T H sound properly. Patty's tongue gets caught in the split in her front teeth and Catherine is afraid she'll bite her tongue off.

Th Th Th, Miss Stritch keeps saying. She writes it on the blackboard: *The man crossed the road*. The proper pronunciation and the wrong pronunciation beside it: *The* and *De*. They have to read it out.

They all say it together: "De man crossed de road."

She says: "Listen to yourself speak the word *The*."

It's hard to listen to yourself speak. *The*, the way Miss Stritch says it, sounds awful posh and *de* looks dead dopey when it's written down like that on the blackboard.

Imagine going around saying *the* all the time. Imagine having your tongue caught in between your teeth like a goofy goof? Patti thinks. They get giddy then. They start to titter and dig one another.

"Now pay attention girls," Miss Stritch goes. "Try to make an effort. Say it together. Repeat after me: *The* man crossed *the* road. " She keeps pointing her finger at her tongue tip. There they are with curly tongue tips, trying to say *The* properly. She makes them keep it up until their tongues tingle. It's not that difficult, she says and they'll get the gist of it soon enough. It only needs a bit of practice. It's on to one syllable words then. She writes the word clown on the blackboard. "Clown," she says real poshy woshy. They have to repeat it after her. She corrects them and says they have to say: *Clown* not *Clow-in*. Beside the word clown, she writes it the way they say it: Clow-in. They're in stitches then. Listen to yourselves speak the word clown, she says again. She writes *Down* beside the word *Clown* next. They're supposed to say; *Down* and not Dow- *in*. then it's *Girl*, not G*ir el*. The girl walked down the road. The clown fell down the stairs.

The next lesson is very important Miss Stritch says. It's all about words ending with Ing: *Do-ing Chew-ing, Be-ing, Close-ing*. The important thing is, you have to pronounce the G at the end. Miss Stritch's eyebrows go up when she says Ing. Patti's mouth is jaded. Vera says she's jacked. Then Miss Stritch is doing R sounds. She writes Rolo and Ring and Bring on the blackboard. She says: you have to roll the Rs around in your mouth like a boiled sweet. She demonstrates: Rrr olo! Brrr ing! Rrrr ing!

They're all fed up with elocution, but Miss Stritch is not finished yet. For the last lesson, she makes them recite bits of stupid poems.

The rain in Spain falls mainly on the plain
How Now Brown Cow
Pitter Patter Raindrops.

Then, she wants to draw their attention to a few common mistakes in their inner-city speech and pronunciation. It's

Come here, not *Comeior,* It's *Dublin,* not *Dubilin.* It's *School,* not *Scoo- il.*

"One last word," she says. "Repeat after me: New Town Mount Kennedy!"

No one is listening. They're all fed up. They think it's dead dopey learning to talk posh. No way would they talk posh and say, ing outside the school, so what's the point of paying throppence a lesson? There's pieces of paper going round under the desks, with funny drawings of Miss Stritch. There's one with her long tongue sticking out and another one with her sideways pony tail, and another one with her stripy crossed legs. Some of them think elocution is crap. No one wants to turn into little poshy woshy's, especially Patti.

Outside the classroom they're all pretending to talk posh. They're putting on the posh voices and saying: *Newtown mount Kennedy* and *The rain in Spain falls mainly on the plain.* They're stretching their lips like elastic into all kinds of funny shapes. They're showing off the drawings of Miss Stritch in the yard.

"Your gettin' very grand all of a sudden," her granny Connor says.

"Get-*ing!*" Patti says and granny says: "God protect us," and laughs, her half funny, half angry laugh.

It might be for the better. It's not that any of hers is common, but it's no harm, her Ma says, to learn to speak properly.

"It's nice to talk nice and have manners," she says.

16

THE LIBRARY

She's reading the Water Babies by Charles Kingsley. It's a terrific adventure story about a raggy little chimney sweep called Tom. Tom discovers this underwater world, when the fairies turn him into a water baby. Tom was *amphibious*, and that means he could live on land and in water. Tom lived on water-cresses and water-gruel and water-milk. It was written years ago in 1863 and it was Charles Kingsley's most famous book. She found it in Capel Street Library. A lovely book with a deep blue cover, with a picture of Tom as a water baby on the front.

Capel Street Library is her favourite place to go, especially in winter. After helping granny in the market, she goes there in the afternoons. It keeps her out of trouble and away from the flats, granda says. Granny thinks it's a waste of time. It's a couple of doors away from Brereton's pawnbrokers and not far away from the old drunken house. It has a shiny black door with a brass knob and knocker, orange and black tiles in a diamond shape in the hall, and a wood coat- stand with brass hooks like question marks. The staircase is very posh, dark brown polished wood, with a leather banister rail and brass studs like a necklace along the edges. It twists round up to the first floor, where the children's section is and further up to the second floor, where the adult section is. There's this nice clean toilet, with toilet paper and teeny bars of white soap and a smell of Dettol. A cleaning woman with a blue smock, mops out the place every day. They're allowed to use the toilets and that's terrific, because Patti has to use them a lot.

They were allowed to get library tickets, Patti and her brother. One of the uncles signed the form with their names and addresses. The tickets are blue, like the colour of their Ma's medical card. You can get two books out on loan for two weeks at a time.

"Bookworms!" Granny calls them. "Little bookworms!"

Granda says: "Leave them be."

Granny says: "Are their eyes not bad enough already, without makin' them worse starin' into books?"

Granda doesn't answer. All he does is ruffle his newspaper. Granda likes reading. He thinks reading is good exercise for the brain. He likes Westerns. He has his own Western book collection in his book shelf. He made it himself and covered it with the same mauve wallpaper to match the wall. He's always reading a book at the fireplace. He falls asleep in the armchair, with the book still open on his lap. Her granny couldn't be bothered with books. She says she has more to do with her time, than sit around reading books.

The library rule is, if a book gets lost or damaged, they have to pay to replace the book, so they always keep the books in granny's place, away from the kids. Sometimes, they fall asleep in the library in the big leather chairs at the window. There's a warm brown radiator like the ones in school. It's nice with the heat and the quiet and the smell of the books. Patti loves books: adventure stories and ghost stories and sea stories. Every book has a different smell. Sometimes they have the whole place to themselves, except for the librarian who keeps nodding off behind her desk. Some of the shelves are empty. There's a nursery rhyme section with a few crappy toddlers books like: The Three Bears, Red Riding Hood, Jack in the Beanstalk, The Little Match Girl. She must've read The Little Match girl ten times over, since she learned to read. The Little Match Girl is the saddest book she ever read. It always makes her cry.

Her brother is mad into Huckleberry Finn. Patti likes it too. At home, they share books sometimes. It's mostly Patti sharing, because her brother doesn't like to read girly books. With Huck Finn, she reads when he's not reading, a few pages at a time. She likes the Famous Five books and Pippi Long Stocking. Pippi is one of her favourite characters; she makes her laugh out loud. Pippi is the strongest girl in the world. She has red hair and odd stockings. She lives alone with her horse and her monkey. She sleeps with her feet on the pillow and her head under the covers, like Patti. She's not afraid of anyone either, because she stood up to a burglar when he broke into her house and she bashed him.

Sometimes, if they're not reading, they look for strange words in the dictionary or do a bit of homework. When the librarian falls asleep, they sneak upstairs to the adult section. There's loads more books up there. They mosey around the bookshelves without anyone noticing. The other librarian stands on ladder-steps, stacking books. She allows them to look, but they can't take out any books.

The tramps and the bag ladies from the Iveagh Hostel sit near the other radiator. They fall asleep behind last week's newspapers or just stare out the window at the traffic. Around where they sit, there's a stale sour smell of Red Biddy and dirty clothes. This scruffy old man, with a long white beard is there a lot. He has a sack coat tied with twine, a nose like a rotten strawberry. At the reading table, he reads the same books, every day. Big hard covered art books with coloured pages of nudey women, with roundy bellies and small diddies. Not a stitch on them; angel baby's flying over them in some kind of garden. Trees. Peculiar shaped trees she never saw before. The scruffy man calls them over with his yellow finger. He wants them to look too, but they keep away from him at the far end of the table. He laughs back at them with his rotten teeth.

At five o'clock sharp, the Librarian rings a bell to say they're closing. She gathers all the books from around and stacks them on her desk. Sometimes, on the way out if no one is looking, Patti slides down the banister rails. She got the idea from a Famous Five story. You'd think it was dangerous, but it's not, as long as you remember to hold on tight to the banister rail. The only thing is, she has to watch out in case someone is watching, because this day, on her way down, she saw the beardy man watching her from the bottom, but she couldn't stop herself half way down. There he was, with his rotten teeth, grinning all over his face. She had to do a runner out the door and she didn't stop until she reached the flats.

17

THE GRANNIES

Everyone says the grannies can't look at one another. Maybe it's because one is a northsider and one is a southsider. The Liffey passes between their two blocks of flats and when you cross Church Street Bridge, it's like you're in a different city. On the southside, it's all steep hills: Christ Church Hill, John's Lane Hill, Saint Audoen's Hill, Oliver Bond Hill. Her granny on the southside says that people from the north side are quarehawks indeed; her granny on the northside says you couldn't trust a southsider as far as you could throw them. They dress different too. Her granny on the northside wouldn't be seen dead in a head scarf; she always wears a felt hat, with a fancy hatpin at the side. Granny Connor loves head scarves; she has a drawer full of coloured scarves in her sideboard, a different one for every day. She covers her head with the scarf, makes a big fancy knot under her chin. One of her favourites is a pure silk scarf with a picture of some tropical island. It's like a painting of paradise with parrots and palm trees and the sea in the background. Granny does a trick with the scarf. She holds it up to the light when it's sunny and you'd think the waves were moving and the palm trees were swaying.

"Birds of Paradise," she says. They can see the sun shining through the scarf, and the bright colours of the parrots.

She can read tea leaves and tell fortunes, but she never takes money. For the reading, you have to pour your tea without a strainer, so the leaves stick to the bottom of the cup. There's a message in the leaves. Granny knows how to read the message. Sometimes the neighbours bring their cups for a reading. For ages, she just sits staring into the cup, she moves it this way and that. They watch her face. They tell her out straight, they don't want bad news. For starters, they don't want any more babies. If there's money coming they want to know; if they'll win on the

pools, or the church draw, if they have a rich aunty or uncle in
America, who might leave them a small fortune.

Granny just laughs. She says: "Maybe it's a miracle youse want."

She told Patti, when she grows up, she'll marry a dark haired
man from the southside, that she'll have dark haired babies like
her Ma, that one day, she'll live in a nice house with a garden.

"The leaves never lies," she says.

She likes to wear long skirts and Fair Isle cardigans. When
she's cooking, she wears a flowery wrap around pinafore. In the
scullery there's a black gas stove, but she prefers to cook her potatoes over the fire. She has this old-fashioned iron thing like a
grate, that goes on top of the coals. Her kitchen is always full of
smoke from the potato-fire. When they're cooked, the potatoes
are black on the outside and white on the inside. She makes you
eat the potato skins. The skins, she says, have all the goodness
of the potato. You can't leave anything on your plate. If you do,
she gives a big speech about the Great Irish Famine.

"If the people'd had those skins in the Famine, they wouldn't
have perished." That's when it starts. Then she's on about people so thin from hunger, if they turned sideways you couldn't see
them at all. She's talking about human skeletons, with mouths
full of weeds and grass and pebbles. She bangs the table and
says: "Ate that for Godsake," if you even think about leaving
something there on the plate. The uncles can't leave nothing
either; they move the potato skins around the plate. They make
a pile at the side. They start to get up. Then they sit back down
again. The potatoes on the southside have a smoky taste that
Patti likes. Her granny likes them salty. She shakes the Saxa
packet to smother them with salt, then she adds a dollop of
country butter from the dairy.

She loves raw onions. She makes onion sambos. She butters
two turnover slices from Catherine's bakery. She cuts up a Spanish onion into rings. She spreads the onion rings on one slice of
the bread. Then she squirts on lashings of YR brown sauce.
Then salt. Loads! A big shake full from the packet. She puts the
other slice on top. She fills her mug from the enamel jug. She's
not a heavy drinker, but she likes a little drop of porter to wet

her lips. In Murtagh's bar beside the flats, they sell the black porter by the jug full. The barman fills her white enamel jug for one and six. It's the jet-black stuff with no white head. It smells a bit like the Liffey, when the tide goes out, but she likes a sup with her onion sambos.

"Ahh!" she goes, "That's grand." She wipes her mouth with the back of her hand.

She only has a few teeth left; long ones here and there, like rusty nails, but she wouldn't have false teeth for all the tea in China. She prefers having her own teeth. At least they're her own, she says. The aunties have her tormented to get a new set from the Cornmarket dental hospital. They keep saying the new teeth will take years off her, but she won't hear tell of it.

Her eyes are the same colour as the Liffey; sort of greenish, sort of brownish, with twinkly bits that sparkle. When they look at you, it's like they're looking inside your head, down, down deep, so she knows what you're thinking. She has big hands with pointy knuckles, that make shapes in the air when she talks. She's always stirring something at the stove; stew or cabbage or coddle. She talks funny; she says kittle for kettle, sauhages for sausages, cohages for cottages, mate for meat, tae for tea. She's one of a set of twin girls, but Patti never met her twin. She walks funny too; with quick little steps, she pushes herself up John's Lane Hill to shop in Thomas Street, her straw messagebag hanging on her arm. She gets breathless and has to stop sometimes. In winter, she wears ankle socks and cor- duroy boots. During Summer, she wears leather sandals with no socks. When she laughs, she shakes all over; her arms, her shoulders, her belly and her bum; it's a huge big wobbly laugh, like she can't stop herself. She splutters and chokes and some- times she has to get a drink of water.

"Oh dear God!" she goes. "Oh God t'night!"

She'll only wear a coat, if it's lashing out of the heavens. There's some old coats hanging on the back of her bedroom door. Sometimes if it's real cold in winter, she throws them over the bed on top of the quilt.

Sometimes, Patti sleeps on the southside, during the summer holidays. She squeezes in, beside Aunt Annie and Aunt Rita at the foot of the bed. Her granny sleeps at the top out on the edge, with Aunt Jinny at the wall. The uncles are in the other bedroom, Paddy, and Joe and Fran. Through the wall, they hear them, coughing and talking and arguing. After they go to work, granny goes in to tidy up and air the place. There's a smoky, sleepy smell in there. The ceiling has brown stains like old fashioned maps. Granny coughs and rubs the smoke away with her hand. She gives out hell about them smoking in the bedroom.

"Look at that ceilin'. They have the place destroyed with the cigarettes."

Then she strips the beds and opens the window wide.

She's not like other grannies, Patti thinks. She's hard and soft at the same time. Her Ma always says, she's a very good mother; for food and fires and nice clean beds. Except cigarettes. She hates cigarettes. She gives out hell about her Ma smoking. She says she smokes like a chimney pot. Every Friday, she buys cigarettes and divies them out to the uncles. In the sideboard press, on a shelf, she keeps the Sweet Afton boxes under lock and key. She says it's the only way to keep them from choking themselves to death.

"Giz a smoke Ma," they always say, when she's at the gas stove. They have her tormented, poking and nudging her in the arms. She hits them with the dish cloth, chases them with the sweeping brush.

"Get away! Youse have me scourged," she goes.

They can see the Afton boxes, stacked, like a yellow brick wall, behind the glass door of the sideboard. Uncle Paddy sits there, staring through the glass at the cigarettes, but granny won't give in. He bites his nails down to the quicks and still she won't give in. They have a quota; granny allows them a certain amount of cigarettes every day. Once they smoke their quota, they can't have another cigarette. That's the rule in granny's place. She has to stretch the cigarettes out for the week, she says, otherwise they'd be gone in the first day. She sends their shirts to the Swan laundry on Monday and they come back like new, in cellophane covers on Friday. She has to make sure the uncles are spic and span for Sunday mass. She examines them from head to toe. She gives out if they didn't polish their shoes properly or comb their hair into a neat shape. That's when she goes after them with a clothes-brush and a hair brush to tidy them up. That's when they go all sulky.

They go: "Ah Ma. For Godsake!"

She makes them stand still, while she brushes them down; first the shoulders, then the arms, down the front. Next, she turns them around and does their backs.

"Yous're like overgrown childer," she says.

Then she checks their hair. She reaches up and combs the front. She tells them to make sure and get the whole mass and not to attempt to leave before the end, while the priest has his back turned.

"And another thing! No bad language. No fightin' or atein' one another. Keep a civil tongue in your heads. Don't make a holy showa me on the Sabbath."

Sometimes, the uncles have rows, over cigarettes, or clothes or the newspaper, but there's no cursing allowed. Not one single curse can pass granny's hall door. That's the rule.

Sometimes they don't talk. They just sit there and listen to the opera on Radio Eireann. In the alcove, on an old chair, there's a brown wood wireless with holes and knobs at the front. Granny twiddles the knobs to tune it in. She hits it and punches it to get rid of the crackle. If it doesn't work, she opens it up at the back with her pliers. She takes out the insides, but before she knows where she is, there's wires all over the place. It's dead cosy, with just the two of them, a big pot of tea on the table. Her fire is blazing, maybe the smoky smell of potatoes bubbling on the grate. The blue dresser in the kitchen has a door that pulls down into a table. When her Ma visits, granny gives them all sugar or lard or brown sauce on bread. She opens down the dresser. She takes out bread. She takes a big spoonful of sparkly sugar or a dollop of dripping or a shake full of sauce and spreads it thick. The kids love the sugar and lard, but Patti prefers the brown sauce. She's always giving her Ma advice. The most important thing, she says, is to pay your way. Especially the rent.

"The roof over your head," she says pointing upwards.

She always pays her way. She wouldn't owe anyone a half-penny. She settles all her bills, every Friday, straight after she gets the pension. She has no callers to her door, except the man from the Royal Liver Friendly Society.

18

THE KINGS SHILLING

Patti wouldn't tell a soul about the Kings Shilling. It's supposed to be a secret, the biggest, hugest secret any granny ever had. She has a war pension from the British Army. Some people call it the Kings Shilling. Patti's granda was a soldier in the first world war, the war that killed gillions of men. The pension is not much, only a couple of pounds a week, but it helps her out with the messages and bills. She has to buy stacks of messages for the aunties and uncles, pay her rent and all her bills.

Patti never saw her granda, but she knows what he looks like. She saw this old scratchy brown photo of him in his uniform. It was before he went to war. He wore a kind of tunic jacket, with a turn-up collar and brass buttons, this funny looking hat, pointed sideways on his head. It's only a small photo and his face is blurry, but Patti thinks he was very handsome. The aunties make him sound like a film star.

"Very good lookin'," Aunt Rita said.

"Very handsome indeed," Aunt Annie said.

"Six foot tall, sandy hair, massive clear skin with sparkly blue eyes," Aunt Lilly said. She wishes she could've met him, but he died, only months before she was born in Saint Kevin's hospital. They said his poor gassed lungs were never right after the war and he was lucky to live so long.

Her Ma told her she will never forget the day he died. They were all gathered around him in Saint Kevin's hospital. Earlier, the priest heard his confession and gave him extreme unction. He must've known he was dying, because he said goodbye to everyone. He whispered in a rattly voice into Ma's ear. He said her coat was a lovely shade of blue, it matched her eyes to a T. Then he gave her hand a little squeeze. A curtain around them swayed then, and a peculiar breeze blew in from the corridor. It went dead quiet then. Granda's breathing got real bad. They could hear the death rattle in his throat. They started to say the

Rosary. Granny's face darkened as Aunt Jinny took out blessed rosary beads. Coughs came from the uncles, who were bunched together on one side of the bed. Then there were the shaky, sobbing voices of granny and the aunties with their arms linked. A nurse in a white apron appeared with a bowl of holy water. She felt for a pulse, then listened for a heart beat. She shook her head and they all knew he was gone. The nurse closed his eye lids. They all stood there for a long time just looking at granda. They said he looked the picture of peace, with all the pain and fear gone out of him. Granny stayed longer than the others. They all went to Thomas Street to buy the black. Aunt Jinny rushed home to sew the black armbands on her Singer sewing machine.

They all believe you have to suffer in this world to get to the next. Patti likes to think of him up in Heaven, watching over her baby sister and brother. Her Ma says she knows he's in Heaven, because he suffered a lot in this world. Poor granda had to wait all those years for his peace. She first heard about the war pension in her granny's bed one night. The whispery voices of the aunties talking in the dark. It was all about the pension and how hard it was for granny to get it, how she had to fight the British Army tooth and nail for the couple of pounds a week. And after all poor granda went through and what he had to suffer with the shell shock and everything. Patti pretended to be asleep, but Aunt Jinny said, little piggies have big ears.

Her granny still gets angry. She puts her hand to her forehead.

"That bloody war!" she gives out. "That bloody massacre of a disgraceful war!" Sometimes, it's like the war is still on in granny's. It's like granda is still out there, in the trenches, fighting the Germans. Granda was one of the lucky ones, who came home. He wasn't killed in action, so that's how come he became granny's husband and her Ma's Da. Him and granny had twelve children after they got married.

"He was gassed out of it, " granny says. "His lungs near tore out of his chest."

She says his regiment were smoked out of the trenches, like rats from a tenement hole. One day, a huge ball of poison gas came rolling out of nowhere. They had to bail out into No-Mans- Land, a dangerous place between the trenches, where they could get blown to atoms. The war gas blinded them and choked them and some of them died. A lot of the time, when they were moving from one place to another, they had to eat seaweed and grass to stay alive. They saw things that can never be told, like nuns being attacked by soldiers and the holy habit's reefed off their backs. There were big war-rats in the trenches that went after the wounded soldiers. They picked at their open wounds when they were asleep.

"They were nearly ate alive," granny said.

Heaps of Irish men died out there in the trenches. Granda was with the Royal Dublin Fusiliers. Aunt Jinny told her he fought in the Battle of the Somme and the Dardanelles. Her granny says he was well built, as strong as a plough horse. Before he went away, people gave him blessed medals and scapulars and holy pictures with special war prayers. In the trenches, he had heaps of miraculous medals around his neck, so maybe that's what saved him. After he was gassed, his lungs were so bad he had to go to a military hospital to recover, but he never did fully recover and they had to send him home in the end.

"He was invalided out," Granny told her.

Before he went to war, they got engaged to be married. Granny waited for him like a lovesick sweetheart. They were going to tie the knot as soon as he got back. Granny was only sixteen when she first met him.

"Sweet sixteen," she says, "and never been kissed."

When she thinks back, it was hard, not like a love story at all. Granda was different when he came home from the war. He walked with a limp and had the shell-shock bad, like he imagined he heard bombs and explosions in his head. Like he was still in the trenches and he used to hide and cover his head to make it go away. He hadn't a breath to draw, especially during the night, because his lungs were so badly damaged. Other times, he used to march up and down the room, like a soldier with a pretend rifle over his shoulder. He'd do it in the street too and make a holy show of granny. Sometimes he'd kneel down and give thanks that he survived the war, other times, he'd go nuts.

It was hard for him too, when he first came home. Everyone gave him dirty looks. All of a sudden, no one liked him. He walked up the stairs of the house, where he lived in Golden Lane, with his two step sisters. He was expecting a big welcome, but the sisters ganged up on him because he was wearing his army uniform. One of them took off her shoe and threw it at him, when he came through the door, then the other sister grabs this delf plate off the wall and throws it after him, as he escapes down the stairs. While he was in the war, his sisters joined the IRA. Poor granda had to run for his life, with the step sisters after him. He does this runner pronto to his pals place in Patrick Street. His pal says: "Ya bloody eejit! Get that uniform off quick before you're killed." They had to hide the uniform. Granda had to lie low in his pals place until him and granny got married.

It's a pity, Patti thinks to have a granda that you can never meet. When she heard the story, she thought he must've been very brave. She never saw his grave, but he's buried in Mount Jerome. At first she thought it was a special burial place for dead soldiers, a place like with plaques and wreaths and stuff, but it's only a graveyard. She heard there's supposed to be heaps of protestants buried up there, as well as catholics and that it's not a patch on Glasnevin Cemetery on the northside. It's a bit sad, because her granda doesn't even have his own grave. He's sharing with other people. She's not sure why, but nobody wants to talk about that. They don't want to talk about wars anymore, they say.

19

THE HUNGRY HILL

It's time to forget about bloody wars, granny says. It's time to lay that ghost to rest. Her granny has heaps of other stories to tell. There's fairy stories and banshee stories and famine stories. Patti likes the famine story, The Hungry Hill, but granny has to be in the right mood. If she's jaded she won't tell it. She has to pester her first.

"Ah go on granny, tell us, go on."

Then she puts on her special story face.

"Right so. The Hungry Hill."

And just like that, she starts off like a talkie doll.

"They tramped the roads, they begged at doors for scraps a food. They were proud people. The woman wouldn't go into the poor house with her childer; she'd die first. One day, they left their mud cabin, took to the long windy road that brought them to a town a few miles further, but the town was deserted and notices were stuck up all over the place about the deadly Cholera. The scourge! On past the town they go and out onto another road, along the way, they met more hungry people. Like the walkin' dead, they were. They chanced their arm and asked for bread at a house up a narrow boreen, but the maid held a hankie to her nose and pointed up the mountain, where a soup kitchen was run by Quaker people . . ."

"What's Quaker people?"

"Quakers were a different religion to ours. They were good-natured people, who tried to help out. Down the country, they boiled big pots of soup in makeshift kitchens to feed the starvin' people."

"So, what happened next?"

"The mean oul maid shut the door in their faces. Up the rocky bendy road, they went, but they were too slow on their feet and the Quakers were well gone by the time they got there. Nothin' but a big empty soup pot, like a cannibal pot. There was a grand smell of soup in the air, but not a bone left. They climbed further up in case the Quakers were gone to another village, but the road got too steep and the woman was wallfallin' with the hunger and so were her children, so she lay down near a stone wall with them all huddled into her and it's said, they died there at that wall. All died, bar one of the childer who made it down the mountain to another village, where the Quakers were set up again and it was her told the story to her own daughter and her to hers."

Granny goes quiet then.

"Now that's enough, I'm weary with all that talkin'."

She starts to yawn. Patti can see her few teeth and her tonsils.

"Don't be annoyin' me any more. I've a splittin' headache."

"There's more isn't there? Ah go on, tells us the next bit, about the horrible landlord."

Granny presses the sides of her head, like she's trying to get the famine pictures going again. Her eyes kind of wander off, like she's looking at something miles and miles away.

"Wait," she says. "Let me think."

She drinks a sup of porter.

"The oul land lord had plenty of food for himself in the big house, but he wouldn't share with his tenants, he'd see them die first. Some stayed put in the cohages and cabins and died t'gether. The landlord burned all the cholera cabins on his land the next day. Thick black smoke covered the side of the mountain."

"Why were they so poor?"

"They only had the small bit of ground they rented from the landlord, they lived on potates and sour milk. They had to do farm work to pay the rent. When the blight came over the land, they were starvin' with the hunger. They got the fever bad and couldn't work."

"Why didn't they grow cabbage or go fishin'?"

"Em . . . well the ground was rottin' with blight, so they couldn't plant anthin' and the smell! Now that smell was like the divil himself, risin' up from hell. A putrid, disgustin' stink! Remember, it was a rocky mountainy place, the land not good at all."

"Could they not have killed the cow an ate the meat?"

"No, I told ya before, they had to sell it. Now listen. Shut up for a minute and listen. Their bony bodies were collected afterwards and buried in the famine graves; a huge hole they threw everyone into. In them days, there was no money for funerals."

"Like the Holy Angels?"

"Yeah, I suppose so, but no one wanted to bury them cause of the cholera . . ."

"What's cholera?"

She wipes her forehead with the back of her hand.

"Cholera was a contagious disease, you could catch it easy, especially from the dead, so they had to pay people to bury them. Drunkards and bowsies, some of them, lookin' for drink money."

Granny blesses herself with her finger and thumb.

"What about rabbits?"

"What about them?"

"Could they not catch rabbits?"

"The people were very weak, too sick to go chasin' rabbits."

"Or ducks?"

"Are ya listenin' or am I talkin' ta meself?"

"Yeah, course I am."

"Stop fidgetin'and sit easy, I tell ya and listen! "

"Granny."

"What? "

"Ya know the way we live on an Island?"

"Yis."

"Ya know the way there's crabs and cockles and muscles and loads of fish in the sea?"

Granny looks at the ceiling, she shakes her head, from side to side, blows a big mouthful of air into the room. Patti knows she's fed up with her.

"The sea was miles away, didn't I tell ya that already. Tell your Ma to get your ears tested in the eye and ear. Now where was I? Ya have me all mixed up!"

"What about the ghosty part?"

"Oh yis, I nearly forgot. The famine dead is restless spirits. At night they rise up out of the mass grave. If you were to go that mountainy road of a dark night, you'd be sure to meet them. They're the walkin' dead of the Hungry Hill. They walk in the rags they fell down in, the bones sticking out of them underneath, the eyes eaten away. They walk this earth for evermore. "

She stops then. She blesses herself and digs Patti in the arm to do the same. They sit there listening to the seagulls and the traffic noise through the window. Then her granny puts her head to one side, says she needs a little lie down after all that.

20

LOADSA MONEY

She smells of apples and oranges, parsley and thyme, all mixed up together. She has bright blue eyes with gold flecks. Nice pinky smooth skin and silvery grey hair. She buys prize bonds and sweepstake tickets. Everyone says she's loaded. On Sundays, she wears fox's tails or her mink stole with real leather gloves. It's her other granny, the fruit and vegetable dealer who sells in the Daisy Market. Granny is roofed in, a long- term tenant of Dublin Corporation. A rent man collects the two and six rent money, every Friday afternoon. Jack writes out a rent receipt and hands it to granny. She reads the News of the World on Sundays; every other day it's the Herald. She starts with the deaths on the back page, in case anyone she knows died.

She makes stacks of money in the market; blue backs and greenbacks and brown- backs. She's mad about horse racing. Lester Piggott is her favourite jockey; Lester never lets her down. She backs favourites and outsiders. She backs doubles and cross-doubles, trebles and cross-trebles, Yankees, bets to win and each-way bets. She always has a horse running in the two thirty at Carlisle, or Chepstow or Pontefract. She studies the form every afternoon in the racing pages, with her reading glasses taped together in the middle. She could tell the men a thing or two about horseracing. She's in the know about trainers and jockeys, she knows all about hard ground and soft ground, and middling ground, and what ground suits what horse best. She knows about weights and measures, or if a certain jockey is too fat or too tall for a certain horse, or if a certain horse is not up to the mark.

On market days, she wears a blue denim money pocket, tied around her black skirt. Over her money pocket, she wears a flowery bib. Underneath all that, she has on a pink bony laced-up corset, which she calls her stays. It's supposed to keep her kidneys warm and all her wobbly bits in place. For Sunday mass, she dresses up real posh, in her mink stole or her fox's tails. Lately, she's all in beige: a felt beige hat, beige leather shoes, a beige bag and gloves. Beige and brown is supposed to be a new contrast, the very latest colour style. It's beige this and beige that and it's dead boring, Patti thinks, like when the sky looks dirty after loads of rain.

On Sundays, after mass, she makes Irel chicory or Nescafe on half milk, half water. Then she puts on the dinner. On the step outside the door, she sharpens her carving knife. The steely sound goes around the fish-market walls and comes back in an echo. She only buys the best cuts of meat; it might be pork shoulder or a roaster chicken or silverside corned beef. She might buy cakes out of the Kylemore for their tea and sometimes she makes apple cakes if she has time.

At night, she keeps her teeth in a tumbler of fizzy Sterident. They grin through the glass, over at granda's teeth in another tumbler. With their teeth out they look like two big babbies. It's like a chemist's shop in their bedroom, with all the medicines. There's roundy boxes of coloured tablets, cough-bottles, ointments, inhalers, Friar's Balsam, Wintergreen, bandages, lint, bags of cough- sweets. Granny gets bad asthma attacks. It starts with a shiny pink face and a wheezy sound in her chest. It gets louder and her face goes dark red. Her eyes go bulgy and watery and the dark red turns to purple. She grabs at her clothes and tries to breath. She roots in her pockets for her inhaler. She squirts it a few times down her throat. It takes a while, but it's the only thing that works. She has to sleep sitting up, propped up on her bolster pillow. She usually falls asleep with her rosary beads between her fingers.

Every morning, she squeezes the tube of Max Factor makeup and rubs it into her face, then she dabs cream- puff powder on her nose and forehead. She runs a comb through her hair, puts on her money-pocket and that's when she's ready for the market. After the market, she empties out her takings. She stacks it up on the table, silver first; half-crowns and florins, shillings and tanners and thropenny pieces, coppers next; it's pennies and two pence's and the whole table is full of money. She has hiding places in case her money is robbed. The money-pocket goes in the space under the dressing-table drawer. If her takings are good, she's usually in good humour, but sometimes she says, "That Daisy Market is gone t'hell."

She's no skinflint. She got the three lights for over the table and the wall lights to match and it must've cost a small fortune. They're the height of grandeur and worth ever penny. They came in a big wooden box called a tea chest, wrapped in loads of straw.

"They're all the fashion!" Granny says, switching the lights on and off to show the effect. They all stand outside, to see into the lighted window and it looks dead cosy in there. Granda says it's like a lighthouse and just wait until the electricity bills come in.

When she hears about the lights, granny Connor says:

"Maybe it's three lights they want. Would one light not be enough?"

Patti tells her, the three lights are all the fashion on the northside, especially with the dealers, but she only makes a face and says, there's nothin' wrong with her tiered chandelier. She means the fibreglass chandelier she bought in Frawley's, that looks like an upside down wedding cake. If she only knew, it's like a different world on the northside; some of the other dealers have mirror tiles over their fireplaces, and beige radiograms and the swanky velvet wallpaper, everyone is talking about. They leave their hall doors wide open so people can see in. Everyone wants to feel the velvet wallpaper, but they have it covered with plastic sheets in case it gets dirty. The woman in the wallpaper shop says it's called Flock and it comes all the way from France and it's very expensive.

In the flats, they rent the tellies by the week from a place in Talbot Street called RTV Rentals. It costs a bomb to rent and you never own the telly. Uncle Willie got the chance of this second hand hardly used set. They're always tuning it in. They have to work on the zigzags and the snowy dots and the wavy bars across and the lines down. Uncle Willie and her Da have to work together, one holding up the bunny ear aerial and moving it around, the other fiddling with the knobs. They argue and give out hell about the telly. They try to coax it to work. It gets on her granny's nerves, especially if there's horse racing on. She gives the telly a few belts. She hits the screen and the sides. It's a bloody jalopy, she says. She'd shoot the bloody thing if she had a gun. But sometimes after forever, they get the picture working and they watch Green Acres.

Green Acres starts with a man called Oliver and a woman called Lisa singing to each other. Oliver and Lisa are a married couple who moved from New York to the country. Lisa has blondy hair. She wears long false eyelashes and long cocktail dresses. It's dead funny, the way she throws the dishes out the window instead of washing up, the way she couldn't care less about housework. All she does is laze around on the couch all day. She dresses up for dinner, but Lisa can't cook. All she can make are hot cakes. They're either too floppy, or too hard. She bangs them down on the table. She talks kind of strange, like she has something stuck in her mouth.

"I'm Home Honey," Oliver says.

"OLIVA, you vant a hot-cake?"

"Oh sure honey," he goes, even though you'd know he doesn't.

"Comving vight up daa ling."

They live in a country place called Hooterville, with miles of fields all around them, but all Lisa wants is to be back in New York. Oliver is a lawyer but all he really wants is to be a farmer. They have crazy neighbours, who all wear dungarees and baseball caps.

In the song, Oliver sings: *Green acres is the place for me, farm livin is the life for me, land spreadin out to far and wide, keep Manhattan just give me that countryside.* Then Lisa goes, in her Hungarian voice: *New York is vhere I'd raather be, I get allergic smelling hay, I just adore the friends I knew, daaling I love you but give me Park Avenue.*

Granny says, "that blondy one in the Green Acres is stone mad, throwin' good delf out the window."

Granny prefers Quick Silver, a quiz show with Bunny Carr as the quizmaster.

Everyone is shouting; *stop the Lights*. It's like a new saying around town. On Tuesday nights, they watch Quicksilver; even if the telly is not working they watch bits of it in- between the wavy bars. Her granny likes Bunny Carr, especially his immaculate grey suits and snow-white shirts. He starts the quiz all smiley and friendly:

"There's no need to be nervous. Sure it's only a bit of fun. And sure you can always, *Stop the lights,* " Bunny says to the contestants.

Granny laughs at that. She thinks it's gas. Bunny says they're giving away loads of money for nothing.

"You'd never get rich on Quicksilver," Granny says. She'd like to have a go herself, only she might be a bit nervous. She'd know the easy questions, like the two p or the three p ones, but some of the dearer questions like the half crown ones are very hard. If the contestant doesn't know the answer, Bunny gives them hints by prompting them and sometimes he nearly answers the question himself.

Another programme she watches is Monica Sheridan's cookery show.

"Here's Monica," granny says and sits down at the table.

Monica talks to the camera. She looks straight out of the telly into the kitchen, like she's just in the next room. She measures and mixes and pours. She uses a lot of baking powder and yeast and Pyrex dishes. She wears an apron and she always uses gloves when she's lifting something out of the oven. She's working in this fancy kitchen full of shiny pots and pans. She only has to reach out and there's a shiny pot or a bowl or a plate, like magic. She follows recipes. She has a plug-in electric mixer. She cooks peculiar things; things you wouldn't eat, like cauliflower cheese and beef Wellington. She cuts up a melon into skinny slices, puts cherries on top and she calls that an appetiser.

"That Monica can't cook for love nor money. What's she doin' with that cauliflower? It looks a holy show covered in cheese," Granny says.

***

Sometimes on winter nights, in front of the fire when the telly goes fuzzy, granny likes telling history stories. You see her rolling up her sleeve and that's when you know. Oh God! She's going to tell the missing elbow story. The same story over and over. The story she's never to forget. Ever! It's all about the Troubles and the 1916 Rising. What it was like up Church Street; the barricades and the shots fired and the bullet-holes and the rebels hiding out in the houses. The women running back and forth with messages to the Volunteers. Some on bicycles and some on foot. The whole place was like a bombsite. All the looting downtown, with people going nuts, robbing stuff out of shop-windows, like clothes and kettles and delf, prams and bikes and basins. And then the good part, the part she really wants to tell. How she was nearly killed and lost her elbow-bone, when she was delivering fruit for her mother to a shop in Grafton Street. There was this big commotion near Capel Street Bridge, hundreds of people all rushing down Parliament Street from Dublin Castle. She could hear men shouting to get back. Shots were fired then, people had to lie on the ground with their heads down and that's when the car hit her. Her pram was turned over, she remembers apples and oranges rolling over the road and she tried to catch them, but she couldn't move. A good soul of a gentleman ran with her to Jervis Street hospital in the middle of all the trouble, with the blood dripping out of her.

"Very lucky to have the arm, " she says.

The miracles the doctors worked on that crushed arm. They inserted steel rods and pins to stop it falling asunder. Granny was in hospital for weeks.

She holds up the arm.

"Go on don't be afraid."

"Oh God! Patti hates the feel of it. The skin is creased and papery, the flesh underneath soft and squishy, like warm fresh bread.

"It won't bite," granny says, with her sleeve rolled up.

There's no elbow bone, so she can't use it properly. She has to mind it; she keeps the crooked arm close to her chest, like a new baby. It's her war wound, she says. She was only nine, when she lost her elbow, so she did her bit for Ireland.

Her granny has her imagining it all, with the place in bits, like in a war film, the sandbags, the rebels hiding under the beds or in the attic. Sometimes, she mixes it up with the Black and Tans. Here's the Tans up Mary Street, a gang of them in a huge noisy tank: them shouting up curses at the windows in their English accents, the people shouting back curses and jeers at them, them aiming up with their tanks and guns. The cries and the squeals of the women and children when the shots are fired.

They were bowsies, most of them, who couldn't get work in England.

When she was a kid, she had to work hard on her mother's stall. She always says you shouldn't be afraid of hard work. Patti knows about hard work, lifting bags of potatoes up the steps of the Daisy Market. Delivering fruit and vegetables to shopkeepers. Collecting turf from the depot in Benburb Street, running for messages, to the butcher and the bakery, to the bookies with bets, to the druggist and the dispensary for medicine.

"Hard work never hurt anybody," she says.

Granny told her another story. It's a bit romantic. About her and granda in the olden days when they were courting. They used to meet at Nelson's Pillar. It was still the roaring twenties. A scratchy photo shows her with long black wavy hair and her face creamy white. Her hands crossed over one another, a bit shy looking. She was wearing a lovely handmade dress with a dropped waist. That dress, she told her, was midnight blue velvet. She swanked in that dress. She was very stylish back then. A bit of style never killed anyone, she says. And it doesn't cost that much to smarten yourself up. Here's granda, up O'Connell Street to meet her. He's rushing. A bit out of breath in a long, tan crombie coat and tweed turn-up trousers. His hair in a calf's lick at the front. There's granny in her swanky velvet dress on her way up Henry Street. Maybe a little breeze shaking her long black hair. The two of them meeting in the crowded street under Nelson, their faces a bit yellowy from the streetlight. It was what she calls a romance. They fell in love. She showed him the bad arm with the missing elbow. He didn't mind. Bad arm or not, she was a real smasher, he said. They got the tram out to

Kingstown. They watched the sailboats. They sat on a seat near the bandstand and ate the marshmallows granda bought at a kiosk. She had to be home early, so they didn't dilly-dally. It might've been the new Free State, but it was still very strict.

"Free State is right," granny says. "There was nothing free about it."

She remembers a fierce storm all of a sudden, foamy waves sloshing onto the pier. Granda took her arm. They ran for the tram. Granny says the rest is history.

On Sundays, they walked in Steven's Green and listened to the brass band. Afterwards they sat in a little teahouse off Grafton Street. They saw stage shows at the Theatre Royal. Her Da gave his blessing. Not at first. Her Da was very particular. They got married. They still have their wedding presents in the glass case; bone china, coloured glass and silver spoons. They had Patti's Da, the biggest baby ever born in the Rotunda Hospital. Maybe the biggest baby ever born in Ireland.

"Nearly fourteen pound weight and you'd think he was a year old," granny says.

A photographer came and took his photo. In the photo, he looks like a little Italian with his dark hair and eyes.

Patti's Da grew up. He met her Ma at a dance in Dun Laoghaire. They started going everywhere on his bicycle, with her Ma on the crossbar holding down her dress. They got married not long after granda Connor died. They had Patti. She was born in the Rotunda Hospital on a wet May night. It was Friday the thirteenth and her Ma was mortified, because that's supposed to be unlucky. She told her a stork delivered her and left her on a window ledge outside the ward. Eight and a half pound she was. It's not something her Ma will ever forget in a hurry.

21

THE DAISY

"Why is it called the Daisy?"

"It's because years ago masses of wild yellow daises grew there and you'd think you were out in the country," her granny says.

That was before they built the markets. The poor people made posies out of the daisies and sold them outside the chapels. But today, it's a terrific market. You can buy anything: fruit, vegetables, fish, chickens, clothes, shoes, candles, holy pictures, toilet rolls, delf. The walls of the Daisy are whitewashed. It has a tin roof, so when it rains, it's dead noisy. There's fat cats that sit on the windowsills. They're high jumpers; they jump to catch the fish-heads the men throw at them. It's like a circus game and the highest jumper gets a whole fish for itself.

Work starts early in the fruit and vegetable market. From the flats, they hear the sound of the brass bell ringing and that means the market is open. There's always a queue of horses and carts waiting to get in. When the big front gates open, they start to move forward. The market men call out to each other in loud voices. The echo goes around the brick walls and up to the glass roof.

"Are ya there Joeboy Boylan? "

"Are ya there Tommo?"

The Daisy Market opens soon after. The women dealers are on the road from cockcrow in their white cross over smocks. Every day, except Sunday, they come in from different parts of the city: East Wall, Finglas, Cabra, pushing three wheeler basket carts on iron wheels. There's Catty and Nanny and Biddy and Bridey and Molly. There's the fowl dealers down the steps who sell chickens and rabbits. There's the women who sell second-hand clothes and shoes. Her granny's stall is the best in the Daisy, being on a corner site, that attracts all sorts of people on the lookout for a bargain. She only sells the best of fresh produce, so her stall is always packed with customers.

At the stalls, there's different kinds of talk between the dealers, but it's mostly about body stuff and diseases. It's about gallbladders, gangrene, amputations, piles, septic throats, ulcers, varicose veins, kidney stones. A new kind of operation, called a *Section,* you get in the Rotunda Hospital. To demonstrate, they make a sign of the cross on their belly.

"Like a hot cross bun," one of them says.

"More like a knife and fork job," another one says.

An amputation is when you have your leg or your arm removed. The leg goes blue first, then green, then black. If it's gangrene, it rots and sometimes it falls off by itself. It's mostly men who got their leg off. You see them hobbling along on crutches, with their trouser-leg turned up at the knee. Some lost their legs out in the Congo and some lost them from too much drink.

Sometimes there's fights between the dealers over customers. Granny say's it's only jealousy. It's usually between Nanny and Catty, or Biddy and Nanny, or all three of them. Sometimes granny has to butt in to stop them tearing each other to pieces. Catty doesn't get many customers and maybe it's because she has a little beard and moustache. Her voice is faraway and shaky.

Biddy says: "Catty's potatoes are like herself, ancient and hairy and full of eyes, her caulies saw better days and her onions are only disgraceful."

Catty wears a long coat, a wide, banged down hat over her forehead, so you can only see half her face. She looks out at Biddy from under her hat. She says her merchandise is fit for a bishop's palate. Biddy is funny. She dances gigues and reels for the tourists. She wears a small black hat with a peacock-feather. She puts on powder and lipstick in the little mirror on the windowsill. She gives Patti kisses on the cheek.

"There chicken," she goes, with a big sloppy lipstick kiss.

She calls her a little smasher. When she dances, she lifts her skirt over her knees and you can see fat wobbly legs and garters. Everyone claps. Granny thinks she's a scream.

"You're stone mad," she tells her.

They go to Dignam's on Friday's after the market closes. They have a singsong in the snug. Sometimes they get sozzled and Mister Dignam has to warn them over and over to stop singing so loud and drawing attention to his respectable establishment.

"Keep it down now girls," he says, pointing his finger, but that only makes them sing louder. Her granny is not a drinker. On the odd occasion, say like Christmas, she'd take a small sherry to wet her lips, but mostly it's a small ginger ale. She'd prefer to back a horse in Aran Street bookies, or go home and soak her feet in a basin of hot water and Epsom Salts.

She knows all the important people in the market, especially the salesmen with the brown shop coats and the pencils behind their ears. On Mondays, she settles all her bills and buys more stock. She has a bit of a chat with the salesman first. She picks out a case of oranges or a barrel of grapes. She starts the deal. She makes an offer. She tells them the fruit is half rotten and only fit for the bin. She winks at Patti. If there's a bad orange or an apple in the box, she says the whole box is rotten and that's how she gets it cheaper. It's one of her tricks.

"Who's goin' to buy that? Sure the whole box'll be rotten by tomorra."

There's no shortage of well-to-do customers at her stall. There's the Jew men and the protestants, there's the chipper owner and the draper called Mary, there's the women from the houses and the women from the square and the women from the flats. There's bag ladies from the Morning Star Hostel who ask her for an apple. There used to be this nice well-dressed woman granny knows from town called Kathleen. Kathleen used to shop for bargains in the Daisy on Saturdays. She went to Moore Street first and sometimes she'd wander up to the Daisy to browse the stalls. Granny used to give her a big smile when she came in with her messagebag. Then she puts on her posh voice.

"Oh there you are, Kathleen. Isn't it well your lookin'? "

"Oh hello Annie."

They always had a little chat. She only bought the best of stuff: Beauty of Bath apples, William pears, Canary tomatoes, a bit of parsley and thyme.

"I've lovely York cabbage just in," granny says.

She'd take a few heads, she says, but her bags are nearly full up.

"Those Moore Street girls, won't take no for an answer."

"Oh I know. For God's sake, they'd poison you down there if you weren't careful."

Then she gets out the good brown paper bags from the half-pound bundle she bought in Evans's.

"How's all yours?"

"Oh grand. And yours?"

"Oh well as can be expected."

The others watch, Biddy and Nanny and Catty, their eyes slanty and jealous, behind their stalls. They're only jealous, because Kathleen won't buy anything from them. She'll only say:

"Hello there girls, isn't that a grand mornin' thank God."

Then granny gets the good stuff out of the press, the stuff she keeps for her best customers. She gives her a shiny purple plum.

"Here. Try that for flavour."

Kathleen takes a bite.

"Nice and juicy. Full of flavour. Oh go on, sure you might as well give us the pound."

She wipes her mouth with a white cloth hankie.

"I've nice blood oranges too."

Granny cuts an orange with her pen- knife, lets the red juice spill onto the ground and it's like the orange is bleeding.

"That'll put blood in your veins."

"Right so, a half a dozen."

Kathleen pays granny and says hello to the other dealers and goes for a look around the market. They all say a big hello, like she's real important.

"She's very La-Di-Da, that Kathleen," Catty says.

"That's a lady!" granny says, "A real lady!"

Granny told Patty, she has a son who's a writer. He used to buy fish every week in the fish market. They used to live in town in the tenements, but they moved out to the sticks, miles away from civilisation to a place called Crumlin. The Corporation were giving out houses like presents, but granny wouldn't be moved from the city, not even if they paid her disturbance money. She got a house all right, the Dublin Corporation sent her out the same letter they sent Kathleen Behan, but she burned the letter before any of them could see it and that was the end of that. No way was she going live out in the Wild West in the shade of the Dublin Mountains.

Friday is the busiest day in the Daisy. It's queues everywhere. The women from the flats buy cabbage and potatoes, apples and bananas. The posh protestants order carnations and prunes and honeydew melons. They always want some herb they never heard of. They want marmalade oranges to make marmalade. You'd know them by their tweed costumes and bullet-proof stockings. They come in on the buses from Harold's Cross and Phibsborough and Terenure. Everyone knows they have get togethers in their houses, what they call parish mornings. At the stall they talk to each other about the rector or the cannon or the chaplain in their church. Granny says they want the best of stuff for half nothing, even though some of them are rotten with money.

The jewmen are always friendly, especially this nice man called Mister Jackson. Mister Jackson is a smart dresser. He wears a long trench coat, called a Mackintosh, and a brown Trilby hat. He's in the jewellery business. Has a shop on the southside. He lifts his hat.

"How are you today Annie?"

Granny says, "Oh very well. " He's what she calls a gentleman.

The egg man from County Meath brings in trays of his best brown eggs and sometimes he keeps her a few spotty duck eggs. It's called barter. He swaps her a tray of eggs for a tray of fruit and vegetables. She always trims his cauliflowers and cabbages and sometimes she peels him a banana.

"All the way from Jamaica," she says. "Have a bite; it's good for the brains."

He always laughs at that. He thinks she's a scream. He thinks they're all a scream. He talks to the women for a while. Biddy might tell him a few jokes about Paddy Englishman. His brown van with the wood beams is always parked outside the market gate. He has the back opened out like a stall, where he sells his eggs. The eggs still have bits of feathers and dirt, but he says that's because they're so fresh.

They're all bingo-mad in the market. They go to the Father Matthew Hall and Saint Anthony's Hall and the Tivoli. The bingo-balls jump around the plastic box; they go pop and pock! Then they come out this tube and the number lights up on a big screen behind. The man calls out the numbers in bingo-talk: Two fat ladies for 88, clickety click, two little ducks for 22, legs 11. Busloads of people come up from the country on Thursday night. If they win the jackpot they get a free taxi home. Patti marks a book. It's allowed. No one says anything. Except if she has a full house or a line, she can't shout check. Someone has to shout it for her. One night, she won a full house on two fat ladies and her granny got fifty quid, the biggest prize in the Tivoli.

PART 2

22

THE MEETING OF THE WATERS

Uncle Willie says that travel broadens the mind. Uncle Fran says, the pilgrims were great travellers; they walked in their bare feet to all the Holy shrines in the world. He wouldn't mind going to Lourdes, he says, to cure his bad hip. A girl in Patti's class went on a pilgrimage to Lourdes for a cure for polio, but she stills wears crutches. Some day when she grows up, she might go on her travels, maybe to the Isle of Mann, or the Canary Islands. She's only been down the country once with her granny.

Sometimes the dealers go out for the day on Sundays. It's called a mystery tour and it takes you to lovely places down the country. They were all jealous in the flats, because she was going and they weren't. Everyone was calling her a culchie. Her friend said it was only oulones who went on mystery tours. The sky looked dull, but her granny said the weather was to take up nice, according to the forecast on Radio Eireann. They walked down the quays. They passed three bridges to get to the bus stop near O'Connell Bridge. Granny's feet were killing her in her good Sunday shoes. There was a queue of women with messagebags, some of them from the Daisy Market. The bus was a special tour bus with high back seats. The driver was leaning against the Liffey wall, with a cigarette stuck in his mouth. He kept looking at his watch. Then he opened the door and started to give them a hand coming up the steps.

"Mind your step now ladies," he says.

They find good seats with white hankies on the backs and granny says they're travelling in style today. The driver starts up the engine and a cheer goes up.

At the traffic lights, they wave out at people crossing O'Connell Bridge. The people look back at them like they're mad. On the quays, there's hardly any traffic. They pass a couple of horses and carts loaded up with furniture and scrap metal. They know one of the drivers from the market. Granny smiles and gives him a wave, but Gidda doesn't see her. Gidda is miles away, holding up the horse's reins, like a cowboy on a wagon train. They have a guessing game to see where they might be going; her granny thought it was Bray, Bridie thought it might be Drogheda, someone at the back said, the Rock of Cashel and someone else said, the Lakes of Killarney. But all the driver does is laugh. Through the microphone, he says none of them got it right and they'll just have to wait and see. It didn't matter where they were going. It didn't matter if they never stopped. It was nice just being in the bus and going somewhere. It was terrific having the window seat and it was smashing she was the only kid on the bus.

It went a bit quiet, then the driver started telling jokes, Paddy Englishman and Paddy Irishman stuff, so everyone cheers up.

"That's more like it," Bridie says.

"He's a ticket, that busman," granny says, taking out her hankie.

All of a sudden, they're all in convulsions. There's the rattly noise of paper and they start to open bags of sweets. Granny has iced caramels and bulls eyes. Bridie has acid drops. There's the sound of munching and chewing and then someone starts to sing: *When You're Smiling*. Everyone *joins* in. They root around in their handbags. One of them takes out a Baby Power, another one takes out a square bottle of Gordon's gin. Granny said it was a bit early for that carry on.

But it didn't matter, because they were going down the country and everyone was having a great time. The singing is over and it goes quiet again. After a long time, they're outside the city, on a country road, with trees on one side and fields on the other. There's sheep with their lambs, spotty black and white cows, all the different greens of the fields, light green and dark green and yellow green. It's like being in a different country, where everything is dyed green. The sheep are not as white as she thought they'd be. The cows are bigger. The driver talks into the microphone. He tells them to watch out for the mountain up ahead, called the Sugar Loaf. They heard of that mountain before. Everyone watches. It looks huge and crooked, like a sideways hat, but after they pass, it seems to go straight again.

"We're in the Garden of Eireann ladies," the driver goes into the mike.

"There's a song about the Garden of Eireann," Bridie shouts.

"Can anyone give us a few bars?"

No one seems to know that song, but a woman remembers another song about Wicklow. She starts to sing in a quivery voice. The bus goes faster and they go deeper into the country. The woman with the Baby Power falls asleep and her hat falls to one side. Granny reaches over and gives her a nudge and she jumps awake and rubs her eyes.

"We're nearly at the mystery sight," granny says.

Patti hopes they'll be stopping soon, because she needs to go to the toilet. They turn very slowly into a narrow road. There's trees everywhere. They stop in a car park, with a sign saying: Forest Walk.

Bridie shouts; "Stop the lights! We must be at the mystery site."

"It's just a short stop to stretch the legs," the driver says, so they all get off the bus.

There's no toilets. They can't find toilets anywhere. Everyone is bursting. Patti has her ankles crossed. Some of them are doubled over. How are they supposed to manage without bloody toilets, they all want to know? The driver leans on the side of the bus and lights a cigarette. He says there's plenty of cover and shady trees in the forest.

"Are you coddin us?" Bridie says, with her hands on her hips. "Do you know we're all ladies here, born and bred?"

Granny gives her a dig in the arm.

"He's only gettin' it up for us," she says, but he isn't. He just stands there, with the cigarette hanging out of his mouth. The trees are tall and closed in at the top, so you can't see much sky. The ground is spongy and covered in plants. Her granny is raging about her good soft leather shoes she bought in Arnotts. If she'd known, she'd have worn her market shoes.

There's no one else in the forest. It's dead quiet, except for the sound of birds high up in the trees. They all crouch down behind the fattest trees; a long line of women with hats and scarves and pulled up skirts. A roaring gushing sound, like when a water main bursts and the corporation waterworks are called. Patti goes a bit away from them behind another tree. Someone says: it won't do the trees any harm. They're all in stitches. Then they hear it on the way back to the bus, the sound of a waterfall coming from somewhere in the distance. Bridie said it sounded like Niagara Falls, and the busman said, that wasn't the only thing that sounded like Niagara Falls. Bridie said that was disgraceful vulgar talk in the company of ladies and children.

Everyone was complaining about the mystery tour. Outside the bus, they ganged up on the driver. There was nothin' in this bloody place only trees; what were they supposed to do with trees? Did the driver think they were in a fairy story, like the Babes in the Woods, or The Three Bears? They wanted somewhere with a bit of life, they wanted music and a singsong. They wanted monuments and country stuff. They didn't pay good money for a bloody forest in the arsehole of nowhere, with no toilets. The driver was cool as a cucumber. He says there's very good toilets at the next stop and plenty of water and a grand little pub. Someone said, there better be. So everyone was happy again. On the bus, the driver makes an announcement. He tells them, The Meeting of the Waters is the next stop. It's where two rivers meet and it's very popular with city people and American tourists.

"So it's on with the mystery tour ladies," he says, starting up the engine.

At the mystery sight, the driver parks near the riverbank. There's picnic tables and grass and a small wooden bridge. This was more like it, everyone said. They find a bench and sit down for a while. The river is low, like a stream, the water as clean as tap water.

"Begod, that water is only massive," Bridie said. Then she takes off her shoes and stockings, says there's nothing like mountain water for corns and bunions. She dangles her feet over the edge. The driver tells her to be careful she doesn't fall in and drown. Then they all crowded into the pub for teas and drinks. It's packed with tourists and yanks, all bunched up at the bar. First, they order pots of tea and scones, then it's glasses of stout, then it's small sherries and gins and whiskies for the journey.

All of a sudden there's a man with a cowboy hat playing the organ. They all want a singsong, so they call on one another to sing. The driver comes over with his pint of Guinness. Someone starts to sing: *Pack up Your Troubles* and it's like a hooley in the flats. They want to dance then. You can't have a singsong without a dance. Then the bar lady moves back chairs and makes a space on the wooden floor. The man in the cowboy hat starts to play a foxtrot. The driver takes Bridie's hand and leads her onto the dance floor. A few old yanks ask some of them up to dance and it's like a ballroom. Granny's face goes scarlet when a tall man with a tanned face asks her up. She has a shockin' bad arm, she says, and pulls up her sleeve to show him her 1916 elbow, with the yards of bandages wrapped around it. The man gives a little bow, smiles and moves off to someone else. The yanks are having a great time.

"This sure is some shindig," one of them says.

Granny says it's good sport all right and it's nice to get away for the day.

Bridie says it's the best do she's been at in years.

There's Irish dancing then and Patti is allowed to join in.

"Go on, get up and dance. "

Granny nudges her in the arm. The man in the cowboy hat sits down and another man takes his place and starts to play the fiddle. They all join hands and dance a reel in a big circle. After a good few dances, the driver looks at his watch.

"Lets get this show on the road. The mystery tour must go on ladies," he shouts through the music. He says he has more Irish mysteries to show them, more places of historical interest on his list. But the hooley is in full swing and they won't be moved. He orders another pint and stands with his arm resting on the bar. He'll give them ten minutes, he says. But after the ten minutes, they want more drinks and some of them want to go and some don't. A few of the posher ones say it's disgraceful and they're missing the whole day, but the others want one more drink for the road. Just one more. Her granny pretends it's Christmas and has a small sherry, just to please them.

It takes ages to get them out of the pub. They're all in great form on the bus. There's more songs; someone sings the sad song about Picardy and the roses that shine there, then someone else sings: *It's a long way to Tipperary*. They're on a narrow mountainy road, with sharp drops down one side. You can see for miles across a deep green valley with a silvery stream, like a very long snake. If a car comes the other way, the driver has to pull over and there's hardly any room. Her granny blesses herself and Patti says a prayer to her guardian angel. She has a strange feeling in her head, her ears do a popping thing and she goes deaf. The sun peeps out at a sign for Glendalough. The driver turns into the car park and pulls the brake and says he'll give them round towers, if that's what they want. He'll give them lakes and mountains and plenty of crumbling ruins. But some of them are already asleep. A few more are tipsy and some of them are sozzled. They don't want to get off. Granny wants to stretch her legs. So does Patti. A few of them get off the bus to have a look around. They don't go that far, because the driver says they only have twenty minutes. They walk a bit around the nearest lake. They see the second lake and the round tower and the chapel ruins, where saint Kevin the hermit priest lived. They didn't dilly dally, because the bus driver was waiting.

It was starting to get dark when they got home. The bus leaves them back to O'Connell Bridge. That was a grand day, her granny says, but the next time, they might go a bit further, they might chance The Blarney stone, or The Lakes of Killarney.

23

A WHOOPY CUSHION

They're all a bit nutskies in her granny's. They do tiddles to make her laugh, so she can't stop and she nearly chokes.

"We'll do tiddles," they say.

One of the aunties would have her down on the floor, tiddling her all over on her tiddle bits. *"Tiddles! Tiddles!"* They'd say and go ninety, under her arms, down in her belly and her sides. She can't catch her breath and the tiddles make her laugh and laugh more. It's like she's going to burst, but the aunties won't stop until she gives them a good kick.

They have this whoopy cushion they put under the Herald and when you sit down, it farts and people think it's you.

"It's only a joke," they say, but it's only funny if it happens to someone else.

They do a thing with a chocolate box. They take the lid off. They tell her to take a sweet.

"Have a lovely chocolate sweet," they say, holding out the box in front of her.

"Are ya sure?"

"Course I am. Go on, they're lovely."

She picks out a brazil nut. She goes to take it, but she can't. The Brazil nut is stuck to the box. It's a pretend sweet; an empty plastic mould turned upside down.

They do another trick with Brutlax chocolate.

"There's a nice bar of Cadburys," they say.

The Brutlax chocolate has the same purple and silver wrapper as Cadburys Dairy Milk, but there's this medicine inside the chocolate like senna pods that makes you run to the toilet. She didn't know about it the first time, so she ate the bar of Brutlax. It tasted lovely, like normal chocolate, but then she got the shocking pains like she was being stabbed with invisible knives. You're supposed to laugh at that too, even though you're stuck in the toilet for hours.

"It's only a joke, dya get it?" they say. She gets it, but she doesn't get it at the same time, so she has to pretend she does.

"I get it," she says.

Her Ma says it's bad enough to be fooled once, but never be fooled twice. It was her own fault, because she wasn't wearing her glasses, so she couldn't see the mould was plastic. It was the same with the Brutlax chocolate she thought it was Cadburys. She won't be fooled again, she says. She knows all their tricks now, about pretend chocolate sweets and pretend bars of Cadburys. You can only buy the Brutlax chocolate in the chemist. She'd know it the next time if she saw it.

A fox was standing beside the bed one morning, when she woke. There it was, with starey eyes looking up at her and she thought she was dreaming. It was only a stuffed fox; they put it there to give her a little fright, but it was the spitting image of a real fox.

"Give him a rub. He won't bite, " Aunt Dinah says, so she covers her head with the blanket until they take it away. One of the dealers was selling the fox in the market and granny got the loan for the night. In the flats, everyone was talking about the fox. They had it out on the front step and all the kids were terrified.

A real crab was walking up the hall on the red and white tiles, when she came home from school one day, with another one behind it trying to catch up. There's granny, hiding behind the kitchen door with a big grin on her face.

"Sure, they're only havin' a race to see who's fastest."

Another day, a dressed up dummy was hiding in the coalhole, when she went to get a shovel of coal. In the dark, she thought it was a real woman with pearly white teeth. It was another one of granny's jokes. A pair of wind up chattering teeth that rattle across the floor and try to bite your feet: chatter chatter chatter, all over the place until they come to a sudden stop under the table. Granny thinks it's gas and keeps winding it up again and again.

Then there's another new jokey thing that came all the way from China. Granny says this yoke would make a bear with a sore head laugh.

"Just wait and see," she says, opening a cardboard box.

She lifts out a laughing delf China man with a bald-head and a fat belly. He's sitting on a toilet pot, and there's a cistern with a pull chain behind him. Granny does a demonstration on the table. She presses a button and his trousers fall down over his knees. Then she pulls the little chain and the toilet makes a flushing sound. Then the man stands up and you see his fat bum. She presses the button again and the trousers go back up. They're in knots at the table. They keep pulling the chain. It's a bit rude, but it's the funniest thing they've ever seen. Everyone wants the China man on the toilet pot. In the market, they're queuing up to buy them. The dealer said they're selling like hot cakes and she'll have to order a whole shipment from China and put the price up. They don't show it to granda. Not yet.

24

RASPBERRY SUNDAYS

Granda mightn't see the funny side of the funny China man. It's not the kind of jokey thing he'd encourage in a hurry. He's a bit old-fashioned. He still wears long johns in bed. At night, granda's braces are down over his trousers, his bootlaces are opened and his hair is tossed. Before he goes to bed, he winds up all the clocks, the old-fashioned chimes clock on the sideboard, that was a wedding present, the smaller brass clock on the mantelpiece and the blue roundy alarm clock, which granny says would wake the dead. Granda opens the chimes clock at the front. He sets it by the hands. At the back he winds it up with the special key. He might take a spoon of Epsom Salts in water, or he might fill the hot water bottle if it's a cold night. He bolts the hall door top and bottom. He switches off all the lights. In the bedroom, he puts his teeth in a separate tumbler, next to granny's. They read the Herald between them in bed. They divide it up and swap over. He crumples the pages. There they are in bed, with their teeth out and their glasses on, the white bolster like a snowy mountain behind them. The two of them making newspaper noises under the light bulb. The two of them nodding off and twitching until granda gets up and switches out the light.

He used to always bring Patty with him, every Sunday after mass, into the pub around the corner. She was allowed to sit on the high stool beside him to keep him company. Granda looks at the barman and the barman nods and pours her a glass of raspberry cordial. She holds the glass up to the light. It's lovely if it's sunny out. She likes how the light flows through the tumbler, making the red raspberry light up, like a sacred heart lamp.

It's dead smoky in the pub. Granda gets his pipe to light after ages. Most of the older men smoke pipes, but the younger men smoke Sweet Afton or Players Navy Cut. There's glass ashtrays on the counter, overflowing with butts. It's a porter and whiskey smell and a smell of men's overcoats, all mixed up. It's nice and cosy in there, before the men get drunk, before their faces go red and their voices get too loud. Before they start fighting and arguing with one another. She's the spittin image of her Da's people across the eyes and chin, they say, and where did she get them lovely stylish glasses? Then they let her have a little taste of stout. It won't do any harm. It's allowed.

"Not too much now," her granda says. "Just a drop." He holds his hand under her chin in case she spits it out. They all laugh then, when she makes a face. She prefers orange she says. Sometimes a man will buy her a bottle of Club Orange with a straw. She always gets a packet of Tayto and loose change for sweets. First, the men bang their pockets with their hands. Then they root around in the deep parts and rattle the small change. Then they take out a few pennies. She's not allowed to mess or rock on the stool. She has to sit easy and be a good girl. She's not supposed to earwig or ask umpteen questions.

The pub gets crowded after the last mass at twelve o'clock; the snug is usually packed with women from the flats and the square. They ring the brass buzzer for service. The barman goes back and forth to the hatch with glasses of creamy stout. Then it gets louder. There's curses and shouts from the men about racehorses and football and the bloody government. The women in the snug start to sing and the barman gives out. She knows by granda's face. He rubs his chin first. Has another sup of stout. He lifts her down off the stool. It's time to go home. He leaves her up to the gate. He tells her to go straight home for her dinner. He tells her to tell her granny he won't be long. There's granny, bent over, sharpening her knife on the side of the step.

"Granda says he won't be long."

Granny nods, like she doesn't believe him. She straightens up. She tests out the knife-edge for sharpness with her finger and thumb. In the steamy scullery, she carves the chicken and chops the cabbage. Her face is hot and red. She tells Patti to make herself useful and set the table. Willow plates, knives and forks, glass salt and pepper shakers. Brown Chef sauce. Coleman's Mustard. Nice clean shiny lino tablecloth, with squares like wall tiles, with red roses in the middle.

There's army medals in the sideboard drawer, with dusty striped ribbons and Patti wonders was he in the wars, like her other granda. They won't let her touch them.

"Mauler's off," they say if she lifts one up to get a better look. She's not supposed to touch things. Maybe they're not his. Maybe they belong to someone else in their family. It's none of her business. She heard one of the aunties saying they might be worth money some day. Granda never touches them. All his stuff is up high on a shelf in the scullery: his tools, his screw box, his shoe last, his gun. His gun is an old-fashioned-looking yoke, wrapped in a yellow dusting cloth. He stands on the stepladder. He takes it down carefully to clean and polish it and granny gives out hell. He blows the dust off first; then he checks all the moving parts to see if they're in working order. He takes things apart on the bath board. He holds the gun up. He looks through the barrel and pretends to pull the trigger. It's all right, because it's not loaded he says, but granny says it's dangerous and tells him to put that gun away out of her sight. He shines it up with silver polish and wraps it back up. Next he takes down his shoe last. He mends his good shoes with pieces of leather. He hammers steel nails into the soles of his black work boots.

Friday is payday. It used to be throppence, and then it went up to four pence. She can buy a packet of Smarties or two Trigger bars or two Macaroon bars, or two penny toffees and five pink mice. Her sisters always eat their sweets outside the shop as soon as they buy them. They never save any for after. It's pull open the wrapper. It's throw away the paper. It's one big bite, then gobble gobble gobble. Then it's big chocolate faces.

Then they'd say, "giz some," when Patti gets her own stuff. They do a war dance until she gives in. Then they take a big huge bite, a horse's bite, all the way down the Trigger bar and there's hardly any left. Sometimes, in her Ma's place she has to eat her stuff in the toilet with the latch on. You're not supposed to eat in the toilet. You can get diseases. German's come out of the toilet into the sweets and down into your stomach, especially if the window is open and there's a breeze and you have a cold; *Breezes and sneezes spread diseases.* One of her aunties on the southside says that. Patti stands up on the wood toilet seat. She shuts the window. She hopes she won't sneeze.

25

A HOOLEY

In the flats they have hoolies. It might be after a wedding, or it might be after a wake, or it might be at Christmas. It's dead brillo, with the place full of people. It's like in the old drunken house where they used to live. Everyone in good mood. The place spinning with the music. All the chattering voices. Granny, with her mouth organ and spoons; Uncle Willie with his accordion, some old man from upstairs with a fiddle. All the happy faces, all the clapping and all the feet tapping. The stout bottles stacked up in crates in the scullery, the ham pot bubbling on the gas stove full of pigs' feet. Patti with her brother, watching. The two of them listening and no one telling them to go to bed.

In the back bedroom all the overcoats are heaped on the bed. Granny's brother Johnny does MC. He stands on a crate in the middle of the floor, taps his glass with a fork, and calls on people to sing. First up are the good singers.

"Now ladies and gentlemen," he says in his hoarse voice. "Be quiet and no talking."

The room goes dead quiet then. If someone even mutters during the song, he gives out hell. Then everyone has to clap.

"Lets hear it for the very talented Misses Roche. Put your hands together and give her a big round of applause."

Granny might sing or she mightn't. She'd have to be in the right mood. It's the same with her mouth organ and her spoons. If she sings, her voice is trembly, especially when she sings: *Picardy*. It's like she's half crying, half singing at the same time. Someone always sings *Kevin Barry* and *Danny Boy*. Some of them have hard tinny voices, that break up in the middle of the song, but the MC makes sure everyone gives them a round of applause.

The table is moved back for the dancing. The good dancers take to the floor. The room shakes and spins around them. The best place to watch at a hooley is under the table. They sit on the wrung and watch all the feet, dancing feet and tapping feet, granny's tan leather slip-ons, granda's black hobnail Corporation-boots, all the furry slippers and the brown working boots, a woman with sausage shaped legs and no ankles, a man with holes in the soles of his shoes, the MC's black shoes on the upside down crate.

Granny has her hankie out. She's mopping her forehead. She's hot. There's rain on the way, she says, she can feel it in her bones.

"And now for a Paddy Englishman joke."

Granny's brother standing up on the stout crate. He makes a mike out of his fist. He splutters out the words of the joke. He's in stitches. They all are, except granda; his eyebrows are gone together in an angry bunch. He sits in his flowery armchair smoking his pipe, his mouth making that funny popping sound. His bootlaces are open and ready for bed, his shirt collar off, so his neck looks bare. His eyelids are half closed. He might be fed up or just tired, Patti thinks. He rubs his eyes; maybe he wants to wind up the clocks. Her granny's face goes red with the laughing. She roots in her pocket for her inhaler. She aims it into her mouth. She squirts: P'quaw! P'quaw! It's a sign she's getting an asthma attack, Patti knows.

Her Da's face is shiny. He's in charge of the stout, opening bottles with his corkscrew in the scullery, filling up glasses sideways like a real barman, making sure the white creamy head goes to the top. The cork pops out every time and the creamy stuff spills down the sides of the bottles. He rubs his hands together. Someone lifts up the pigs' feet. They're heaped up on the blue willow turkey plate and the steam makes a hot cloud over the table. They peep out their heads from under the table.

The smell! All the hands digging in, all the hairy feet and toes and the sound of the munching.

The men say: "Now we're talkin'."

The women say: "That's some feast and no mistake."

Her Da says: "Bedad it is."

He bends down under the table. He hands them two ginger ales.

"Here," he says. "Drink that."

The ginger ale has a beery grown-up taste. On the floor, there's spills of stout, bits of gristle and fat. Granda's boots are off with his feet stretched out in front of him; then he's yawning out loud. In a minute, he stands up and picks up his boots. All he says is "Goodnight all."

Her Da says he'll wind the clocks later on and granda goes to bed.

It's story time then. They all have to tell a story: It can be a ghost story, or a funny story or a recitation. There's loads of stories about Monto, a place down town, where they used to live.

After the Monto stories, her granny catches her breath and takes out her mouth organ. She runs it across her lap first. She blows into it a couple of times to get her note. She plays the same tune every time and each time she gets breathless and has to stop. Aunt Dinah sings a very sad song, about a girl who fell in love with a butcher boy. He left her in the lurch and she was heartbroken, so she ended up hanging herself. After the song a woman says: "That song should be a lesson to all them young ones with romantic notions in their heads." Then Aunt Dinah has a surprise. She has Babycham in her handbag. She lets them have a little taste. The bubbles go up Patti's nose and make her a bit dizzy. Aunt Dinah says champagne is in a different league to stout.

26

THE LIMELIGHT

In the Limelight Lounge bar, it's all green spotlights and green leather seats. There's no messers allowed in the Limelight, only good singers. They drink lime cocktails and Bols Advocate. They have ballad sessions and talent competitions on Friday nights. Her Aunt Dinah won prizes for her singing; she sings Dicey Riley and Peggy Gordon and the Butcher Boy. Everyone says she has a lovely voice. The Limelight is her favourite pub. She brings home the coloured glass ornaments that they get free in the cocktails: there's swords, fishes, tigers, giraffes, birds; they're all on display in the glass cabinet on the top shelf.

Sometimes they dance around the kitchen table, Patti standing on Aunt Dinah's feet, pretending to be her dance partner. They do waltzes and foxtrots and the tango. She's learning to jive and twist. Aunt Dinah is pally with her Ma, even though she's her sister in law. She thinks her Ma is funny. Her Ma says Dinah's a real smasher. She could've been a model in a fashion magazine. She lives life to the full, even though she's delicate. Patti knows what she means: Aunt Dinah's eyes are a greenish kind of blue, like the seaside in a postcard. They always have a bright lit up look. She's very thin with slim legs and ankles. She's always done up to the nines. She does her eyebrows and her nails; she plucks the stray hairs first, then she makes an arch, with a Miner's eye-pencil; she files her long nails with an emery board and paints them with Cutex pearl polish. She dabs on nail varnish to stop the ladders going up her stockings.

At Halloween she dresses up for the Tramp's Ball in the Mansion House. The first time she went as the Merry Widow. A photograph shows her standing on O'Connell Bridge, in a long black dress, a big old- fashioned bonnet and parasol. Next time, she's a gypsy girl, in a red satin puff sleeve blouse, gold dangly earrings. She rubbed in Tanfastic overnight to make her go brown. In the photo, she's holding up a tambourine. Her face is dark and shiny, her teeth white and pearly and you'd swear she was a real gypsy girl.

Patti sleeps with her sometimes. It's a long narrow room, through granny and granda's room. It was a present from Dublin Corporation, when granda became a caretaker. It's the only flat with three bedrooms. There's two holy pictures on the wall; the Sacred Heart with his chest cut open, so you can see his heart, and Our Lady with her sad crying eyes. The eyes follow you everywhere. It's spooky as anything, especially at night when the yellowy light shines in from outside. Aunt Dinah says it's only the artist's trick to fool you and you should never be afraid of a holy picture. But it feels like they're always watching. They kneel down at the side of the bed. Patti prays for the dead babies and the holy souls in purgatory, for the black babies in Africa, for her Ma, that she'll buck up and be happy, that the Russians won't come marching up Greek Street in their hobnail boots, or press any buttons and start World War Three.

Dinah wears a nylon baby doll nightie to bed. It might be lemon, or it might be lilac; that depends on her mood. She has a talcum powdery smell. She wears twin sets and tight skirts and Glen Abbey nylons. She steeps her good clothes in Lux flakes overnight. She boils her underwear. She's funny. For one of her jokes she makes clothes soup. She puts all her underwear in the big pot. She boils them up like a coddle. When they're done, she says:

"Would ya like a bowl of soup?"

"Yes, I would, one bowl of knicker bocker soup please. "

She lifts up something with a fork, puts it into a bowl with water and Patti lets on to eat it.

"It's gorgeous, only maybe a bit more salt," and Dinah shakes in a few Lux flakes. They go into stitches then.

She does another trick with her thumb and first finger, so you'd think her finger was cut in half.

Coty L'aimant is her favourite perfume. It has a red satin bow tied around the black bottleneck. It smells fab, like bunches of fresh flowers. She gives Patti a little spray before they go out. Aunt Dinah says it's sophisticated. Some Saturdays they go to the Rainbow café in O'Connel Street. They always sit in the window-seat under the rainbow. They can see everything from there, the Liffey and O'Connell Bridge, the monument, with the big statue in the middle of the road. Aunt Dinah orders orange sodas. Then she plays the jukebox, a few dancy songs, to put them in a good mood. They watch people going by. They might sit there for an hour or more and Aunt Dinah might fix her makeup in the compact mirror. Or she might sing along to the songs on the jukebox. Or they might jive with Dinah leading. In the Rainbow café, you can dance between the tables, as long as you don't knock anything over. If you break something, you have to pay for it.

Aunt Dinah's hair bounces and shines under the Rainbow lights. She washes it in a sachet of Clinic shampoo, and then rinses it out with a jug of cold water. She puts in rollers to make a curly flick. She backcombs the top with a special comb with beads between the teeth. She lifts a piece of hair up and pushes it back. She looks a bit mad with the hair sticking up like that, until she smoothes it over and then it's like a little beehive.

"It's all the fashion," she says.

She wears real leather gloves with a hole and a button, so you can see the back of her hands. She has slingback shoes with pointy toes. Her Ma says it won't be long till she gets the key of the door on her twenty- first birthday. The fellas do wolf whistles when she walks down the street. She goes a bit red and crosses the road. She has a chap in-anyway, so she couldn't be bothered. Her chap is nice looking with black wavy hair and a motor car. He always wears a suit and a tie. His car is turquoise, with three doors. Her granny says he's from a comfortable business family and lives in a semi-detached house.

There's this crowd around the door. Aunt Dinah is in the bedroom getting ready for the dress dance. She's wearing an orange organza dress with a stole to match. She's putting on her black patent slingbacks. Her chap knocks on the door and the kids ask him for money.

"Grushy grushy grushy," they shout and you'd think it was a wedding. Granny answers the door and gives them a look and they run away pronto. The taxi's engine is running; it's like the ones they have for weddings or funerals, long and black and shiny. Her chap's arms are full. He brings Dinah a pink and white orchid in a round plastic box, a box of chocolates in the shape of a book with gold pages.

He looks dead neat. Has on a black suit and dicky bow. His face goes like a beetroot when granny tells him to sit down on the visitor's chair. He leaves the orchid and the chocolates on the sideboard. He folds his arms.

"Will ya take a drop a somethin'?" granny asks. He nods his head, but she's already opening the press and pouring him a Jameson in a large whiskey glass. He says:

"Thanks very much."

His hand looks a bit shaky holding the glass. He loosens his dicky bow and opens his collar. He sips the Jameson. He makes a face. He stands up when he sees Dinah done up to the nines. He looks at her dress. He gives her a smile. He says nothing, but you'd know he thinks it's fab. Dinah smiles back and goes over to the mantle mirror. She sprays her hair one last time, with Colet hair lacquer. Her chap looks at his watch. He hands her the orchid and chocolates.

She says "Oh thanks. That's a lovely box."

He sits down again. He fiddles with his dicky bow. Granny gives him a hand. She knows all about dicky bows, she tells him. There isn't much she doesn't know about dicky bows. He stands up again while she makes the bow, then she pulls his lapels together, like he was one of her own sons.

"There, that's better, " she says and stands back to get a better look. She looks over at Dinah at the mirror, tells her to hurry up. Then she feels the dress material.

She says: "You wouldn't buy a dress like that off the rail. That organza was worth every penny, even if did cost a small fortune in Hickey's Fabrics."

Aunt Dinah looks at granny through the mirror, like she wants her to shut up. Then it's time for the Babycham toast, just a small sup from tiny glasses. It's time to go then. Outside everyone wants to feel her dress.

"Oh look! Oh looka the lovely dress!"

They're all pushing and shoving to get in close. The black taxi backs up and they jump into the back seat like film stars. All they can see are faces at the back window. Dinah's smiley face and her chaps shy face. Dinah's long black satin glove to her elbow, waving, like she was Elizabeth Taylor.

"He's nice. Not too forward, a well reared chap," granny says afterwards.

You'd know by her face she liked him. You'd know by her face if she didn't like him as well.

The next day she tells them all about it. The dress dance was out of this world. She had a ball. It was in this plush hotel, out far, overlooking the sea. It was all red carpets, sparkly chandeliers and linen serviettes. The four-course dinner was fab. The band played till all hours. They had champagne and a new cocktail just out she can't remember the name of. They danced the night away. They had their photo taken by a photographer, with the two of them standing at the foot of the staircase smiling. Her chap was a good dancer. They did the Twist. They jived the feet off themselves. The seagulls were squealing over the fish market wall when the black taxi left her straight home to her door. She even saw the milkman with his horse walking through the flats and he handed her the two bottles of milk.

27

THE MILKY WAY

From the top balcony they watch the sky; there's Patti and Jimmy and his friend Kinger. There's the half-moon, lit up like a pearly banana; there's roofs and stacks of chimneys and the far away lights of O'Connell Street. There's the big dome of the Four Courts, just around the corner. She loves that big dark blue sky, especially when it's starry; the dotty bits spread out, like her polka-dot dress Aunt Jinny made for her

"It's the Milky Way, isn't it?" Jimmy says.

"I think so," Patti says.

"It's a constellation," Kinger butts in.

"A constellation?"

"Yeah."

He read that in a science book, he says.

"They're up there, past the stars, past space, aren't they?" Jimmy says.

"Who?"

"The dead babies."

"Yeah course. They're probably watchin' us now."

"It must be billions and billions of miles away, Heaven."

Jimmy has his elbows spread sideways along the balcony.

"Trillions," Patti says. "You'd have to get ten rockets."

"No!" Kinger butts in again. "It's well past the moon. No rocket'd get there."

"How do you know?"

"Cause."

"Cause what?"

Kinger doesn't answer. He goes quiet. They all do. They just stare up at the banana moon, then down at the empty flats. All the games are finished for the night: Rounders and Relivio and Kick the Can. All the trolley wheels are quiet. There's echoing voices from the flats across the road, with the Ma's calling in the kids for bed: "Mar eee! Ros a leen! Caar mel! Con cep

150

ta! Joe boy! Christy." In a minute, it'll be their names being called. She wishes she had binoculars or a telescope. Heaven must be further than the moon, further than the Milky Way even. Maybe Kinger is right when he says no rocket would get there, Patti thinks.

There's supposed to be a man in the moon. If you look hard, when the moon is high and roundy, you can make out blotchy shapes, like a pimply face. Her Da said there'll be another man on the moon some day. The race is on to get there between the Americans and the Russians. He read this space article. It said in years to come they might all be going to the moon in rockets. If you had plenty of money, you might go there on holiday. But that's all in the future.

Her Ma says: "Shurrup about the bloody Russians. "

She thinks their Da has Russians on the brain.

When there's a bright moon, they watch the sky from the lookout glass in the scullery window. Her Ma climbs up on the bath board. She pulls back the net curtain. The kids want to know when is the baby coming back from Heaven.

Ma says: "That's enough about Heaven."

She's not as bad now. She might be getting better. Her granny says: "All in good time." That's a good sign, when she says that. She sees a little sparkle in her eye, she says. A teeny weeny one. And where there's hope there's life. Her tealeaves are a bit better. She's drinking enough tea: Pots! And you'd want to own Liptons. And for smokes, you'd want to be Mister Players Please. She won't tell about Ma's leaves, what she saw there in her cup, only it's something good, something happy- go- lucky, by the smiley look in her eyes.

28

THE LEGION OF MARY

They smell of chapels and silvermints. They carry black handbags full of holy leaflets. They wear Mary Banger shoes. One has a black perm, the other one wears a pink hat like an upside down poe. They're the women from the Legion of Mary. Sometimes in the flats they say the rosary against the fish market wall. They make up pretend altars out of fruit boxes and chairs. They cover them with a plastic tablecloth. They kneel down on the hard ground. If they see someone on the balcony, or at a window, they call them down to pray. That's why everyone hides. Sometimes they sing hymns.

Her Ma says: "It's well for them, nothin' better to do, but knock on doors and pray and sing hymns."

Her Da says: "Leave them be, they're only spreadin' the holy message of the Holy Catholic Church."

But her Ma hasn't time for praying at walls. Her Ma hasn't time to bless herself. She says: "They'd want to try out holy matrimony for a change."

"Tell them Legion women were gone ta bed," she goes, when she hears their special Legion knock. From the bath board lookout, she peeps out through the holes in the net curtain. There's the two of them, with their arms full of leaflets, standing on the step. There's the two heads, one with a perm and one with a pink hat.

They keep you talking for the duration. They go on and on about the Blessed Virgin and Jesus. It's stuff they already know from catechism. Stuff they learned over and over in school. They give her Ma a headache, with all their holy talk and she has to take two Aspro's when they're gone. If Patti answers the door, they say:

"Is you're Mammy in?"

"Em . . . she's gone ta bed."

"Oh! Is you're Mammy not well? "

"No."

They try to look past her into the hall, but she keeps the hall door closed over.

"Tell her to come to our meeting at the Legion Hall for the special blessing."

"Ma has no time, but she might have time next week."

One of them opens her bag, takes out the Legion leaflet and a holy picture.

"Give her these."

Patti takes them. Anything to get rid of them, she thinks.

They'd know all about it, if they didn't answer them. They won't go away. They say Hail Marys into the letter box.

"Hail Mary."

No answer.

"Full of grace!"

They all have to stay real quiet in the kitchen. Ma warns them.

"The Lord is with thee!"

They stay for ages and look through the letterbox again. They finish the prayer off and let go the letterbox before walking away.

Her Ma says them Legion of Mary women are old maids who were left on the shelf. There's no harm in them, but they'd give a saint a pain in the head. There's some who were rejects.

"What's rejects?" Patti asks.

"They're very religious women, who wanted to become nuns, but they weren't up to the mark and got turned down by the nunneries."

"So?"

"So, the Legion of Mary is the next best thing."

"Oh right."

She tries to explain. What she means is that the Legion gives them special powers to say the rosary in public and knock on doors and give out leaflets. They always want her to go to meetings, but she has more to do with her time, than gallivant in Legion halls, she says. The Legion hall in Church Street is where they have their meetings. Members are entitled to a free cup of

tea and two Marietta biscuits. The lights are on every Tuesday night at half seven. They hear them saying the rosary. It's
the widows and the old maids and the old shawley grannies all
bunched up together in there.

* * *

It's her Da's favourite magazine. A very holy book that comes
in the letterbox every Monday by early post. It's called The
Messenger. Da reads every bit of it, from start to finish, all the
articles and the advertisements and the prayers. Stories about
the missionaries out in Africa, the Holy Ghost Fathers and the
Little Sisters of the Poor. There's pictures of them dressed in
white habits with black babies in their arms. The babies have
big white teeth and woolly black hair.

"The Messenger is right," her Ma says. She always puts it
up in a safe place in case the kids pull it to smithereens. They
always want to see the black babies in the pictures.

Her Da says her Ma'd want to read that holy book herself,
but her Ma says she hasn't time to bless herself, never mind
read The Messenger. Patti reads it sometimes after he's finished.
There's always a good short story about the life of a saint or a
martyr. There's some cranky letters to the editor, about the fires
of hell and damnation. About purgatory and limbo. You can
send money to the black babies, or have prayers said for your
soul when you die. You can get indulgences for the remission of
sin. It's like this: you save up indulgences, like the Green Shield
stamps. You can get a free indulgence by going to a novena or
saying certain prayers or fasting. The more you have the more
sins are cleaned off your soul. Her Aunt Jinny is saving them
up. She goes to all the novenas. Her Ma says when Jinny dies
they'll have her place all ready and waiting in Heaven. There'll
be a red carpet laid out for her. And Patti can imagine her in
heaven, on a big comfortable armchair, her hair all up in a bun,
her lace mantilla on.

The priest goes around the doors with bundles of leaflets
about the men only sodality on Monday nights.

"Oh yes Father," her Da says, and takes a leaflet to read.

154

The priest says he'll be relying on a good attendance to fill out the chapel. Da tells him he can rely on him.

"Yes father I'll make sure to be there."

Her Ma gives him a look. She's maybe thinking: All the sodalities and novenas her Da attends, he'll surely get to Heaven as well.

There's loads of chapels with men only sodalities; there's Aran Quay and Adam and Eves, Halston Street and Church Street. Up the hill, John's Lane and Saint Audoen's. The men go to the sodalities, before the pub. They're always down in the back seats, or bunched up near the back door, where they can slip out easily. They half kneel on one leg, with their brown Rosary beads dangling and their head's bowed. They answer the sodality prayers in a kind of low groan, like they're giving out. It's different in chapel with just men. It's all overcoats and soft caps and coughs. It's all men who want to be holy for half an hour. It's like they don't really want to be there, but the parish priest will be after them if they don't attend. He'll make a show of them out in the street when he sees them. If a woman comes into the chapel by mistake, all their heads turn at the same time, soft caps and baldy heads and hair oil heads. The looks they give her, like she did something bad, like she walked into the men only part of the pub instead of the snug.

Chapels are nicer when they're nearly empty, Patti thinks. Sometimes on the way home from school, she goes into Halston Street or Church Street. She can sit for a while in peace, light a candle if she has a penny. If there's smelly tramps on the back seats snoring, she goes up to the front. The widow who cleans the chapel always gives her dirty looks. She sweeps real fast all around her, and then she polishes the brass plaques in the pews. She rubs in Brasso. She shines real fast with her duster.

"Tuh Tuh" she goes. There she is with her brush and Brasso, with a big face on her. Under her black coat, she wears a dark blue nylon smock, and over her head and shoulders, a huge shawley black scarf. The smell of the Brasso mixes with the smell of candles, and mixes with the smell of the tramps. The widows like to clean churches and do the altar flowers. They go to all the masses. They get special indulgences, for cleaning chapels, and there's a queue a mile long waiting. The only thing is they have to be very good living. That means they have to get Holy Communion every morning at the half seven mass.

"Young one," the widow whispers, "We're closin' in a minute," but Patti knows they're not, they don't close until eight o'clock, so she lets-on not to hear. She closes her eyes tight. Then she hears the sound of the widow's footsteps, then a creaky sound. She opens her eyes. There's a strong smell of cigarettes, a twist of smoke coming out the side of the green curtain. The widow is having a sneaky smoke in the confession box. When she comes back out, she wipes the smoky air with her yellow duster, as if a duster could rub out the smoke. Patti pretends not to see. She closes her eyes again.

You're supposed to have respect for the widows, because they're always in mourning. You have to get their messages and smile even if you hate them. You have to call them Misses this or Misses that, even if you never called them that before.

"Hello Misses Clarke," even if they're cranky so an so's. If you go for a message and they don't give you a penny, you can't put on a face. They link one another going to chapel. They don't wear powder or lipstick; it's all washed clean faces, combed back hair, tidy, neat, respectable. Some of them wear the black for years; black coat, black shoes, black seamless stockings.

29

THUNDER AND LIGHTENING

They're over at the Liffey watching the swans. The mother is teaching them how to swim. They're in a V behind her, their heads down, like they're shy. They're lovely. Like real cute kids. Their feathers are greyish, not gone white yet, like in the ugly duckling story. They follow her everywhere. If she turns, they turn. If she moves her head, so do they. If she stops, they stop. The mother swan looks haughty and proud and dead pretty.

"The young swans are called cygnets," Jimmy says pointing. He read that in a library-book.

It goes darkish all of a sudden, the sky first then the Liffey. The water goes dark, dark green. A loud bang comes from somewhere far down by the docks near the Alexander Basin. The mother swims away fast, the cygnets follow behind her, with flapping feathers. They disappear under the bridge.

Another bang.

"Did ya hear that?"

"Yeah."

"Oh God. It's thunder!"

"Lets go."

They better leg it quick. To be near water is dangerous. It's something to do with electricity and overhead wires. Mirrors are dangerous too. So are knives and forks and spoons. So are batteries and pots and pans. A few kids with eel-nets, start to make a run for it over the bridge. Jimmy pulls his jumper up from the back of his neck and covers his head, so it looks like he's headless. They make a dash for it too, across the quays, past the Four Courts and Coalman's rope weavers, and in the end-gate. They see her then. It's Ma. She's outside the door, calling the kids down from the balconies. She's blessing herself then, half covering her face with her other hand.

"Go up quick and get them down for Godsake."

Next, she has Patti by the cardigan sleeve shaking her.

"Stop it."

"Get them!"

More thunder claps only louder this time and then it starts to rain. Out of the heavens. Bucket loads. She has to drag them down the stairs, especially Anna who's hiding in a corner covering her face. The flats are empty, except for a few people out on the balconies. Doors slam then. Inside it's dark with the curtains closed over. Patti sees the dressing-table mirror has been covered with a sheet. Her Ma shakes holy water around the place, drags the babby and the kids in behind the bedhead. She's saying her prayers real fast: "Holy Mary Mother of God pray for us sinners now and at the hour of our death. Oh Sacred Heart of Jesus I place all my thrust in thee . . ."

Her fingers are in her ears then.

"Ma."

"Shush."

Lightening then. A big flash. Glittery blue light like magic through the curtains. It flashes across the ceiling, lights up the black wallpaper trees and behind the bed, where they're all huddled. Their faces are lit like holy statues. The babby starts to bawl his head off. Then they're all whinging.

"Oh MAAA! MAAA! "

"Oh Sacred Heart of Jesus spare us!" She keeps saying.

"For Godsake it's only thunder Ma," Jimmy says, but she won't listen. They sit on the side of the bed. They wait for the thunder to stop. All the legs are sticking out from behind the bedhead. All of a sudden she jumps out with the babby in her arms, does a runner out the door and opens the coalhole. She half drags half pushes the others in.

"Get in there quick," she shouts.

"They'll be manky in there Ma," Patti says, but she's not listening.

They're all afraid, because it's pitch dark in the coalhole.

"The boogyman, the boogyman is in here," Franey shouts.

After a long time, they can hear softer rain on the windowpane and they know it's over.

It goes dead quiet.

"It's all right Ma, it's all over. Youse can come out now."

"Are ya sure?"

"I'm sure," Patty says.

She peeps out her head then, the kids are in a bunch behind her like the cygnets in the Liffey. She has the shakes. She lights a Player and sits on the side of the bed. It must be her nerves from the thunder, Patti thinks. She says thunder and lightening is a sure sign that God is angry at the world. She'll leave the sheet over the mirror. She'll wait for a sign. She won't use a knife or a fork. A pot or a spoon. There'll be no lights switched on. It'll be like this until the sky clears and God calms down again.

"I'm goin' out," Jimmy says, and off he goes, all slouchy shoulders. She shouts at him to come back.

"Gallop after him," she says. "Get a hold quick."

"He's all right Ma," Patti says.

She pulls back the curtain, looks out through the top windowpane. Over the fish-market it's all dark hanging clouds, like maybe God is still angry at the world. In the flats the doors open one after another. The Ma's give out about the thunder and lightening. They fold their arms and watch the sky. They rub their belly bumps. Clothes drip from the washlines. There's a big brown puddle like a lake, out in the middle of the flats. In no time it's full of kids. They splash and mess and drown each other. They have puddle fights. Then it's the Ma's shouting over the balconies:

"Get outa that puddle quick and don't be ruinin' them good Clark's shoes."

The next day, her Ma asks granny to read her leaves. Granny says as far as the weather is concerned it's going to take up fine for the weekend. There's no more thunder or lightening that she can see. Good things are on the way and it won't be long before the sun is shining. Then she gives her one Sweet Afton out of the sideboard to cheer her up.

30

THREE DELF BIRDS

Everyone says that they're all the go in ornament fashion. Her Ma thinks they're gorgeous. Everyone has them over their mantelpiece or in their hall: the three delf birds with their wings spread like they're really flying. Granny Connor has them over the sideboard in the kitchen. Her other granny thinks they're very common and not in a million years would she hang them on her walls.

So what if they're common? Patti thinks they might add a bit of colour and turn the winter garden into a summer garden in her Ma's place. Her Ma likes to shop on the southside, in Thomas Street and Meath Street. It's mostly window-shopping, or what she calls browsing.

"I'm only browsin'," she says, or "I'm just lookin'," if a shop assistant comes over.

She has her eye on the three delf birds in Frawley's. They're on display on a dummy wall, beside the household section. There's three sets of birds to choose from, all in different colours.

"They're like birds of paradise," she says staring at the wall.

"The birdie birdie," the babby says in the go-car.

"Pity you can't buy one at a time, instead of the whole set. "

They're a bit pricey at twelve and eleven a set, she says, but she thinks Sloans Loans might have them.

Sloan's Loan's is across the road from Dublin Castle in Parliament Street. It's a huge shop with glass windows that turn around the corner into Lord Edward Street. They sell everything in there: clothes, furniture, bedclothes, clocks, ornaments, suits, jewellery, the three lights. Her Ma says it's some shop all right. You don't need money and it's dead easy to buy something. Here's what happens. First you look in the windows. Then you look around the showrooms. You can browse if you're not buying. You pick out what you want to buy. You fill in this form. You don't have to pay. Not a penny. You pay by the week with interest. And here's the best part; no one knocks at your door, so the Da's in the flats don't know. What they don't know won't kill them; that's the rule. The only thing is, the kids are not allowed to mess, so she always warns them before they go in.

It's like magic when they get there, because Sloan's Loan's have the very same delf birds as Frawley's. But her Ma looks past them at all the other fancy stuff in the window. She's not that gone about them birds, when she sees them up close.

"Maybe they're a bit too common; sure they're on every wall, north and south of the Liffey," she says. But she has her eye on other stuff. She makes a big turn with the go-car. She pushes in through the door and a bell chimes like a chimes clock.

It's everything all at once in there; all the fancy stuff they can never have. They walk around in a bunch. A salesman in a grey suit watches from a desk. Her Ma has her eye on these fab candlewick quilts. A sign says: *Latest pastel shades*. They're on display on a table near the window; one in blue, one in lemon and one in pink. They're half out of the cellophane packets, spread out, so you can see them properly. They have nice flower patterns and leaves.

"Aren't they massive! Them candlewicks'd make any bedroom look like a palace," she says.

"Not too dear either. Only a few bob every week, what ya wouldn't miss if ya were careful and paid over six months."

She moves to the stairs.

"Grab the end of that go-car," she says. Patti steps backwards down the steps, holding onto the go-car.

Downstairs. A real double bed all made up nice, with a yellow candlewick and this dead brill headboard, like a beige dressing gown at the top. It's fab! Makes you want to lie down and dream and dream, Patti thinks. The sunny yellow of the candlewick, the pink flowers and green stems. Her Ma stands back. You'd know by her face, she's flabbergasted.

"That's gorgeous," she says. "That's only out of this world!"

All of a sudden, the kids make a run for it and start to climb up the bed.

"Get down quick or I'll be taken in a squad car."

Her Ma's nervy face. Here's the man in the grey suit, rushing down the stairs to give out to them. She tries to drag them down off the bed, she grabs arms and legs, but she can't get a hold. It's like at home, when they're all jumping on the bed, making springy noises. The yellow candlewick is all creased. Franey does a back flip. Anna does a front tumble and jumps off the bed. Then she does cartwheels across the carpet. It's all a mess now Patti knows, and they might get barred from the shop. Her Ma tries to flatten out the candlewick creases and you'd think it was her own bed she was making. She smiles at the salesman with her Cornmarket teeth.

"Don't worry Mister," she says, "I have them well under control."

He gives her a look and scratches his forehead.

He says: "As long as there's no damage done Misses."

She tells him she'd pay for any damage and that she's only browsin' today, but she's very tempted by them lovely candlewicks. He walks away with his arms behind his back.

Then they see it, a lovely sofa over at the wall.

"Begod, that's nice," Ma says and sits herself down to try it out. Then the others plonk themselves down beside her. There they are, sitting on top of one another on the sofa, except Patti who's trying to watch Anna. Anna is up to mischief again, skipping around the showrooms. She knocks into something and the salesman looks over.

"This sofa is very comfortable indeed. It'd go nice in the kitchen."

Here's Ma, rubbing her hand over the soft material. Here's Franey, climbing over the back and jumping off. The babby wants to do it too. He's kicking and twisting and trying to get out of the go-car.

"Stop messin' I said and behave! I can't bring youse anywhere."

"Ma, lets go home." Patti says.

"Not yet. It's early. I've oceans of time."

She's biting her nails and watching the bed; she's dead nuts about that yellow candlewick. The salesman comes over; he says there's a discount price on bedclothes for the next week and her face lights up. She's over the moon. She'd love one she says.

"As a matter of fact, I'd like one of them candlewicks in each colour. That yella one'd be lovely for Easter and that blue'd be nice in winter and sure white and pink are for all seasons."

She stands up. She'd like new pillows too, she says.

"And sheets; them candy- striped flannelette ones. With the heat of them sheets in winter sure you'd never be cold."

They remind Patti of sticks of rock. The salesman is all smiley now. He goes away and comes back with a cup of tea for her Ma and a huge pink form.

She says: "Thanks very much, now where do I sign?"

The salesman shows them to a desk. He pulls out a chair. He points at a line at the bottom of the page, but first she has to tick a line of boxes. It's all questions on the form. They want to know all her business: stuff about wages, stuff about any other loans and stuff about their Da. Her Ma has a think first; she looks kind of dreamy, like when she's making up a story in her head. Then she ticks all the boxes real fast and signs her name in big huge writing with a fountain pen. She tells the salesman that her husband has a very good job with fantastic wages. Only thing is she can't remember the name of the place.

"Hasn't he?" She digs Patti in the arm.

Patti says: "Umm" and nods. Her Ma goes on a boast then. It's like she can't stop herself.

"Very brainy my husband. Could've had any job he wants. Used to be a clerical officer with The Port and Docks but he was cut out for better things."

The salesman takes back the form. He has a look at what she wrote. He's nice. He has on a suit and tie. He scratches his head. He sits down and does a bit of writing.

"That's grand, Misses," he goes after a good while.

"No trouble at all."

And would she need more bedding, or a bit of occasional furniture? Or the delf birds that are all the rage?

"The delf birds might have to wait," she says. "The delf birds wouldn't keep you warm of a cold winter's night, would they Mister? The delf birds are flying on every mantelpiece wall in the metropolis."

So the salesman goes a bit red, then he has a little laugh. He tells her to have a look around while he does the paperwork. They're allowed. As long as they don't break anything it's ok. There's jewellery and ornaments in glass cabinets. There's new coffee tables just in with brass tips on the legs. There's companion sets and coal-buckets her Ma'd like, but enough is enough she says and they'd better go home quick, before they buy up the whole shop. There's just a few formalities. The items she chose will be ready to collect in a couple of days, the salesman says. She warns them on the way home: no tell tales about Sloans Loans. No stories about candlewicks or sheets or pillows.

"Lips are sealed," she goes, and puts her finger to her lip.

They're as bulky as anything, when they collect them on the pram. A big stripey Sloan's bag. Yards and yards of cellophane covers. This gorgeous smell of new off them when they unwrap them.

"Aren't they lovely? "

Her Ma spreading out a candlewick on the back bedroom bed. It's the pink one first. She pulls it and flattens it this way and that. She fixes it neat as a hospital bed. Then she stands back against the wall to see it better. They all have a feel. They run their fingers along the soft fluffy fringes of candlewick stuff, around the shapes of the flowers. They all want to go to bed early.

"Only for a minute and no messin'."

So they all jump under. They pretend to go asleep with their eyes shut tight.

"That's enough. It's too early for bed." She shakes them up like it's morning. She starts to pull the candlewick off the bed again.

"Your Da. He'll have a fit if he sees them candlewicks."

Patti knows what she means. He'll have more than a fit. He hates anything by the week from Jew men or Sloan's Loan's or Cavendish's.

They hold one corner each. They shake it first, like a washed sheet. They walk towards each other into the middle. They fold the candlewick carefully from the edges into four neat squares, then wrap it back up in the plastic like it was never opened. Then she hides them in behind the bedhead and covers them up with an old blanket. She says she'll put the quilts on the beds when their Da is in work. Then they'll take them back off again before he comes home.

"Ma. It's a bit stupid having lovely candlewick quilts if you can't sleep under them."

"No it's not. They're only for show. Sure they'd only get destroyed on the beds at night."

"Maybe Da'd like them."

"Noshatall! He'd lift the roof."

It's always the same. It's always what her Da doesn't know won't kill him. It's like all the Da's live in this other place. A special men only place of pubs and darts and pigs' feet, of Sunday-suits and sodalities and boiled tripe.

A few days after. There's a big commotion. It's all shouts and bangs and door slams. There's murder over the candlewicks. Patti and Anna are playing a game in the wardrobe. Patti has on her Annie Oakley suit. It's a Wild West game. They have the babby's reins. They're pretending to be in a stagecoach. Anna is in front as the horse, with the reins around her waist. Anna making horsey horsey sounds: Meha ha ha! Meha ha ha! It's Saturday. They're fixin' ta make camp soon on the high rocky mountains. There's outlaws and Indians out there. There's noise from the other bedroom, where the kids have set up camp with sheets tied to the headboard. Then there's another noise. Quick footsteps. The sound of paper. Then cellophane. It must be the Sloan's bag. She knows. It's the candlewicks. He must've found them.

There's the crinkly plasticky sound of the wrapping. Ma's quieter footsteps. Da shouting at her in moany giving-out voice.

"What's all this?"

"Wha'?"

Ma's whispery voice.

"What? What? Sloan's bloody Loan's!"

In the wardrobe, they try to keep still. It sounds like he's reefing out the quilts from the bag.

"Send them back from where they came from! Back to Sloan's bloody Loan's."

"Leave them," Ma says in a shaky voice. "Leave them be."

But Ma's shaky voice is too shaky. It won't work. If it was stronger maybe like the other Ma's when they give out hell to their husbands. Maybe if she was more of a targer, Patti thinks.

Paper sounds. Cellophane dragging along the floor. Heavy footsteps down the hall. The hall door slamming, glass shaking and it's like the Irish earthquake again.

In the wardrobe Patti has her hand over Anna's mouth. Anna is wriggling like a squirmy snake. Then she kicks open the door with one big kick. The door swings out and the mirror rattles.

"Oh look!" she says.

There's her Ma sitting on the side of the bed.

An unlighted Player between her fingers.

Cellophane all over the place.

"It's the candlewicks, isn't it Ma?"

Ma looks up with her eyes half closed and watery.

"Yeah. Course it is."

She looks down again. She picks at her nail. She says: "What matter?"

"I just knew he'd find them. We should've hid them somewhere else Ma."

"Where else?"

"I don't know. Somewhere! Anywhere he wouldn't find them."

The kids are all outside. The lovely candlewicks are all bunched up on the step. There's more down the other step, some in the stripey Sloan's paper, some in cellophane, sunny yellow and baby pink, sea blue and snow white.

Heads appear over the balcony. They all start to gather them up quick before they get robbed or get dirty. They all have armfuls of candlewicks. They half drag, half carry them back to the bedroom. They have one last feel before they're wrapped back up. All the hands having a grab before the bag closes.

"Lemme have a feel."

"Go way. Maulers off! Other people have to lie under them quilts."

But they won't stop grabbing. She tries to fold them back up the way they were. Fold and tuck, fold and tuck, until they look like neat squares. Then into the cellophane covers and the stripey Sloan's bag. The way they're wrapped up it's like they were never opened, Patti thinks.

"There, you'd never be the wiser. Everything is shipshape," her Ma says. She loads up the pram with the wrapped candlewicks.

Over in Sloan's Loan's she tells the salesman she changed her mind. She makes up this fancy story about a parcel of swanky bedclothes her cousin sent her from America. She says they've sufficient in the bedding department for the time being. The salesman's face is all surprise. All he says is: "Ok Misses." Then he starts to unload the pram.

Maybe it's as well, her Ma says on the way home. But she doesn't mean it. You'd know by her face; sort of sad, sort of lonely and a little bit nervy. She wanted them candlewicks. She wanted them bad, Patti thinks.

"There's plenty of time for grandeur and candlewicks," she says making the bed that night. Smoothing over a sheet, with her palm, she bucks up. She has on her offer it all up face; the one that knows she can't have this or she can't have that.

She says: "What you never had you never miss and sure them heavy candlewicks would be murder to wash and how in the name of God would you dry them?"

31

THREE BRASS BALLS

You're not supposed to ask questions, that's the rule on the northside and the southside. *Why* is the worst word in the world and *what* is nearly as bad. Sometimes Patti forgets and asks anyway. This day it was a question about the three brass balls.

"What are them brass balls for?" She asked pointing upwards.

They were still living in the old drunken house. The first time she saw them they were on this long queue in Capel Street. There were all kinds of people queuing: women from their street and strange women they didn't know, old grannies with white hair, red faced spunkers with bundles under their arms, a few gypsies wrapped in check blankets. They had all kinds of stuff loaded up on prams and box carts. Over their arms the women carried the Sunday suits, in their hands they held pairs of polished shoes.

The three brass balls were hanging like giant doorknobs over a black hall door. There was a big window and a porch with steps leading up to it. The window was piled with stuff: sparkly jewellery, clocks, radios, cameras, a set of binoculars in a leather case. She wanted to know what the brass balls were for. First her Ma puts on a face. Then her face changes. She says it's just a pawnbroker's sign, the same as a stripey pole outside a barbershop. Patti knew what a barbershop was but she never heard of a pawnbroker.

"What's a pawnbroker?"

"It's like a bank only different."

She wasn't sure what a bank was either.

The people on the queue were starting to moan about the queue.

"You'd think they'd let us in early and them inside countin' all their money."

"Bloody robbers and the money they're getting from us."

Then the black door opened and there's this big rush forward.

You don't see many men in pawns because it's mostly the women that pawn things. They pawn them on Monday morning and get them out on Friday or Saturday:

Sunday suits.

Holy Communion and Confirmation outfits.

Clocks.

Shoes.

Wedding rings.

Radios.

Bikes.

Toys.

Birdcages.

Holy pictures.

Electric fires.

The Da's are not supposed to know. They sort of go stone blind from Monday to Friday.

It's only if your stuck. It's like you get this loan of money for a loan of your stuff. You're not getting nothing for nothing, her Ma says. You have to pay interest on the loan. If you don't pay the interest on time your stuff is sold at auction. There's a special display case with jewellery for sale. They have auctions every few months for unclaimed items. The trick, Ma says, is never let anything go to the pawn. I'd be a sin to let the pawnbroker sell your stuff for profit.

She says: "It's people like us that's keeping them pawnbrokers in the height of style. They're worse than banks, but I suppose they're handy when times is hard."

On Monday mornings, there's always a queue down the street and around the corner. They have to drag the prams up the steps. There's two high wood counters, a snug with a glass window. In there it smells of mothballs and dust and shoe polish. The pawn man shouts out at them over the counter.

"NEXT!" And the line moves up.

"Put them up here!"

He thumps his fist on the counter. He has a look at whatever they have. He makes a close examination; then a closer one.

"How much were you looking for?"

"Em . . . sixteen Jimmy."

He shakes his head. He makes a face.

"Can't do. Ten and six is all."

"Ah sure the box is worth more. Make it twelve? It's only till Friday; true as God Jimmy?"

"NEXT!" He says.

He calls the next customer.

"Oh all right so. Gimme the ten and six for Godsake."

The pawn man looks up. Writes out a ticket real fast.

"Ten and six. Black shoes with laces in box and the name is?"

Or.

"Rose gold wedding ring. No box and the name is?"

He knows the name already, so he stamps the ticket. It makes a thumpy noise and leaves a blue mark.

He points to the end of the counter where there's another queue to get the money.

"NEXT!" He says again.

There's always another queue for the shop on the corner. It's called a fancy good's shop. It's where the women get married all over again, with the brass wedding rings. Her Ma calls it *Camouflage*. They're supposed to look like gold rings, but you'd know they weren't. After a couple of days they go black and blue like eyes after a big fight. The pretend wedding and engagement rings are displayed on velvet trays in the window. The woman with the white shop coat says:

"You'd never guess they weren't the real thing would you Misses?"

She lifts out the tray. She holds it over the counter.

"You're spoilt for choice," she says, but the rings all look the same, like the ones in the middle of the barmbrack at Halloween, Patti thinks.

"Style like that you wouldn't get in the Happy Ring House downtown Misses."

"No, I s'pose so." Her Ma says.

"Here. Try one for size."

Her Ma holds out her hand. Sticks up her ring finger. There's a red mark where her wedding ring was. The woman tries the ring, but it doesn't fit. It won't go past the swollen joint, so she tries another and another. It's like they're in a real jewellers. The woman says: "Take your time there Misses, there's no hurry" then she moves on to the next customer with the tray of rings. They're all trying them on. A line of ring fingers is held up over the counter. Her Ma is very particular. The ring has to look just right. It can't look false or showy. Outside the shop, she pulls down her coat-sleeve. It's just to tide her over.

"It's on'y till Friday," she says with her eyes down.

The trick is to polish the ring with Brasso every day to stop it tarnishing and leaving a mark. The other trick is to keep the ring finger out of sight. Her Ma is like a magician, the way she makes her finger disappear. At home it's all long cardigan sleeves, so you don't see her finger. Her Da'd have a fit if he knew. So might the grannies. On the northside and the southside, the grannies give out hell about pawns. They think pawns are common and vulgar and not for the likes of them.

32

A MISSING HOLY BIBLE

Aunt Jinny says the holy bible is the most important book in the whole world and no catholic household should be without one. All she wants to talk about is her fancy new bible. She bought it by the week on the HP on what the bible salesman called easy terms. She had to wait weeks for the delivery from Rome, where it was supposed to get blessed by the pope. This Friday when it arrives, there's a bunch of kids around the salesman's motorcar. The nosey parker's are gawking over the balconies. Aunt Jinny takes in the parcel with a big smile on her face.

"It looks awful holy," Patti says.

"It should look holy, for five and six a week," granny says.

Jinny gives her a look and says that holy bible is worth every penny and there's some things you just can't put a price on. All she does is boast about her new bible and you'd think she won the pools, she's so excited. She pulls off the brown paper. Inside is a white cardboard box with a diamond pattern. There's gold and white waxy paper around a black leather cover. More paper between the pages. Sideways the pages are gold with a satin string to mark them.

"Isn't it only beushiful!" Jinny says, rubbing her hand over the cover.

"It's well wrapped anyway," granny says.

"Can I have a feel?" Patti asks.

"Wash your hands first, before you touch that blessed bible."

She washes her hands.

It's dead neat. Has old- fashioned writing. Colour pictures of the miracles on shiny paper; The Wedding Feast at Cana. The Dividing of the Seas. A lovely cute picture of Moses in the wicker basket at the edge of the river.

She keeps her bible safe in the white box on top of the wardrobe. She won't let anyone near it, especially the uncles. So it's a big mystery when it goes missing. There's a big commotion in granny's. It's only a few Sundays after it was delivered. It's time for bible reading after ten o'clock mass. Up Aunt Jinny hops on the wobbly green chair in her high heels.

"Get out of the way," she says, even though no one is in her way.

Things go flying though the air then, all the stuff on top of the wardrobe, her holy pictures and photographs. Then it's all the shoes under the wardrobe, all the clothes out of the wardrobe. She pulls them off hangers and off shelves. She searches under the bed and behind the bed.

"Did ya see it?" She goes to granny in the scullery.

"See what?"

"The bible."

"No."

"Was there anyone in there?"

"Where?"

"Where d'ya think? In the bedroom."

"Em . . . no . . . I don't think so, although I couldn't swear to it."

Granny goes about her business and starts to chop a cabbage.

Aunt Jinny is like a mad woman, her hair and her face all tossed and angry and red. Out comes her rosary beads and then she's down on her knees, leaning on a chair. Then she's saying the rosary in the kitchen, under the picture of the Sacred Heart. Fifty Hail Marys, five Our Fathers, five Glory Be's.

"Get down on your knees!" she shouts.

"What' s up?" Uncle Paddy asks. "Is someone dead?"

Aunt Jinny is going a mile a minute, with Our Fathers and Hail Marys and Glory Be's, all mixed up in her mouth. She has the rosary beads held up over the chair, her head bent low, like in chapel. Patti is jaded. A whole rosary, all together at once and at this hour of the day, she thinks. Granny hasn't time to bless herself. She's at the gas stove, boiling water for the cabbage. She looks up to the ceiling with her funny look. Shakes her head sideways, as if to say: What's all the commotion about? She lifts the lid off the teapot. To calm Aunt Jinny down she makes a pot of tea. Aunt Jinny's hands are shaking when she stands up. She kisses the beads, makes a big sign of the cross on her forehead. Here's granny, quickity quick, with the teapot and mugs rattling under her arm.

She sits down and stirs the tea. She pours.

"Throw that down you gullet and we'll say a prayer to Saint Anthony for the safe return of the Holy Blessed Bible."

But Aunt Jinny is raging. She grinds her teeth.

"I'd swear on that Holy Bible, if I had it, it was taken by . . ."

She stops. She looks down into her tea.

"Who?" Granny says. "Taken by who?"

"Who? Who d'ya think?"

Granny looks out the window.

"Traffic out there t'day, " she says, even though there's hardly any traffic. She goes quiet then. She closes her eyes. She blesses herself. Then she goes into a mutter of the Saint Anthony prayer. Aunt Jinny puts more sugar in her tea with the big spoon. She goes: Tuh Tuh Tuh. She rocks a bit in her chair, like granny, when she's telling a story.

"I'll be taken for whoever it was. I'll swing for them! I'll take their life! I'll . . . I'll . . ."

She looks at Patti then. Her big blue marble eyes across the table. Patti looks out the window.

"Did ya see it?"

"Nope."

"I hope you're telling the truth and shaming the devil," she says.

Granny gets up. Her chair scrapes the lino. She gets the YR sauce bottle from the dresser. She plonks it on the table. Then she cuts up a Spanish onion real quick and it makes her cry. She makes onion sambos and shakes on sauce. She holds the bottle upside down with one hand and hits it with the other to loosen the sauce. She switches on the wireless. It's all crackly opera music coming through the brown holes at the front. She thumps the wireless with her elbow. Through the crackles they listen. The room fills up with the big voices.

Afterwards she reads the leaves. She says it's a bit of a puzzle all right, where the Holy Bible went, but the way the leaves are spread out, in that peculiar pattern, it looks like it's on its way back. No mistake! She tells them to look for themselves. They look. All Patti can see are tea leaves in squiggly shapes. Some bunched up and some not bunched up. Maybe something like a daisy chain. Maybe ants crawling in a crooked line. Then granny grabs the mugs and washes them under the tap. She hums the opera song. She rakes up her potato fire.

The prayer to Saint Anthony works. She was right about the tealeaves. It's a couple of days after. Granny is lying down, snoring with her scarf still on.

"Was there anyone in this room?" Aunt Jinny says when she comes home from work.

"I didn't see no one, I was fast asleep wasn't I? I'd a headache all day'd kill a plough horse."

Then Aunt Jinny is up on the chair, holding the bible box. Then she's opening up the box to make sure nothing is missing. Crackly noise of tissue paper.

"Is that the bible you're holdin'?" Granny asks.

"Yis."

"Oh thanks be to . . ."

"I suppose it got legs and walked back," Aunt Jinny says, turning a page.

Granny yawns, then she sits up and fixes her scarf.

"Only the Lord above knows what happened. I told ye it was comin' back, didn't I? The leaves never lies."

"Tea leaves is right. It was Saint Anthony, worked that blessed miracle," Aunt Jinny says, real snappy.

She blows on the cover of the bible and brushes it over with a chamois duster. She turns pages. She examines every bit of the bible for damage. All the miracles, all the psalms and gospels. Everything is still the same; Jesus with his long hair, crossing the red sea, the sea parting down the middle, like there's a magic pathway, Moses is still in his basket, like any other baby, and the Wedding Feast at Cana has a crowd of happy looking people with big vases of wine in the background.

"Where was it, 'n anyway?"

Her granny is sitting on the side of the bed rubbing her head.

"Exactly where I left it. Amazin' that, the way it came back itself."

"Mirac'lous!" Granny says.

Aunt Jinny is mad happy, but she's going to hide her bible from now on. Somewhere where no mean maulers can rob it, she says. She's talking real fast with her teeth together, like she has pins between them.

The next day her Ma asks granny for a smoke out of the sideboard. Granny gives her one Sweet Afton. With her head bent over, she lights up from the gas stove.

"I hear the bible's back," she says.

"Will wonders ever cease? It's some mystery and no mistake."

Then granny wets the teapot; two big handfuls of mauve label tea.

"Jinny's delighted. Chuffed goodo! Might keep her happy for a while."

Granny laughs.

The kids are playing in the bedroom. Ma wants her leaves read. Granny takes her mug and twists it around in a half moon shape. She peers into the bottom with creased eyebrows. She puts on the dark face, the face that means what she sees there in the mug is a secret. Ma takes a few deep drags from her Afton.

"What?" she says and granny looks at the ceiling, then nods over at the babby in the pram. The babby looks up at her.

"The goo' boy, " granny says in babby talk.

It goes quiet in the room for a while. They can hear traffic and the kids playing cowboys and Indians in the bedroom.

"Are ya sure?"

"Was I ever wrong?"

"Oh for the love of the Blessed Virgin."

Patti watches her Ma's face. She looks nervy all of a sudden. She nearly eats her sweet Afton; takes long deep drags.

"Don't start now with that mockery talk. Remember what the Lord taketh, he giveth back. Sure isn't it God's will?" Granny says.

She blesses herself, tips her forehead, chest and shoulders. Then she gets out her porter jug and makes two creamy milk stouts. The stout mixes with the milk and goes light brown.

"Drink that up now," she says.

Patti watches the two of them grow brown moustaches.

They lick their lips at the same time.

33

A NEWSFLASH

There's a newsflash on the radio. The newsreader says he's sorry to interrupt the programme. He has on a sad serious voice. They know before he says it. They were waiting for news. The pope is dead. He died following a serious illness. There'll be more detail in the main bulletin, the newsreader says. Everyone was saying he was at deaths door. Her granny has out her tissues; she dabs around her eyes. She blesses herself and pulls the blind down half way. On the main news, it's all about the pope. They hear the lonely dong of a mourning bell in the background. A reporter says there's thousands of people praying in Vatican Square in Rome. There's thousands more outside, lining the streets. Rome is in mourning. A black smoke signal from a special chimney in The Vatican means that the pope is dead. There's Irish nuns and priests praying among the crowd. There's every nationality. Heads of state are arriving as he speaks, the reporter says.

In the flats, people have their blinds half down. Long Paddy is running around spreading the story, he doesn't know that everyone knows already; he thinks it's new news. He blesses himself and genuflects in the middle of the yard. He wears black armbands sewed onto his sleeve. He spits out the words; "The Po Po Pope is De De dead. L lorda m mercy on the Po Po Pope. M may he r rest in p peace."

At first, everyone is running around the courtyard: "The pope is dead the pope is dead." It's all they talk about, on the balconies and at the washlines. Then it goes all quiet. Your supposed to walk and not run. You're supposed to whisper and not shout. You're supposed to pray for the dead pope and the new pope. All the chapels are packed out the doors; there's crowds of people with bowed heads praying. There's queues at every statue to light candles. There's more queues for confession. It goes on all day into the evening. In school, they pray for the dead pope and for the new pope, when he's chosen by the special council of cardinal's. They attend a special funeral mass. They have Benediction. It's like the whole neighbourhood is turned into a funeral. All of a sudden, everyone is holier than ever. People start to get the early morning mass and Holy Communion, even when it's not Sunday. The Legion of Mary hall is packed. Her Da has his ear to the radio all the time, waiting for the latest bulletin from Rome. He says everything changes when the pope dies. Her Ma says change is not such a bad thing sometimes and Da gives her a look.

On the southside, Aunt Jinny reads her bible with the sweeping brush jammed up to the bedroom door. She kneels down in the kitchen and says the rosary. She spends hours in Adam and Eves chapel lighting candles and praying. Granny says if she's not care full she'll get Old Maids Knee.

In the pulpit, the parish priest gives a long sermon about the pope and other popes in history. He waves his arms around in the air. He says it's a testing time for the Holy Catholic Church, a time to take stock, a time for reflection and every catholic should examine their conscience and there's not a soul among them who's not a sinner. He slams his fist down on the pulpit and everyone jumps. Then he's on about the evils in the world that threaten the catholic faith. He's on about pop music and dancehalls and drinking. He's talking big words, that nobody understands, like promiscuity and communism and everyone is fed up. He reaches his neck out far over the pulpit and wags his finger out at them and it's like it's all their fault that the pope is dead.

34

A CARD OF NEEDLES

Her Ma is afraid of the gypsies. She always says don't talk to them gypsies, don't even look at them. You see their dark drunken faces peeping from doorways. You see the stacks of bottles beside them. They drink red biddy and cider and whisky. Sometimes they have fights, with bottles flying and broken glass everywhere, and you're supposed to cross the road if you see them.

"Keep moving and don't look at them," Ma says, if she spots one.

The men have dirty faces, the women have long tangly hair. Under the bundles of check blankets, they have their babbies wrapped up tight. Sometimes you see a dark head, sometimes you don't. Ma says sometimes they pretend they have babbies, so people will gave them money. They're a bit like the fairies; the way they take kids away. Here's what happens. They talk nice to you. Then they grab your arm. They hide you under their long skirts and blankets and take you deep into the forest. You'd grow into a half gypsy child and talk gypsy language. They might put curses and spells on you, because you're not one of them. You'd be roaming the roads forever, singing gypsy songs and begging. You'd be lost forever like in the fairy world. The gypsies have special powers. Patti is afraid of them too. Except for one.

There's this nice pinky faced, friendly gypsy who sells cards of sewing needles. The card is in the shape of a basket of flowers. Every summer she comes round the doors. Her babby peeps out from the coloured shawl with its big dark eyes. The gypsy says: "God bless this house and all who live here."

Then Ma says: "God bless the babby and isn't she a picture of health."

The gypsy can tell fortunes, if her palm is crossed with silver. Ma usually does a trade with her; she might give her sugar or soap or cigarettes for a card of needles. If she has money she gets her palm read. The gypsy does the readings at the hall door. This day, she takes her hand. She holds it up. She squints hard. Then she examines it She makes a frown. It's what she sees in the palm. It's what the different lines mean. She tells her she'll cross water, but Ma blows out smoke into her face and says the only water she'll be crossing is Liffey water. But the gypsy's face is dead serious.

"Wait Missus, there's more."

She says there's money coming her way, so Ma's face lights up.

"H'much?" is all she wants to know.

The gypsy can't say for sure. It might be a small fortune, but the crystal ball'd tell her more. She has the crystal ball in her bag. She can gaze into the crystal ball, if she crosses her palm with silver. Ma says she's no time for crystal balls.

"Go on Ma, get the crystal ball," Patti says. "Maybe you won on the Mater Hospital pools."

She says she hopes so and it's about time her luck changed for the better. It's about time her boat came in. The gypsy says there's more yet in her palm, if she wants to hear. Ma says nothing. She drags hard on her Player. Here comes the serious stuff. It's all about babies. If you're getting one or if you aren't. If it's a boy or a girl. If it has black hair or fair hair. Patti heard it all before, loads of times.

Then her Ma blesses herself and sticks out her hand.

"Go on, but don't give me bad news."

The gypsy goes quiet. She holds her hand up to the light. She fiddles around with her fingers. It's not clear. Not yet. She wants another cigarette. She can't concentrate with the noise of those wild childer in the background. Ma says she's none for herself, hasn't a butt, and her children are not wild at all, for her information. Her children are very well reared. She pulls her hand away. Then she shoo's the gypsy out of the hall and bangs the hall door behind her.

"Bads grant to that gypsy," she says.

They watch her from the window. The gypsy saunters through the flats, with her shopping bag full of needles, her long skirt flapping in the breeze, her carpet slippers dragging behind her.

35

A FAMOUS AUTOGRAPH

Aunt Jinny is chuffed. Her bible is safe in a secret hiding place. No one is allowed to cross the bedroom door when she does her reading. She likes to read straight after mass with her good clothes on. She always dresses up smart for mass in her Sunday best. In chapel, people always watch her when she walks up to get Holy Communion. She looks like a Spanish lady with her lace mantilla covering her head and shoulders, Patti thinks. Her Ma told her that there's loads of fella's after her, but she wouldn't have a bang of any of them.

The bible salesman calls every Friday at six on the dot. The angelus bell is usually still ringing when he knocks. Aunt Jinny is always ready with the bible money on the sideboard. Sometimes he dilly-dallies on the doorstep; takes ages to write in his book and ages more to tear out a payment receipt. One Friday, out of the blue, he makes this announcement; he says his first name is Paul after Saint Paul and she can call him by his first name if she wants. Aunt Jinny's face goes red. She just stands there with her arms folded, like she doesn't know what to say. Then he hands her the receipt. Then he asks her would she by any chance, go out with him on a date to the Top Hat ballroom on Saturday? Aunt Jinny goes redder. After ages she says she'll think about it. The bible man waits on the step. She looks dead serious. Then, after forever, she says:

"No. It wouldn't be right, what with yourself being a bible salesman and sure I'm not one for dancehalls and, in any case, I always wash my hair on Saturday night." Then the bible man goes red. "Okey Dokey," he says and closes his book with a snap.

Granny says if she doesn't hurry up, she'll be left on the shelf. There's loads of old maids around where they live. Everyone makes jokes about them. Old maids are women who were left on the shelf, because no one wanted to marry them. They stay single forever, same as a bachelor. It happens after you're about twenty-eight or twenty-nine; you're over the hill then and it's too late to get a fella. A good few are in the Legion of Mary, some work in sweetshops and more work in the factories. When Patti first heard of being left on the shelf, she thought of the shelf in her granny's scullery with all granda's stuff. She thought of Miss Stoke from the empty lonely shop in Mary Street, sitting on the shelf in her blue nylon shop smock, she thought of Mary Bassett, the animal woman, with all her sick animals beside her on the shelf. Old maids have to stay there forever and ever, like the holy souls stuck in limbo or purgatory.

She knew her aunty couldn't be an old maid. She knew none of her aunties could be, even though some of them are more than twenty-eight or twenty-nine. It was Aunty Rita who told her, it's just a way of saying that some girls just can't get a fella, no matter how hard they try.

"Why?"

"Cause."

"Cause what?"

"Cause they're plain Jayne's, or they're fat, or they have a ronnie, or a stutter or . . ."

"Aunt Jinny is not an old maid is she?"

"No. I never said she was."

"Aunt Jinny is not a plain Jayne, or fat and she hasn't got a ronny or a stutter."

"You're right there."

Aunt Rita takes out a Woodbine, lights up and takes a big drag.

"Aunt Jinny is gorgeous looking, with her long black shiny hair and she's in the fashion too, has all the latest styles from Paris she makes herself. And she wears high heels."

Rita picks at her lip with her finger. There's lipstick on the cigarette top, a smudged bandy shape of a pink lip.

"Your Aunty Jinny has a bible and rosary beads and she's always in the chapel."

"So?"

"That means she's . . ."

"What?"

"Very holy. See all the holy pictures she has, see all the Saints she prays to; put years on ye."

"It's not a sin to be holy. Ma says she has plenty of chances. Ma says she can pick and choose."

It's no use. Aunt Rita doesn't have the patience for talking. She gets annoyed with questions. Aunt Rita has plenty of fella's too her Ma says. No shortage. But sometimes she's bad with her nerves. That's when the men with the white coats come; that's when they take her in the ambulance, even though she doesn't want to go.

"Sometimes, our Rita lives in a dream world. All she wants are Woodbines and dancehalls. All she wants is Mister Right."

"Would Aunt Jinny not want a Mister Right?" Patti asks.

"Our Jinny couldn't be bothered with dates or Mister Right," her Ma says real smartalecky.

"Our Jinny has more to do with her time, than gallivant in dancehalls."

Everyone knows she's not just a holy Mary; everyone knows Aunt Jinny has style.

Sometimes she lets Patti brush her long black hair. She climbs up on the chair behind her and pretends she's Anna Liffey, from the hairdressers across the road.

"Miss. You have lovely thick hair."

"Oh thanks very much."

"Miss. Would you like it up or down?"

"Em . . . up I think."

"Ok so. A very good choice. Would that be a French roll or a beehive?"

"Oh, I think a French roll. And please Miss Liffey, no back-combing."

"Oh yes, I do agree with you Miss, backcombing ruins your hair. Makes it very fuzzy and knotty."

Aunt Jinny laughs at that, then she stretches around and hands Patti a bunch of hair-clips.

"Try to make the French roll like Princess Grace's."

"Oh yes Miss, that's easy, a French Princess Grace."

The French roll is half pinned up in a twist, only a few more clips to go.

"Mish. You jon't mind me asping?"

Patti with clips between her teeth.

"No . . ."

"Would you. Would you be geshing marrwied soon?"

No answer. Patti knows it's the wrong question. The feel of Aunt Jinny's stiff shoulders through her pink cardigan. All of a sudden, she turns around on the chair, with her hair half up in a bunch. She gives her this look. A bit haughty; a bit disgusted. Eyes starey like big marbles.

"What? What did you say?"

"I was just . . . wondering."

"No I'm not gettin' married for your information. It's like this! Holy matrimony doesn't suit everyone. You only have to look around you. The men gallivantin' in the pubs every night, the women lyin' up in the Coombe twice a year."

She clicks her tongue. She jumps up from the chair, pulls out the French roll so her hair is all over the place.

Oh yes. Patti knows what she means all right. What she means is she wouldn't want to end up with a gang of kids like her Ma. She wouldn't want to end up with a husband who hasn't got the pledge, who has wobbly legs at every hand's turn. She wouldn't want to end up with not a decent shoe on her foot. She knows what aunty wants: she wants style to beat the band, she wants to travel the world and stay in swanky hotels. Patti knows that one of these days, Aunt Jinny'll travel to Paris to see the latest fashions on the catwalk, and then she'll go to Rome to meet the Pope in person. So that's why she won't ever get married.

But that's all in the future, so when they do the Anna Liffey hairdressing game again, Patti has to be careful, not to ask the wrong questions; no wedding stuff for starters, no forty questions. Aunt Jinny reads the fashion and film-star magazines. There's one that tells their beauty secrets, like Clint Eastwood sticks his head in a bucket of icy every morning. That's supposed to stop you getting wrinkles. Elizabeth Taylor eats caviar sambos and drinks champers. That's supposed to be the fountain of youth. There's someone else who does handstands for hours every day, to push back time and Aunt Jinny says that makes perfect sense.

It's allowed to talk about film stars and famous people. Patti wanted to know what famous people Aunt Jinny met. She's seen so many famous people in her day, she says, what with premiers here and premiers there, in the picture houses downtown. The amount of film stars she's seen in the flesh, up that close, so you could nearly touch them.

"Who was the last famous person you saw?"

"The last famous person I saw was . . ."

She has to think about it. She'd nearly swear it was Gay Byrne, but she has to look up her diary of famous autographs. Yes, it *was* Gay Byrne she says at a film premiere at the Adelphi cinema. Her and her friend Betty asked him for his autograph. She says for this special occasion, she was done up in a rose pink fitted dress, one of her own creations.

"That shade of cerise pink was like an Indian summer sky," she says with a dreamy look. She had a bit of ostrich feather over her shoulders to accentuate the dress, black patent slingback shoes and a clutch bag to match. Betty was like a film star herself, in a violet dress and box jacket. Here they go down Abbey Street, all smiles and high heels and handbags, the two of them like fashion models. They're waiting in the crowd outside the Adelphi, when Gay's car arrives. Here's Gay in this long black shiny car, with his wife Kathleen beside him. A big cheer goes up from the crowd when the chauffeur opens the door. Gay smiles and waves. Kathleen does the same. Kathleen is wearing a long dress with a stole to match. Jinny thinks the material might've been brocade. She says the style of the two of them was out of this world. Jinny and Betty try to slice through the crowd with their elbows and bags. They get shoved around this way and that. Aunt Jinny's hair gets all tossed and she has to get her comb out. This cheeky doorman pushes them back, like they were cattle with his fat arms. Gay and Kathleen slither in by this special side door for very important people. Inside, Aunt Jinny and Betty are in the middle seats. All they can see are the backs of their heads, in the VIP seats near the front. They don't really watch the film at all because it's Gay they came to see. She says they paid a small fortune for black market tickets from a woman in the flats.

"How did you get the autograph?"

"Well that wasn't easy, but we got it in the end."

She says everyone wanted Gay's autograph and all they could see were autograph books held up in the air. They had to bash in between the crowds on the way out. Gay wrote fast in her autograph book before the doormen escorted him out through the crushy crowds to his car. Cameras clicked and flashed. They saw the car drive away, with Gay and his wife at the back window. Aunt Jinny says Abbey Street was packed that night. On the way home, to celebrate, she and her friend Betty had two Club oranges in the Four Courts Hotel. Aunt Jinny says you can't beat the glamour and style of a film premiere night.

* * *

Maybe it's a date and maybe it's not a date. Whatever it is, all of a sudden, there's this brown haired fella called Christy with a three-quarter-length trench coat hanging around the gates. He's not bad looking. He's all right. Except for his pimples. This Sunday, they meet him at the end gate. Aunt Jinny says they're going to the pictures and Patti can come to keep them company if she wants. She's not sure at first. She feels a bit like piggy in the middle, but then Aunty Jinny says: "Come on if you're comin'" a bit cranky like. She's done up to the nines, with her hair in an up-style; what she calls: up in curls. She's wearing her new navy and white coat and dress to match, white high heels with a T strap at the front and navy blue gloves to her elbows. She looks lovely, like she's going on a real date.

Christy is all smiles. He stamps out his cigarette and fixes his tie when he see's her.

He looks at Aunt Jinny first. Then down at Patti. He frowns.

Then he says: "Well hello there and what's your name?"

"Her name is Patti. She's coming with us to the pictures," Aunt Jinny says.

He nods an OK. They start to walk towards the bridge. Christy on the outside, Jinny in the middle, Patti on the inside holding Jinny's hand. He sticks out his elbow. He wants Jinny to link his arm, but she won't.

She shrugs her shoulder. "I'm all right," she says, so he walks along beside them with his hands in his pockets. Christy's face is all sharp bones with a bunch of pimples near his chin. He has a Brylcream smell, same as her Da. They walk fast down the quays and up O'Connell Street.

There's a long queue outside the Carlton. They wait in line. At the box office, they stand aside, while Christy gets out the money. It's packed in the foyer. A lovely smell of perfume and popcorn in the air. The usher shows them to their seats and points into the middle of the row with her torch. Christy says: "Ladies first," but they're not sure who sits where, so Aunt Jinny goes first and pulls Patti along by the hand into the seat beside her. Christy goes next, so she's stuck there in the middle between the two of them. At the interval, it's all bright lights, loud voices and shuffling feet. They queue for the ladies while Christy goes to the gents. On the way back, he buys them orange maids and popcorn from the girl with the tray strapped round her neck. Patti says:

"Thanks very much." Christy says: "Your welcome."

It goes dark again and the dark blue velvet curtains swish back.

The film is a bit stupid. A Western with John Wayne and this mad young one in a cowgirl suit with a battered hat following him all over the Wild West. John Wayne prefers his horse and his whiskey. He tries to teach her a lesson. He tries to send her home on her horse. He even slaps her in the bum, but she keeps coming back. It looks mad in the Wild West; all square rocks and dusty paths and creeks where they make camp and water the horses. It's all campfires and whiskey drinkin' and fights afterwards. In the towns it's saloon girls with frilly dresses doing the cancan.

In her handbag, Aunt Jinny has a bag of Iced Caramels. She stretches them across Patti's lap to Christy.

"Here take one," she says. Christy takes a sweet first, then Patti. They make sucky sweet noises in the dark. The coating on the Iced Caramels sticks in her back teeth and hurts for a bit, but it's nice all the same.

It's quiet on the way home with hardly any traffic. There's packs of birds twittering in the small trees beside the Liffey. There's rubbish everywhere. Sweet-wrappers and cigarette boxes blow along in the wind. They cross over at the Halfpenny Bridge. The appleseller shouts out in her singsongy voice: "Beaushy a Bath, five f'r a shillin'. Cox's Pippins, six f'r a shillin'."

Aunt Jinny's highheels make a scratching sound on the path. They don't talk for three bridges, and then Christy does a little cough with his fist to his mouth and asks her did she think it was a good film. Aunt Jinny says it was all right, but a Western is not really her sort of film. Up the quays, a strong breeze all of a sudden. A newspaper blows past them along the ground. They watch a whole page lift up and flap over the Liffey wall. It floats like a raft with a girls face looking up. Then the face sinks and goes under the bridge. It's the News of the World, the English newspaper her granny reads on Sundays. The one with all the scandals about politicians and models and good time girls. The rest of the paper wheelies along and wraps itself round a lamp-post. Loose pages open and close like an accordion. Aunt Jinny pretends not to notice. She has a face on her like she ate a crab apple. Christy's hair is tossed and loose, a big piece down over his forehead.

At the gate they stop.

"Go on in. I'll be there in a minute," she says.

Patti doesn't look back. Maybe they might kiss. Or maybe not. She hopes they do kiss and maybe Christy might be Aunt Jinny's Mister Right.

36

A WEDDING STORY

On the southside they all go to different chapels; Aunt Jinny and Rita go to Adam and Eve's, Uncle Fran and Joe to John's Lane and Uncle Paddy to them all. Aunty Annie is very particular; she prefers to get mass at Saint Audoens up the hill. She likes the short sermons and it's never as packed as other chapels. They have the half- twelve mass and up there no one notices if you're a bit late. It has a man kind of smell, because it's mostly men who kneel in the back pews or stand near the doorway smoking. Saint Audoens is the oldest chapel on the southside, Aunt Annie tells her It goes back centuries and the whole place is bursting with history.

After mass this Sunday, they wait until everyone is gone. They walk up the aisle and it seems like miles. They light candles at the side altars. They sit for a while and say a few prayers. Outside in the main chapel, Aunt Annie tells her in whispers that she might be getting married. She's going steady with this nice gentleman from the Coombe Cottages, a widower with two daughters. His name is Mister Palace, so she'll be called Misses Palace.

"That's a terrific name," Patti whispers. Annie says yes it's a very unusual name.

She's not sure about which chapel she'll get married in. She wants to know how long that isle is, so she measures it with her footsteps on the way back down.

"That'd be a terror to walk up," she whispers. "That aisle must be half a mile long.

You know, it was here in this very chapel your Mammy and Daddy walked up to their own wedding. I remember it well, like it was yesterday. Your mammy looked lovely in her wedding costume. Like a film star she was. Her hair as black as coal under her hat."

"She wore a costume? And a Hat? Was she not in a white dress and a lace veil?"

"No."

"Why?"

"Veils don't suit everyone."

"Was she in high heels?"

"Course she was. The latest."

"And what about her costume?"

"That was gorgeous! A tailored fawn coloured two-piece, out of MacDonald's Ladies Fashions. And her hat! People remarked on that hat and how unusual it was, for months after. "

"Was she very nervous?"

"Yeah. Rattlin, she was with the nerves. Even at'ome, before she left for the chapel. I remember her smokin' like a chimney breast in the bedroom, one cigarette after another."

"That's Ma all right."

"Yeah. Smokin' since she was a kid, your Mammy. Our poor Da was only laid to rest a couple of months earlier. That was a terrible pity he missed the wedding."

"That's awful."

"It was only ourselves in the chapel, although there was enough of us in it."

"What about Da. Was he done up?"

"Oh your Daddy was very well turned out. Had a nice dark suit on. All his family were there and the style of them to beat the band."

"Where was the wedding?"

"In your Daddy's place on the northside. A big do, plenty of food and drink, it went on all night and the next day and the next day."

"Holy God!"

"I'll say this for them, they don't do things by halves down Foley Street. They were talkin' about that wedding breakfast for ages after."

"Breakfast? At a wedding?"

"Yes. It's called a wedding breakfast, even though it's not really a breakfast."

"Was there a honeymoon?"

"No. Not what you'd call a real honeymoon. I think they went on an excursion somewhere for the day. Not that day. The following Sunday, I believe. That was their honeymoon."

"How come there's no photos?"

"You'll have to ask your Mammy about that. I don't think it was allowed. Your Daddy's people didn't want any photographs. So I believe".

"Why?"

"Oh. I'm not sure. In them days people didn't take photos like they do today. But the memories last longer. Who needs photographs, when you have the memories?"

"Will you have photographs taken on your wedding day?"

"Course I will. Mister Palace insists on all the trimmings, including a wedding album with a white leather cover. Mister Palace is very modern in an old-fashioned sort of way."

It's a bit peculiar, Patti thinks. It must be that photographs weren't in the fashion like they are now. Everyone that gets married now has a wedding album with a white cover.

"We weren't made of money," her Ma says, when she asks her about the missing photographs.

"Photographs are lovely to look back on. Your wedding day is supposed to be special, like your Holy Communion or your Confirmation."

Her Ma's face looks a bit dreamy. She bites her thumbnail.

"It was the ferocious fifties. Times were shockin' hard."

"And what about your honeymoon?"

"What honeymoon? Honeymoon is right. People didn't have money for honeymoons. We were lucky to go to Bray for the day. Anyway what's all this forty questions about weddins and honeymoons all of a sudden?"

"Oh, nothin'; I was just talkin' to Aunt Annie."

"About what?"

"About weddins. Aunt Annie says she might be gettin' married."

"Married? Our Annie?"

"She met Mister Right. His real name is Mister Palace."

"Is that so?"

"Mister Palace is very modern in an old-fashioned sort of way. Mister Palace is a gentleman."

"Gentleman or no gentleman, marriage is no bed of roses. She'd want to watch her step. I hope she doesn't rush into anythin'. She doesn't want a ball and chain."

"She's not gettin' a ball and chain, she's only gettin' married."

"Our Annie is a beaushy."

"Maybe she doesn't want to get left on the shelf."

"Yeah. Maybe so. I suppose she's gettin on all right and she's no spring chicken, that's a fact."

She lets a half washed jumper fall into the bathwater, dries her hands and lights a Player.

"I can't believe she's gettin' married. You know she was goin' to be a nun one time.

"A NUN? AUNT ANNIE?"

"True as God. She's a bit holyish our Annie, but a different kind of holy to our Jinny."

"Annie's not nunish. Annie wouldn't wear a nun's habit."

"Oh I know what ya mean there. Annie is some glamour girl now, but it was years ago. She was only a young one. One day she told me mother out straight, she wanted to become a nun."

"Please yourself", me mother said. But all along, she must've known they wouldn't take her into the convent. To become a nun you'd have to have money behind you. Your people have to pay for your keep in the convent while you're a postulant."

"What's a postulant?"

"It's like a trainee nun. Anyway, they don't usually take workin' girls from the flats."

"That's balderdash! The nun's in school say if you have a true vocation, you can go to a convent and become a Bride of Christ."

"Talk proper. Don't start with that wordy elocution talk and have us all baffled. It's not that easy to become a nun. You'd have to live in a house and not a Corporation flat."

"Right."

"You see, they'd take you in all right, but they'd only make a skivvy out of you; they'd dress you up in a nun's habit, but you wouldn't be a proper nun. You'd be what's called a domestic sister. D'ya see?"

"I think so. She'd be like the nice looking nun in our school, the one who does the laundry and the cooking and the gardening?"

"I s'pose so. You couldn't take full vows, or get the silver weddin' ring."

"Is that what happened to Aunt Annie?"

"Annie didn't even get through the front door. She applied to this convent out far near the sea, Greystones, I think it was, wrote a big long letter. A lovely writer our Annie was. There was this big fancy advertisement in one of the holy magazines."

She puts on the culchie voice.

"It said: 'Chaste girls of immaculate character with a true vocation need only apply.' A couple of weeks after, she gets this cranky stuck up letter back from the convent, with a list of expenses as long as your arm. A small fortune they wanted to train her in, money for habits and veils and rosary beads and more money for her keep in the convent. You'd know they didn't want her, the sour sarcastic way the letter was wrote."

"Poor Annie. Did she not try another convent?"

"I don't think so. She never mentioned it after that. I don't know why she wanted to go to a nunnery. Life's hard enough as it is without bein' on your knees prayin' all day."

It's strange to think of Aunt Annie as a nun. Patti tries to picture her in a long white habit. Her shaved head in an egg shape, bowed in front of the altar to take her vows. A silver wedding ring on her finger. She's a Bride of Christ. She's one of the nice-looking nuns with the white seagull head veils. They're a French order who live in a convent in King Street. They always look happy. They walk in two's with their hands up their wide sleeves. Patti wonders what it'd be like, to be a Bride of Christ and have God for a husband. It might be better than the chicken factory, or William's and Wood's jam factory. It might work out. She could sleep in a cell. Say rosaries. Sing hymns. Walk in a nice garden on a sunny day. It's not that bad, when she thinks of it. The only thing is, you can't go out with fellas, or to dancehalls, or smoke cigarettes. There's different stories about nuns. That one about the holy blue pooley might be what her Ma calls, a tall tale. Another tall tale is that nuns can't fart, but Patti knows that's not true for deffo.

If she was a nun she wouldn't be in a closed order, like the Poor Clares. She goes to their convent out in Harold's Cross. Granny puts money in the envelope with her petition. The nuns say special prayers. Granny says they *intercede* on your behalf. Granny has great belief in them, for the holy souls and fevers, for rheumatism and asthma. It's something to do with the oath they took. She says, maybe they do all their talking to God, because they can't talk to anyone else. You ring the bell at the gate. You wait. You hear footsteps. You wait again. You slide the envelope through the black letterbox in the wall. Fingers appear like magic. A cold hand pulls in the envelope and the flap closes. It's dead spooky. There's no talking. The Poor Clares took vows of silence so they can never speak. You hear the footsteps again, inside the wall and the door closing. Patti tried to have a peep through this grill in the wall, but all she saw was a bit of a concrete yard.

"Ma."

"What?"

"Annie is havin' all the trimmings at her wedding."

"Is she?"

"Yes. Mister Palace insists. I'd say she might go to Blackpool or the Isle of Mann or Jersey for her honeymoon.

"Tell her there's nothin' in Jersey only dairy cows and she'd be better off in Blackpool."

"Right."

37

THE TONSIL PINCH

Fights are stupid. The stupidest fights are between the boys. They come up from Sherriff Street and East Wall. They come over the bridge from Pimlico and Oliver Bond. It's usually during the summer holidays. You see them with their war ammo, snotty young fellas with crew cuts and knocky knees. They have sling shots and stones and bows and arrows. They carry long pointy spears they make from wood-pallets. They have sheets of rusty tin for armour plates. They take aim from the fish market wall into the flats. One big stone with a sling shot, then another one. If there's more than a few stones fired that means it's a war.

"Come on yiz shitey Greek Street'rs. WE WANT WAR. WE WANT WAR." They make apache sounds. Do a stupid war dance with their heads down and it's like they're in the Wild West. The war goes on for weeks sometimes, with no surrender on either side. They come back every day for more. The Greek Street boys take aim from the balconies. Sometimes the cops are called if someone gets hurt. If it's a long war that goes on for weeks, the girls join in to help to win the war. Sometimes they're allowed and sometimes they're not. The smart alecks tell the girls to go and play piggy beds or dollies and prams and that's just typical!

Fights! Fights! Fights! Everyone wants to fight. There's fights in the flats. Outside the flats. On the stairs. In the Ice Lane. If you don't fight, they call you a cowardy cowardy custard or a yellabelly. So you have to pretend you want to fight. You have to make it look like you're dying for a fight. You can't come running home whinging, or they'd only send you back out again to finish off the fight.

Your hair always gets reefed, your ponytail or your French-plaits and it's like your scalp is lifting. Once, after a big fight, Patti brought a bunch of her hair home and asked her Ma could she stick it back on. Here's the rules. In a fight, a girl can pull hair and pinch and scrob and scratch with her nails. You're only supposed to bite back if someone bites you first. You can pull tongues and ears. You can pinch tonsils. You're not supposed to kick; that's boys' stuff. Boxing is boys' stuff too. And spitting. She hates that! In a fight the boys spit at each other with big sudsy golliers. They do stupid dances around each other with their fists held up and they call that boxing. They kick each other in the goolies; they twist arms back. They do dead legs.

There's the girl gangs that come up town looking for fights. They hang around smoking near the gates. They might trip you up or say:

"Are ya lookin'?"

So you say: "No."

And they say: "What the fock are ya lookin' at?"

Then you say: "Not much."

In fights some of them are cheaters; they kick and spit and box. They try to break your glasses. They have stones in their fists. Her Ma says they're tomboy gurriers, the ones that don't fight fair.

"Four eyes," they shout and that's when the fight starts.

"Your muddor is gummy."

"My Ma's teeth are brand new, better than your Ma's."

"Your Da is a big fatso."

"He is not."

"A spunker then. A skinny spunker."

"A spunker? A spunker drinks Red Biddy. My Da only drinks stout and whiskey."

"Ya poxy Cow!"

She's not sure what poxy means, but she knows it's something contagious, like leprosy or smallpox, something that makes you feel ashamed.

The worst thing is to be pulled down on the ground in a fight. Here's this young one like a demon on top of you. Her face is in your face. Here's the two of them rolling and wriggling on the hard ground with a crowd around them. Here comes fingers down your throat. A salty taste of skin. Yuk! The fingers are making you choke. Grabbing at your tonsils. It's the worst pain ever. Patti always loses her glasses. She can't see properly so everything goes blurry.

She goggles.

She feels sick.

Oh Mammy. Oh Holy nightmare!

They might be wriggling round for ages on the ground until maybe she bites the fingers. Or knees the young one in the belly. That's how come she learned to do the tonsil pinch. You have to be careful you don't get bitten. You hold the mouth open with one hand. It's very tricky. You push the teeth back. You hope the teeth don't bite off your finger. Maybe you say a prayer to your guardian angel if you have time.

38

NERVES

Her Ma cries a lot. The tears stay still and shiny in her eyes, like the tears in a holy picture. It might be she's not well again. She pulls at her ponytail. She smokes all her butts and bites her nails

"Oh Jesus!" she says to herself and that's when she goes a bit wobbly in the legs and has to lie down. She might need a tonic Patti thinks. She might need Buckfast Abbey. The Buckfast is supposed to be good for your nerves, but her Ma doesn't like it.

"What about a milk stout?" granny asks, but she has her faraway face on, kind of lonely, kind of sad, a little bit nervy.

"I'm grand," she says even though she isn't.

Granny tells her to buck up and get a hold of her senses. She has mouths to feed. Childer to mind.

Aunt Lilly comes in from Finglas and gives her a talking to. She says she'll go melancholy and end up in The Gormon if she's not careful.

"Is that the place beside the Morning Star Hostel? The hospital for mad people?" Patti asks.

"It's called Saint Brendan's for your information. It's where you go if you're not well with your nerves," Aunt Lilly says.

She heard The Gormon is full of mad people with long white hair and steel plates in their heads.

"In Saint Brendan's, they give you ECT."

"What's ECT?"

"They put wires on your head. Give you a dose of the shocks."

"Shocks?"

"Electric shocks."

"Oh My God!"

"It's supposed to make you better. Sometimes it works and sometimes it doesn't. Your Ma is not the only one; Rita had the shocks too, but it didn't work for poor Rita."

Her Ma is not nuts, only a bit sad sometimes she tells her out straight.

Aunt Lilly says: "That's right. It's just nerves, but your nerves can drag you down if you're not careful."

The nerves run in the family. It started with Patti's granda, after he returned from the war. It's all the bad memories Aunt Lilly supposes that made him a nervous wreck; the death and suffering he witnessed in the trenches.

"That bloody war left its mark on whole families," she says.

Aunt Lilly told her, when she was a baby, her Ma left her outside this shop by mistake.

"You were only a few months old. Your Ma wasn't herself. In a trance she was when they found her. Off she goes wanderin' down the Alexander Basin on her travels. Sits there all day on a rock like the Queen of the Sea. Missing all night she was. The shopkeeper saw you in the pram outside the shop. You were taken to The Bridewell then. They found your Ma, God help her the next morning and you were taken to your other granny's."

"What happened next?"

"Your Ma ends up in you know where?"

"Where?"

"Where d'ya think? She needed treatment."

"The shocks?"

"That's right. Your Ma got better. It took a while but she pulled through."

"Then what?"

"They kept you in your granny's. Your Ma didn't even know she'd had a baby her memory was that bad. The rest is history."

***

Sometimes her Ma stops and stares down into the Liffey. On the high part of Queen Street Bridge, where the kids from the southside fish for eels. On the way home from granny's, or coming back from Thomas Street, she stands there like a stuck statue. She looks down through the bally pillars at the green water gushing under the bridge. She tells Patti to bring the kids home. She has that starey faraway look, like she's only half awake. The kids pull at her coat.

"C'mon Ma."

She sucks on the hall-door key, like it's a lollypop.

"I won't be long."

She gets out her smokes and shakes the box. She asks a man going by for a light. He strikes a match and shields it in with his hand. She bends in her head and lights up. Then she smokes her Player real fast all the way down to the butt. They wait on the bridge. Then they wait more while she asks someone else for another light. It might be that she's not well with her nerves, or she's just fed up, or it could be there's thunder and lightening on the way. It might be she's thinking of the babies. That's probably it. She might be thinking did they make it into heaven? Especially Olive Elizabeth. She worries about the devil. She thinks about hell a lot. That Nick fella is never far away she says. She knows what he looks like. He waits for a soul to catch. He bides his time. He's in no hurry. Sometimes when she's not well, she says the devil is on Patti's shoulder where her guardian angel should be. He has horns and a tail and cloven hoofs. She can see him plain as daylight behind her. Sometimes he's in the mirror behind the glass.

"There's no devil in the mirror!" Patti says and she hopes there isn't.

"Ma, it's cold here," she says.

She hands her the key.

"Go home and give the babby a bottle. I won't be long."

It might be long, or it mightn't be long. Maybe it gets dark and the babby starts crying. Da comes in for his tea before he washes himself and goes out again. There's murder then, if her Ma is not there with his tea ready.

The next day, her Ma's face is all changed.

She says: "God loves a trier. Maybe you don't get things right the first time or the second, or even the third time. The main thing is you can never give up."

So maybe that's how come she smokes boxes of Players, that's how come, she looks too long in the river. She's trying to forget and not forget at the same time, Patti thinks.

"You must never forget," she says.

"You must never forget your brothers and sisters who didn't make it in this world."

But that's only half true, Patti thinks, because if you remember them too much, it makes you sad. Her Ma always says: "You have to suffer in this world. You didn't come onto this earth to get things easy. No one is going to lay out a bed of shiny red roses for you to lie down on. No one is going to molly coddle you. You have to offer things up."

39

THE GIRL WITH NO CLOTHES ON

Maybe it was the gypsy who brought the bad luck. Maybe it was because the pope died. They're all talking about what happened to the little girl with the Shirley Temple hair. They say she's a little saint and she'll go straight to Heaven if she doesn't make it in this world. She walked all the way from the waste ground in the dark with no clothes on. It's where they light their campfires and get drunk; the tramps and the spunkers and the gypsies.

The people looking out their windows saw her walking past with no clothes on.

"Not a screed on the poor young ones back," someone said.

She had a look on her face like a frightened kitten. They called out to her, but she just kept walking like she was sleepwalking. They say she was in a trance and shivering and the blood was gushing out of her. An old woman ran out the gate and threw her shawl around her. Then she picked her up in her arms and carried her into the Bridewell Station. In the Bridewell all she did was stare. Then she fainted. The ambulance was called and it rushed her to the Richmond Hospital. The old woman went with her. They gave her a blood transfusion and brought her into the operating theatre.

Patty knows what happened. A dark stranger took her away and took off all her clothes and she must've been freezing. Then he hit her in the head and did horrible things to her. In the flats, they're all out reading the article in the Herald. The headline says; *Vicious Attack on Seven Year Old on Waste Ground.*

This reporter came around asking questions and the old woman gave him the story. Only seven she was and only after making her Holy Communion.

At the door her Ma looks nervy. She blesses herself. She says: "God protect us but the poor girl is destroyed, but thanks be to God she made her Holy Communion."

Goo Chaney says she hopes they catch the maniac before he strikes again.

A few of them say the little girl would be better off dead after what happened to her. She'd never be right in the head after a thing like that. She's supposed to be in a very serious condition, with all sorts of internal injuries. No one is allowed near the waste ground. The police are carrying out an investigation. The spunkers and the gypsies are gone from the waste ground. All that's left are scorch marks and rubbish and empty bottles. Someone found a white shoe, but it was too small to fit the girl so it's not the girl's shoe. It's hard to imagine, being out in the street with no clothes on, trying to hide yourself with your hands, Patti thinks. Her Ma blesses their heads with holy water and tells them not to talk to strangers. People start to keep their hall doors closed because a dark stranger is out there and everyone is afraid.

Then it starts a few weeks after. In the shop he's there behind her, this dark stranger she never saw before. She can smell him; the red biddy and the meths and the pissy clothes. She sees his baggy trousers hanging over his broken shoes. He just stands there behind her and says nothing. Patti thinks he's watching her. Maybe watching her sisters too. Then she can't get him out of her head. In her dreams she sees him, only he's huge like a big shadow on a wall. She wakes all hot from the dream, but when she goes back to sleep he's there again in the shop doorway. It's like he's waiting for her in the dream. She tries to shake herself awake. He follows her home. The stranger in the shop is the same stranger in the nightmare. He starts to follow her around the place. She listens for his footsteps behind her. She stops. Then he stops. She walks. Then he walks. In shop windows, she sees him behind her. He's there in the window of the bike shop in Church Street, he's there at the church gate, always just a few feet behind her.

40

SHE'S FRAMED

Her Holy Communion photo hangs in the alcove between the fireplace and the scullery. Her Ma dusts it with a chamois duster every week. She stands up on the green wobbly chair. She says "I'll go skatin'" but she never does.

That photo frame nearly got broken more times when her Da threw his dinner at the wall. What's nicest about the photo is her dress: a white stand out nylon skirt, spread out over the table, a sprig of Lilly of the Valley at her waist. The under skirts made a crackle noise when she moved. She doesn't like her face in the photograph. She looks dead gawky she thinks.

She has her white net gloves with the frill around the wrist on. Her hands are joined and sticking out, like she's praying. Her hair is done in sausage curls under her tulle veil. That wreath and veil were brand new in a brown cardboard box when her granny bought them from Molly in the market. It came straight out of the Gay Child, Molly said. Granny asked her was she sure it was new and Molly made the sign of the cross on her chest. She says she'd never tell a lie about a holy article of clothing like that. The veil comes down to her elbows with a double row of loops like little S's around the edge. It was made for her everyone said. The wreath is like white flower petals and that was made for her too. She remembers her Holy Communion. It was the best day of her life, but her first confession the night before was the worst part. She examined her conscience; Was she covetous? Did she give backcheek to her elders? Did she curse? Tell lies? Spit? Dead nervous she was on the queue. It was pitch dark in the confession box. She knelt down. She could see the shape of the priest's head when he pulled back the hatch. He leaned his ear to the wire. She could smell dusty wood and silvermints.

"Bless me father for I have sinned, this is my first confession father."

She could hear him yawning a big long yawn. All her sins she had ready; the ones that were true and the ones she made up. The ones about giving backcheek were true, but the ones about telling lies weren't. She didn't curse either, except to say feck and flip and fizz. She doesn't think she was covetous and, she for deffo didn't spit.

"Are you sorry for these sins? "

"For these and all my sins, I am heartily sorry father"

"With a contrite heart?"

"Yes father."

Then she made her act of contrition. The priest gave her the special blessing to absolve her sins, then he gave her penance: One Our Father, five Hail Marys and one Glory be. She knew by his voice that he was the cranky priest, with the yellowy grey hair that gives them hard catechism questions in class. It was nice to have her soul all spotless like the blackboard after it's dusted. It was nice to know she wouldn't go to hell if she died in her sleep. The fires in hell burn forever and you'd roast like a chicken in the oven but you'd never get done.

Her Holy Communion coat was powder blue, same colour as Our Lady's cloak. In chapel, she saw the chalice held up. She saw the priest drinking God's blood. He knocked back his head. He drank it down and wiped his mouth with a white cloth. She saw the holy bread next, a round disc like a white coin. He held it up. At the altar rail, she was rattling. She closed her eyes and stuck out her tongue. Then she felt the Holy bread and she closed her mouth. On the way back to her seat, the wafer got stuck to her tongue and she couldn't touch it with her teeth. It melted a bit. She twisted her tongue into a curl. She pushed it down with the tip. It broke. Then it went down in a lumpy mush. She felt it stuck down there past her tonsils. She kept on swallowing, but it wouldn't go down. She hoped it wasn't a sin. She felt all holy then. She felt hungry too with no porridge for breakfast. You can't eat anything for three hours before Holy Communion; that's the rule so all she had was a cup of black tea.

They stood up at the end and sang Soul of My Saviour. They walked back down the aisle real slow with their heads bowed.

At first it was sunny outside the chapel. Then it was cloudy. Spitty rain fell and they all ran into the school. They got a fairy cake and milk in the school hall. The grown- ups got cups of tea. The lunch woman brought round a big kettle and a plate of scones. The little nun shook the black baby collection box at them the next day. She held up a picture of a black baby in their faces. Then she shook the box more. Patti put a whole half crown in the box to save a black baby. She thought of the black baby, saved and happy in the camp. She thought of it drinking milk and maybe African goody goody made of rice.

It was a few weeks after her Holy Communion, when her Ma bought the picture frame. The frame salesman had his car parked in the courtyard with the boot open.

"It's a very desirable glass frame, with heavy steel screws; it would last a lifetime," he said.

Her Ma thought it was lovely when he held it up. There was a crowd around the car. Everyone wanted the desirable frames; everyone wanted their child's photograph in a frame all of a sudden. It was like when something catches on, like the delf birds or the spotty black and white dogs. That day the Jew man sold loads of frames. He offered special weekly rates and discount for anyone buying more than one frame. Her Ma says she'll be years paying for that frame, but she thinks it'll be worth it in the long run. It's only a half crown a week, what you wouldn't miss if you were careful and diligent. Her Ma says it's ok because the Jew man is not a moneylender; all he sells are picture frames so it's no harm. He Da thinks she bought it downtown in Gerome's photographers. He says he has nothin' against Jew men, but they'd have you up to your eyes in debt. He means the money-lenders who give out loans with interest for weddings and Holy Communion. There's some who do cheques for different shops. Her Ma says they provide a valuable service and some people would be lost without them.

41

A WINTER COAT

It's down a laneway near Strand Street, a tailoring factory that makes children's clothes. That's where they got her Communion coat. The factory belongs to a nice Jewish man her granny knows. He's a real gent, very genuine and respectable, she says. Granny wears her good coat and bag. The tailor meets them at the office door and leads them into a showroom with a green carpet and a long swing mirror. He switches on an electric bar fire. He has a tape measure around his neck, dark hair combed back in straight lines. He smells of something strong and spicy; maybe Old Spice aftershave.

"He's immaculate," granny whispers.

She means his pinstripe tailored suit and his shiny black shoes. He pulls out a rack of coats. With his tape measure, he starts to measure her; length first, arms, back, shoulders.

"Are you looking for any style in particular?"

She's hard on coats, so they want something she'll grow into, granny tells him, not something that she'll be out of in six months. It's a serviceable winter coat they want, with good strong material, not something that'll fall to pieces off her back in no time.

The tailor writes down the measurements.

"Take a look through here."

Some of the coats are covered in plastic. A few have labels attached. Some of them are gorgeous. There's this fluffy mohair one, with a swingy back, in a lovely shade of mauve; there's a beige camel hair travelling coat with real leather buttons, another one the colour of Colman's mustard with brass buttons. But her granny is feeling the stuff of a bright green coat. It's dead hickey looking, Patti thinks.

"That kelly green is nice," she says, so the tailor takes the coat off the hanger.

"Yes yes, a good choice, suit her sallow colouring."

He opens buttons, holds the coat out, and helps her fix her arms into the sleeves. Patti has to walk like a model in a fashion parade up and down the room; then she has to do a twirl. She has to straighten her shoulders and not slouch and imagine she has a book on her head. She has to do this a few times, so she imagines she's walking down a catwalk in Paris France. Her granny says the sleeves are a bit long and the shoulders a bit wide, but the way she's growing, that coat will fit her in no time.

"Take a look at yourself in that mirror," the tailor says.

In the long swing mirror she looks like a little culchie. The bright green is horrible, like the green part of the Irish flag, or a Saint Patrick's Day ribbon. It makes her face look yellow. And worst of all, it's well past her knees, well past the top of her socks. It's dead hickey. She never gets the coat she wants. The tailor stands back with his finger to his bottom lip. He looks at Patti. He knows she doesn't like the coat. Her granny is not sure.

"It's not her shade of green, maybe if it was a shade darker," she says.

"Can I take it off now?"

"You may as well I suppose."

Patti takes off the green coat. The tailor says: "Wait!" He starts to root along the coat rail. He has the very thing, he says, a new type of material that can withstand all weathers. Something between a winter coat and a raincoat. Something stylish and serviceable at the same time. He pulls yards of plastic off another coat on the rail. He takes it off the hanger. It's a duffel. Her granny doesn't like duffels, she thinks they're very boyish and common, but this one is no ordinary duffel. This one is made of red plaid material. The tailor tells them, it's the very latest foam back material and it's selling very well in England and Scotland.

"This one was made for her," he says, helping her on with the duffel.

"That's more like it. That colour suits her better."

The tartan is nice, a red background, with grey and green squares. It has wood toggles and a hood to keep her head warm. She walks up and down the room with her shoulders straight and her head up. She does a twirl.

"Now put up the hood," her granny says.

She pulls up the hood. It feels nice and cosy. She looks in the mirror. She's like Little Red Riding hood, she thinks, but she likes the coat, especially the colour. It's the very latest material and it's not too long either, just below her knee.

"Do one more walk," granny says, so she does the model walk one more time. Then granny checks the hem to see if there's enough letting down room.

"Nice bit of stuff," she says. "Good deep hem too."

One more twirl and granny says: "H'much for the duffel?"

The tailor rubs his finger along his bottom lip. He says he'll let her have it at a very good price. Her granny tells him, business is not that good in the market and things are very slack at present and she hopes he's not going to rob her. He smiles and says the coat was a sample garment, so he can afford to give her a very good bargain indeed. He names a price and granny has a think. She says: "Umm . . ." She looks at the coat one more time. She feels under the arms for growing room, and then she nods her head and says she'll take it. The tailor helps Patty out of the coat and goes to wrap it up. His secretary brings in tea and a plate of biscuits.

"That coat's nice on ya. You'd pay a pretty penny for that coat in Arnotts."

Does she like it?

She likes it. Especially the hood.

"You won't see them duffels walkin' around on their own in the flats, like them cheap grey duffels out of Frawley's."

He brings the parcel. Then they have a little chat. Business is not so good this year. People are not spending, he says.

"You're telling me? The market is gone ta hell."

Then the tailor nods his head and shows them to the door. He says he hopes she likes the coat. Patti tells him she likes it. Loads.

42

UNCLE WILLIE'S LEAKY BOAT

Everyone says her Uncle Willie is very musical. He's always practicing on his accordion. He plays the same tune over and over. No bum notes, that's the rule with uncle Willie. He likes to hang around with people who play music; he meets up with them in the pubs downtown. They play sessions together. Sometimes he brings them home to meet granny, the fella's with the beards and bulky jumpers, fella's with culchie voices and Aran sweaters. They shake hands with granny. They sit in the visitor's chair and granny makes them a big fry-up of sausages and rashers and kidneys. Other times, he might bring home a backpacker and let him sleep on the floor. You might see someone stretched out in a sleeping bag, when you're going to the toilet. The next morning, there's this stranger with tossed hair in the scullery cleaning his teeth.

Uncle Willie is like that. He has friends who send him postcards from all over the world. He's mad about boats and the sea; he joined the sea-scouts when he was a kid. His bedroom wall is covered in scout flags and postcards. The photograph on his bedside locker is of her Da, making his Holy Communion. He has on a snow-white suit with short trousers. He looks like a little saint with his chubby round face and his hands joined.

In granny's place, uncle Willie always gets to use the scullery first. In there, he gets himself ready for a date. Sometimes there's murder, if one of the aunties has a date as well. For a date, he'd be done up to the nines in a suit, shirt and tie. He'd dab on Old Spice aftershave. Comb his short hair with a steel comb and granny nods her head like she thinks he's a real smasher. The aunties have to polish his shoes and iron his clothes and make his bed. He gets breakfast in bed on a Sunday. That's because sons are different to daughters; daughters are for scrubbing floors and cleaning windows, sons are for molly coddling. Sons get to use the scullery first. A daughter has to take her turn; a daughter has to learn to wait.

"Willie is a real craftsman," her Da says.

"A jack of all trades," her Ma calls him. She means he's a carpenter one day and a sailor the next.

Willie smells of wood shavings and French polish and sometimes, on Sunday's he smells of Dollymount strand. That's because he trains out there with the sea scouts. They do canoeing and life saving exercises with the younger boys. On work days, his corduroy trousers hang low on his waist with a loose leather belt. His pockets are heavy with carpenter's stuff: a steel measuring tape, a hacksaw, a pliers, pieces of paper, bundles of cash, a ball of twine. His workshop is in Cole's Lane, behind Moore Street. It's just like a big shed with a corrugated tin roof. In there, it's mountains of sawdust, piled up where he works at the saw bench. He whistles while he saws. Sometimes he listens to the ballads on the radio. When it rains, the tin roof lets in the rain mixes with the sawdust and goes mushy. On shelves along the wall, there's cans of glue, hammers, chisels, nuts, bolts, boxes of nails. In there, you get dizzy from the glue smell. Patti likes the twirly rapid feeling in her head.

Willie makes tables and chairs, sideboards and dressers. They're all his own designs; the latest trend in modern living, he tells them. This day, he makes a low square table with hardly any legs.

"It's Japanese," he tells them.

He paints it up with varnish, makes Japanese designs up the side, but no one wants to buy it. Half-made chairs and tables are against the wall. A light bulb is rigged up with loose hanging wires over the saw bench. The blade twinkles as he pushes the saw back and forth in the light. Willie's face has dots of sweat. His trousers are low at the back, so you can see the start of his bum when he bends over. Ma says he'd want to get a good strong belt to hold up them trousers.

People owe him small fortunes for furniture they don't collect. That's what happened with the new sideboard. It's called a prototype. Willie says it's a new modern kind of sideboard. The kind of thing you'd only see on the continent.

"It was French inspired," he says. "A special commission designed for a special client."

This client was looking for something different, something fancy and unusual. But then the special client didn't want the sideboard when he saw it. Willie was disgusted, because he spent weeks designing and making the Prototype.

Da says: "It's some piece of furniture all right. You wouldn't see furniture like that in Cavendish's."

So Willie says he can have it if he wants it. He can pay him when he has the money.

The neighbours come to see the sideboard. They gawk and stare as her Da and Willie try to carry it in from the van.

"It's a fantastical object all right," one of them says.

"French," Ma says. "The very latest design."

"What is it?" Another one says.

"What is it? What is it? Mother of God, are ya blind? Can ya not see it's a sideboard?"

"A sideboard?"

"Not any oul fashioned sideboard mind you."

"Specially commissioned," Da says, all breathless. "A masterpiece of design and craftsmanship."

There's murder over the French sideboard, but Patti thinks it's nice. Her Ma doesn't like it; she says it has no shape or make. It's roundy and square at the same time. It has bowlegs. And where in the name of God was the mirror? How could you have a sideboard with no mirror? And those doors are very awkward, the way they swing out and them sharp corners would take the eye out of ya.

"Mirrors are gone out," Da says, "have you no style at all?"

So her Ma thinks a bit. Maybe she's not up to scratch on the latest in sideboards and it'd be nice to have more space for the clothes. Uncle Willie says he'll varnish it up next week and put on the door handles the week after.

Everyone is talking about Uncle Willie's new cabin cruiser. So this Sunday, they all walk down the quays to get a look.

They see it banging up against the wall, near a big boat called the Lady Patricia. There's Willie with a bucket emptying out water, with his black sea-scout jumper and black beret on. He gives them a big wave.

"Ahoy there!" he shouts.

The kids are all excited and wave back:

"Ahoy Ahoy," Franey shouts.

Ma says in a low voice: "You'd want your head examined to go to sea in a jalopy like that," but thank God Willie doesn't hear.

The boat is low in the water, like it's going to sink any minute. There's waves pushing against the sides, stout bottles and bits of rubbish caught in at the wall.

"Keep back from that wall," Ma shouts.

Willie shouts up at them; he asks them do they want to go out for a spin around Dublin Bay. Patti doesn't think so. Her Ma says: "God almighty, are ya coddin me Willie or what?"

There's puddles of dirty seawater in the boat. A fishing pole with a line rigged up into the water. He's fishing for Dublin Bay prawns and crabs, he says.

A few sailors walk by in navy sailor suits. Their wide bellbottoms flap in the breeze. Willie points to where a foreign navy ship is docked further down the quays. He says it's open to visitors, but there might be a charge. The kids want to see it. They start to drag out of Ma's coat. She walks down a bit. It's huge and grey with flags at each end. Men are working on different parts of the ship. There's a sound of drilling and hammering. One of the men waves at them and says something foreign.

"Give him a wave," her Ma says. "Say ahoy." They all wave back. "Ahoy there."

Jimmy stands back with his arms folded. Walks up and down alongside the ship. Shakes his head from side to side, like he can't believe it.

"It's a warship with torpedoes," he says.

"No it's not. There's no wars on thank God," Ma says.

"I think he's right. It might be a Russian warship Ma," Patti says.

"Don't you start about the bloody Russians. Are we not bad enough?"

Franey makes a run for it up the gangplank. Anna goes behind him. A man in a boiler suit puts his hands out to stop them. He gives Ma a look. He says something in a deep voice and a foreign accent. Ma rushes forward and grabs Franey's arm, gives it a shake, and wraps his fingers around the go-car handle. Anna makes a face at the man. Calls him *Fatso Watso* under her breath. They walk back to Willie's boat. They're supposed to keep well away from the edge, but Anna keeps messing, running round in circles like a mad thing. Ma keeps shouting at her to keep back, but she doesn't listen.

Willie waves when he sees them. Then he disappears into the cabin and comes back out with his accordion. He wraps the straps around him over his scout jumper. He plays a few notes. Then he starts to play a tune. It's the Skaters Waltz. They know that tune off by heart; Willie plays it all the time in granny's. A few people walking by gather around and listen. The accordion music mixes with the breeze and the seagulls. Willie plays another tune and the people give a few claps. Then he tells them he's preparing for a solo voyage in a few weeks time. He might even chance the Isle of Mann if the weather conditions are right.

"That's great," Patti says.

"God! Is that not a bit far?" Ma says, but Willie just nods. Then she says they better go. That tide is coming in fast and their Da'll be in for his tea.

On the way home, she says, "Your uncle Willie has sea legs. He shudda been a fish instead of a carpenter. He could swim to England and back, like a mackerel no bother."

"Boats is right. That fella'd want t'get his head examined," her Da says when one of the kids tells him about the new cabin cruiser.

"The boat was wocky, wocky," Franey says.

"There's enough trouble in the world, without boats," Da say's.

"At least Willie's a real sailor and not a dreamer," Ma says.

***

The new sign says Alfredos Italian Restaurant. Homecooked Food and Fine Wines. Willie shows her around. Up a creakity stairs, over the angler's supply store in Mary's Abbey, down two steps, through a curtain made of coloured beads.

"Mind the steps," Willie says.

It's fab inside; all red and white check tablecloths and wooden high back chairs. On the tables, wine bottles with candle grease on the outside. More wine bottles in baskets on the white lumpy walls. Up the top there's a kind of bandstand with a low walk-on stage with a piano and drums and a microphone. On top of the piano, a boat with a man standing up with an oar. Willie says it's a gondola from Venice. Alfredo has brown skin and a grey moustache. He talks Italian in a deep choky voice. He cooks all the food himself: pizza and pasta and cannelloni. They can hear him singing in the kitchen, the clanging noise of pots and pans.

"What's that smell?"

"Garlic," Willie says and Patti never smelled that before.

"Look," he says. "There over the counter." She sees the garlic hanging up in net bags, like pretend onions. In the market, they sell them to the posh protestants for the casseroles. Alfredo gives them a piece of bread, like a big Vienna roll slice.

"I bake-a that myself. Work alla day." He's funny, the way he talks. He has on a check apron to match the tablecloths and Patti never saw a man wearing an apron before. She has to keep in the laughing. Out a tiny window, there's a yard, with fruit-boxes and wine bottles and bags of rubbish. Willie sits down at the piano. He has a new night job playing in the restaurant. He runs his hand along the keyboard. He starts to play a soft jazzy kind of tune she never heard before.

"Was that all right?" he wants to know. "Any flat notes?"

"I don't think so."

He plays it over and over until he gets it just right.

"It has to be perfect for tonight," he says.

"It has to be a professional performance with no bum notes."

He told her Alfredo's is the new in-place in town. All the modish people go there now, people with long hair and flowery shirts and cravats. People from theatres and jazz clubs downtown. She thinks he must mean the people who talk like they have marbles stuck in their throat. Alfredo's is up and coming. Willie loves it. He's mixing with all sorts of new people. They chat till all hours after he finishes playing. They drink fab red wine from the best vineyards in Italy. Alfredo gives Willie a bottle for himself. There's a picture of a man in a funny hat on the label and it looks a bit like the monk on the Buckfast Abbey bottle. They have a little taste out of tiny glasses. It's a bit sour, but that's ok, Patti doesn't mind sour. Alfredo smells it first, then he shakes it and then he smells it again. At last he knocks it back and Willie follows.

43
A YANKY PAL

One of the nosey parkers must've told her, because there she is waiting at the door.

"I hope you're not runnin' round with protestants," her Ma goes.

"No. Why?"

"A dicky bird told me. Yanky protestants down Capel Street."

No answer.

"They don't believe in Our Lady."

"They believe in God and they go to mass."

"That's a different mass. A protestant mass, like in Christ Church or Saint Patrick's."

"They have bibles. They read them every Sunday at Sunday school."

"Sunday school?"

"They learn all about the gospel and God there."

"They don't make their Holy Communion."

"They do so."

"They don't."

"They get baptised."

No answer.

"They make their confirmation."

"Are ya sure?"

"Course they do. They believe in the Holy Ghost."

"It's a different Holy Ghost."

"It isn't. There's only one Holy Ghost."

"What about the Blessed Virgin then?"

"What about her?"

"Where would we be without The Blessed Virgin?"

"I don't know Ma."

What's wrong with protestants? Why does everyone hate them? They're not that bad. It's only because they don't believe in Our Lady. It's that bloody nosey parker dicky bird again, the one that sees everything and tells everything. She'd ring its neck if she had it. It must be the nosiest bird in the whole world. It's all because of Betty, Patti's new friend. Betty is from the USA of America. Betty has a yanky accent, a long blonde ponytail, wears lovely American clothes, flowery shorts that go to her knees and ankle socks in different colours. All her clothes are store bought. Betty is very grown up. Patti likes the way she talks. She says sure instead of yes, hi instead of hello. She says: golly and g and awesome a lot. She has a few ordinary words as well, that sound Irish, like kinda and sorta and gonna. Betty thinks Irish people talk kinda cute. Patti likes her. She thinks she's dead neat.

Betty goes to a posh protestant school on the southside. She has to go to Sunday school in Christ Church. They do bible study and sing hymns. It's ok. They're not snobby like some protestants, the old fashioned ones with the tweedy costumes, the meanies who buy fruit from granny's stall and want the stuff for half nothing. Betty told her that they make their confirmation when they're older in America. They have an American preacher who doesn't wear long dresses like some of the Irish priests. He has regular clothes, a suit, shirt and tie. They don't get new confo clothes either; they just wear their best Sunday church clothes. She's glad she met Betty.

She was making a delivery for her granny to a fruitshop in Capel Street. One box of Golden Delicious apples, one chip of Canary tomatoes on top, one chip of button mushrooms. The pram was a bit wobbly, so the mushrooms topple over coming down the step and this nice-looking girl comes over to help her. First, she smiles with a row of straight white teeth.

"Hi," she goes in her nice American accent.

"Howea," Patti says.

"Can I help?" she says, and before she can answer, she bends down and starts to pick up the mushrooms.

She's very chatty. She tells Patti they're new in town, that she lives with her Dad over a diner.

"A diner? Geepers! That's brill . . . What's a diner?"

Betty smiles again. She points to a blue hall door with four long upstairs windows.

"It's on the first floor," she says. "We live in the upstairs apartment."

It's an old closed down place called the Market Café.

"We're turning it into an American diner. We'll do hamburgers and fries and shakes. Dad's making a new sign. Thinks he might call it: Dixie's Diner."

"That's fab," Patti says.

She has to go, she tells her. Maggie the shopkeeper is waiting for her delivery. The mushrooms will go all soggy if she doesn't hurry and she'll get in trouble.

This other day after school, Betty invites her up to the diner.

"Dad wants to meet my new friends," she goes.

Up two flights of bokety stairs. Dust everywhere. The diner is a big long room with red shiny counter. Seats stacked up against a wall. A roundy square jukebox in a corner. Creaky floorboards. A lovely smell of paint and glue. A ladder with a man in denim dungarees working. He steps down when he sees them and wipes his hands in a rag.

"Hi honey," he says to Betty.

Imagine! Your Da calling you, honey?

"Dad meet Paddi, Paddi meet Dad."

Her Dad smiles. He has white teeth and fair hair like Betty's. He's a lot taller than her own Da.

"Well hello there Paddi."

Patti smiles with her mouth shut. Betty's Dad bends his knees a bit to make himself look smaller.

"Bet you kids could murder a soda."

He pulls out stools, goes in behind the counter. He washes his hands. There's a soda fountain half full, like the one in Cafolla's, two plastic oranges floating on the top. He presses a handle. There's a squirty noise. A trickle of orange. He fills up two glasses with sudsy orange and puts them on the counter.

"Workin' like a dream," he says.

The orange tastes lovely, like real oranges.

"It's lovely," Patti says.

"Dad fixed it up so it works, soon as we moved in."

Behind the counter there's a deep-fryer machine and a big fridge.

The fridge is fat and round, like a standing up hot-water bottle. It makes a humming noise, like a stopped car with its engine on.

Betty's Dad goes back up the ladder and starts to peel stuff off the ceiling where there's a jagged hole.

"Dad's working real hard, fixing up the place," Betty says.

She tells Patti that they took a lease. They 'll open when all the hard work is done. They might do ice cream as well. Her Dad has lots of swell ideas. They might start a chain of Dixie Diners around town.

"It'll be real neat when its finished," Betty says.

"Sure will, when it's all cleaned up, when everything's in workin' order," her Dad says. "Specially when the juke box is fixed up."

This day, Betty's Dad makes them real hamburgers on the hot plate. It's the first time Patti tasted an American hamburger. It's the nicest thing she ever tasted, with fried onions and smothered in tomato ketchup.

"It's gorgeous," she says.

They're allowed to hang around the diner. Betty's Dad is always on the ladder, hammering and fixing things. He takes the fridge motor apart. He calls it the icebox. He's working on the jukebox too, so there's bits of it all over the floor.

"Sure'll be something when it's finished," he keeps saying.

"It sure will, Dad," Betty says.

He's getting ready for the big opening. It's any day now. It's next week or the week after. It's maybe next month or a coupl'a months.

"Doesn't really matter. The important thing is, it's gonna happen." Her Dad says.

Betty says her Dad digs the Beatles, and when the jukebox is fixed he'll have all their songs put on so they can play them whenever they want. It'll be dead brill, like the Rainbow Café. They'll be able to listen to the Beatles while they eat their hamburgers. In the diner, they pretend the jukebox works. It's playing Rock Around the Clock. They kind of hum the tune first. Betty is a good dancer. They try out a jive; they sort of twirl each other round in turns, Patti, then Betty; Betty, then Patti. They do double twirls and treble twirls. Next they try out the Twist. They sing the words; *Lets twist again, like we did last summer.* They go down on their honkers and nearly fall over.

"You kids take it easy," Betty's Dad says from the ladder.

Betty stops twisting. Folds her arms, says the Twist is gross.

"What's that?"

"Awful."

"It's only awful, when there's no music," Patti says. "Just wait till that jukebox is finished."

"Yeah, sure," she says, like she doesn't mean it. Betty gets fed up sometimes. She can't wait until the diner is finished, with the jukebox working and folks in. It's kind of lonely living there, she says, with just her and her Dad. She wants to see where Patti lives, but Patti doesn't show her. She's afraid they might call Betty a proddy woddy, so they don't play near the flats. Instead, they go to the handball alley and mess around. They hang around the Banba and browse the bookshelves. Betty's Dad won't let her go further than the next street. In the diner, it's rules rules rules! Betty's Dad is a bit strict sometimes. She'll get grounded if she breaks the rules. They practice walking, with books on their heads. They walk slowly across the diner floor with their hands out.

"Shoulders back. Head straight. Pretend you're a model in a fashion parade," Patti says.

They try it out with straight faces, but they keep tripping over and bursting out laughing. From the ladder, Betty's Dad says they're a couple a swells. Betty says she'd love to talk Irish like Patti and Patti says she'd love to talk yanky like Betty.

"Where's your Ma?" Patti asks one day.

Betty looks down at the floor.

"Mom died a coupla years back."

"Oh! Oh God!"

She shouldn't have asked. It just came out. It always happens.

"Mom got sick. Real bad."

"That's terrible . . ."

"That's ok. I miss her, but Dad says we have to start over. Make a fresh start. He's crazy about Ireland. Great grandpa was Irish. That's how come we moved here."

That's what Betty said, but then she and her Dad disappear all of a sudden.

She misses Betty. She knocks at the diner this day after school. No answer. There's a new blue and white For- Rent sign up over the door. She supposes they're gone back to America. Maybe she'll write. They might be pen pals. She keeps thinking of Betty, back in the USA of America, with her blonde pony-tail swinging. She thinks of her smiling, with her lovely white teeth. She thinks of her Dad calling her Honey. She thinks of the skyscrapers and the sidewalk and a chain of Dixie Diners. She thinks of the white church, with the nice friendly preacher in the white sunshine in New York State. Some day she might go to America herself. She'll put an advert in the New York Times to find Betty. They'll be best buddies. Yes.

44

A BEAR WITH A SORE HEAD

Her Da knocks the protestant side off his egg with a tea-spoon, sets it aside and dips his bread into the soft yellow.

Her Ma says: "Waste not want not, protestant or catholic."

She blows on the white part to cool it and gives it to the babby, but the babby spits it out; "gicky gicky," he goes. Ma says it's a pity about him and the price of good eggs in the market. Da finishes his egg on the white catholic side, roots in his pocket for his penknife. Patti doesn't like the whites either. The nicest bit is the yellow runny part, between the protestant and the catholic side. He starts to carve his wooden block then, the penknife between his finger and thumb, like he's peeling a potato. He works away, until it starts to look roundy at the top like a head. He's at it forever, peeling and chipping, a tiny bit every day. The kids keep watching, but Da says nothing. He likes working with the wood and maybe he should've been a carpenter like his brother Willie, Patti thinks. They can't ask, what he's making, or he'll lose his concentration. Her Ma warns them: "Don't disturb him while he's happy," she says. What could it be? It looks like a little square statue. Her Da likes Saint Francis of Asissi, so it could be him in his brown habit, like the statue in the chapel, or it might be Saint Anthony, like the one in Adam and Eves. He prays to loads of statues.

The whole block shakes when her Da slams the front door; three flats above them, three flats either side. It's like an Irish earthquake, only it's happening in their flats, in Greek Street in Dublin. He doesn't like callers to the door.

"We don't want any loans," he says to the fat little Jew man with the curly moustache.

"We don't want no charity," to the Vincent De Paul people who go round at Christmas. They're not charity cases he tells them.

The Roomkeper's Society can go and shite! Her Ma can't make up her mind about Da; he's a bear with a sore head, he's as quiet as a church mouse, he's very holy, he's dilatory, he's never idle, he's soft underneath it all, he's a bloody scourge, he's no harm, his bark's worse than his bite, he's very good living, he has rosary beads, he gets oceans of novenas, he polishes his own shoes . . .

The Ma's yap and smoke in the courtyard. At the washlines, they rub their belly-bumps in circles. On bad humour days, they give out about their husbands; they're cranky as anything when they're fluthered. They're bloody scourges. Bears with sore bloody heads. Patti knows what they mean. When they're drunk, they kind of totter, like babbies learning to walk. They trip over their feet and stagger. They sing the drunken songs. They piss at the walls and they fight with the walls. They thump them and kick them. Sometimes, they go to the priest to get the special blessing. They make a pledge to the Sacred Heart; it's a promise not to drink. It might be six days or six weeks or six months. It might be forever. The important thing is that they can't touch a drop during that time, or they'll have to tell it in confession and do millions of penance, because it's a mortal sin to break the pledge.

Her Da didn't take a drink till he was well into his twenties. Ma says he was a late starter, but he was a fast learner. When he's drunk, his face goes shiny, his head hangs floppy like a new baby's and it looks like it might fall off his neck. His hands go trembly, holding the cup of tea, and his mouth goes a bit slobbery eating the white tripe he poaches in milk and onions. He gives out about everyone in the universe: her Ma, the kids, the Society man, Jew men moneylenders, the bloody Government, Dublin Corporation, the Russians. When he talks, it's all bokety, like the words get caught under his tongue. Sideways, his mouth says: "Gerrindabed! Whach you doin' up all hours?"

"I'm only keepin' Ma company," Patti tells him out straight. And he gives her a mean look. "Shuzzhup an go ta be-ed I said!"

Now that's an order and she better move pronto. Behind his back, she makes a face. In her head she tells him to shurrup. In her head: Shurrup! Shurrup!

In bed, she sticks her fingers in her ears. His portery voice goes through the kitchen door and through the walls. She wishes he'd shut up, because her ears are sore. Sometimes, it's like he'll never shut up and she has the waterworks. She hates the cold grey winter garden wall. The wall that never shuts up. Her Ma might come into their bed or she mightn't. If she does, she sits up in her slip and smokes. The room goes foggy and choky. Sometimes, they hear fights upstairs on the balconies, bottles coming down the rubbish chute, cats crying like babbies in the yard, the loud singing after the pubs. Sometimes she thinks she hears the headless coachman and the horse's hoofs galloping. He passes at twelve o'clock in the stagecoach. Sometimes there's a sound of footsteps in the flat and she wonders if it's Misses Reilly's ghost.

If they have a fight, you have to pretend not to hear. Everyone hates their Da. It's allowed. If she had a husband, he'd be like one of those telly husbands; say like Oliver in Green Acres. He'd have a business suit and a briefcase. He'd call her Ma darling or honey. He'd buy her flowers. They'd be madly in love. There'd be no secrets. They'd have a sports car and never have fights. They'd live in a house with flowers and grass. She'd have two spotless clean children, all dressed in the latest styles. Maybe they do horse riding and ballet and ice skating, like Bunty in the comic. They'd have a garage. It'd be dead neat.

A rossie her Da calls her. What's a rossie, she wonders and looks it up in the dictionary, but there's no rossie word. She asks the librarian in Capel Street Library, but she only puts up her bushy eyebrow and gives her a look. She never heard of it, she says. But maybe it's slang.

"A cheeky rossie," he says.

A gnat. What's that? It's what her granny calls her sometimes, when she's angry.

A ginnet is another name and Patti pictures a kind of bad fairy, with pointy ears and glasses. There's no ginnet in the dictionary either, only jennet, a type of ass or donkey. She's a noodle, if she breaks something like a cup or plate or a saucer. Children should be seen and not heard. Children should respect their elders. That's the rule on the northside. Sometimes her Ma says that children have to play too. In her Ma's place, with Da not there, there's no rules. It's like, they can tumble on beds, play cowboys and Indians on the chairs, talk with their mouths full, slurp, give backcheek. You're ok as long as you don't whinge, or stick out your tongue, or look too long in the mirror. That's not allowed because that's a sign of the devil.

Other times, her Ma says, that children have to be chastised, or else they'll run amuck. They use belts and canes and legs of chairs. It always happens out in the courtyard, so everyone can see. It's like they're watching a concert, with all the Ma's and Da's gawking over the balconies. It might start at one wall and end at the other. Or it might start at the bottom of the stairs and end at the top. Belts in the legs. Belts in the bum. Belts in the head. Belts everywhere. They call it a good hiding. It goes real quiet after a chastisement. You hear doors banging and glass shaking and it's like the Irish earthquake. Sometimes you hear sobs and screeches. Her Da doesn't give hidings, he only pretends to. It's a bit like when he says he's going to England, but doesn't. He always warns them that if they carry on, they'll all get put away to Letterfrack or Daingean or Artane. Patti knows that's worse than any hiding. You can get sent away easy: for robbing and mitching and cursing.

The men wear old-fashioned looking black leather belts with brass buckles. They never leave them off. It's like they can never go out without their black belts. Her Da's belt looks ancient and worn out. He says he'll take off his belt when he's drunk and that's supposed to mean big trouble. He half stands up. He opens the buckle. He stops. He fastens it again. Then he opens it again, all the way this time, just to frighten them. He starts to loosen it from his trousers. Sometimes he takes the belt off, flicks it in the air, like a cowboy with a lasso.

Her Ma says: "Put that belt back on, before ya break sometin'."

Then, he hangs the belt up, where everyone can see it, over the brass water pipe near the hot press, so it's on display like in a shop window. Ma says he has that bloody belt as long as she knows him and maybe it's time to get a new kind of modern belt.

45

A POISON DREAM

It all started with this dead dopey dream she had. The dream was full of the stupid Ten Green Bottles song. Only it was porter bottles and whiskey bottles, all in a row on top of this hill. She's in the Wild West. There's canyons and rocky mountains, a noise of cowboys and Indians. All the drunken bottles are in a line. It's like this cowboy picture, she saw on the Carlton. Patti is dressed in her Annie Oakley costume she got off Santy. She has a real gun and holster. On her finger, she twirls the gun like a real cowboy. She takes aim. She shoots at the bottles. She's a dead neat shot. They all get blasted one after another. All the pieces of broken glass explode in slow motion into the air. All the drink flows out. Every drop, down the rocky mountain, like a drunken brown waterfall. Then the bottles roll away, like they were never blasted. Here come the drunken outlaws, up the mountain. They're looking for their drink. Then she sees him. This medicine man, holding up a yellow square bottle he calls an elixir.

He says: "Listen up, ladies and gents, this elixir's a miracle cure fa all ya aches and pains, this here's betta than any whiskey."

He's the splitting image of the druggist in King Street. Same hair and face, only he's in this queer three- quarter length coat and bow tie with a top hat.

Patti wakes then. She has this brillo idea. She keeps thinking about the druggist. The druggist who was the old-fashioned medicine man in the dream. The druggist, who people say knows his stuff all right. She goes there for medicine for her granny every week. He's humpy, like Mike Nolan in the sweet shop, has a creased white coat, fuzzy yellowy hair. And his hands! Huge pinky hands with dark stained fingers. He mutters to himself all the time. Out back, he makes the medicine and through a half-door he shouts out questions:

What kind of a cough is it her granny has? Hard or soft? Dry or phlegmy? Short or long? Then she has to try to describe it; it's sorta soft and sorta hard and sorta phlegmy, it's greenish, or yellowish, when granny spits it up and she nearly chokes. He peeps out the half door, scratches the back of his head and disappears again. People at the counter keep ringing the brass bell for attention. There's a big place out back, a kind of hardware stores, a gorgeous mixed up smell; paraffin and turpentine, medicine and glue. It makes her nice and dizzy while she waits. Her Ma always says no wonder that druggist in King Street is on cloud nine all the time.

Patti always has a good look around. It's packed. There's stuff everywhere: jars of barley sticks and cough sweets, tins of Zubes, cards of elastic bands and hairclips and rollers. All the baby stuff is behind the counter on wooden shelves: Vaseline and Borax powder and gripe water, glycerine, honey and lemon. Bluestone. On a lower shelf there's Astral cream and Nivea cream and Cutex nail-polish remover. Under the counter in a glass case, there's more stuff: different kinds of smelly ointment, coloured glass bottles. There's a huge black Coty L'aimant perfume bottle on top of a red satin box. Advertisements up on cardboard stands; medicine for indigestion and heartburn and constipation. A new cure for warts you have to paint on to burn them and she's glad she doesn't have warts. It's here you buy the Brutlax chocolate that gives you the brutal pains and makes you go to the toilet. It's the splitting image of the purple wrapper of Cadburys Dairy Milk. A sign says:

KEEP ON THE GO WITH BRUTLAX.

The druggist sells poison as well; the reddish pink powder her Da put down in their old house for the rats. She saw an old woman buying a brown bagful once. The woman said she had rats in her back yard the size of alley cats. He'd sell her some, she thinks if she let on they have rats. She could say they have rats from the fish market in their coalhole, or under the floorboards. Yes. Her Ma might put it in Da's tea; Da'll go asleep happy as Larry. Up in Heaven, he'll have the peace and quiet like he wants. Up in Heaven the babies don't whinge. Up in Heaven, she supposes, everyone has the pledge. No one gets drunk. Da'd go straight to Heaven for deffo, because of all the Messengers he reads and all the masses and novena's he gets. Her Ma says if she had a penny for all the novenas Da went to, she'd be a very rich woman. Another thing is that her Da wouldn't mind. He'd see Olive Elizabeth and John Michael and his own little brother Pappi. So it wouldn't be a sin. Would it?

Her Ma chases her around the table when she tells her about her idea, catches her and drowns her head with holy water, like a baby getting christened. Then she tries to push the Lourdes holy water bottle down her throat and nearly chokes her.

"Jesus Mary and Joseph. Do you want to get us all taken? "

Em; no she doesn't. She only wanted to make Da happy and Ma happy and all the kids and the babbies in heaven. Ma smokes all her butts. Says the devil is never far away.

Maybe it was a bad idea. Maybe her brother was right, when he said she was dead nutskies. Maybe she'd go to hell and roast like a chicken, only she'd never get cooked. She has to think of something else. The poison dream only happened after he started throwing the plates of dinner at the wall again. Her Ma had his dinner on a glimmer on the gas stove, fried liver and mashed potatoes, OXO gravy and onions. He was dead late, his face shiny and his legs wobbly. It was all black in the pan, the pointy bits of liver at the edges. The gravy all gone and the mashed potatoes like slushy snow stuck to the pot.

"What's this?" he goes, holding up a spiky piece of liver.

"What does it look like? It's sheeps' liver. The best out of Steins."

"Sheeps' liver is it?"

The first bit hits the wall over the chimney like a brick; another bit flies like a rocket over their heads and just misses her Holy Communion photograph for the second time. It hits the ceiling: SMASH! Lands near the pram. And then the whole plate crashes into smithereens. Onions on the floor, pieces of smashed plate. Her Ma on her knees trying to clean it up. The whole lot of them with the waterworks.

It's only a sin if you do it. She wouldn't. Not the poison in-anyway. It was just a crazy idea, like something out of a story-book. It wasn't real.

Her Ma says her Da's a scourge sometimes, but it's only the drink talking.

"How can drink talk?" Patti asked.

"It makes your tongue wag. Ya say things you don't mean."

"Like what?"

"I don't know. Things. Givin' out things. Stupid things you're sorry for after."

Then she tells her one of her graveyard stories. They used to go to the graveyard. A lot. It was when they were court-ing. Ma sat on the crossbar, holding the spade sideways along the bike. Da cycled up to Glasnevin Cemetery every week. He used to tidy up the grave and say a few prayers. He wanted to stay there all night. He squatted down at the side of the grave. Hours they'd be up there in the cold graveyard and it got pitch dark and then Ma'd be afraid of her life. Da had a torch in his pocket for emergencies. Ma didn't like graveyards. Her Ma wasn't Ma then. Her name was Maura. She liked dancehalls and good times. Da was a bit shy. All Maura wanted was a good time. Back then she had a waistline like Olive Oyl, who's Popey's girlfriend, lovely black hair, same as she has today. And her skin! People remarked it was very clear. Every Saturday, up at the top of the hill, she got the tram out to Dun Laoghaire for the dance. Her and her pals always sat on the upper deck to get a good view of the whole city.

"Good times, those," Ma says, "happy happy days."

She looks sad when she says: happy happy days, like it's a million miles away.

It was a secret and it wasn't a secret. It was his little broth-er Pappi in the grave. Da was supposed to be watching him in Dominick Street where they lived in a tenement. Pappi was knocked up in the air by this speeding black car. Da was only a few feet away, playing pitch and toss with his friends. All the windows in the street opened up. One window. Then another. It was dead silent. The big black car skidded and screeched and sped off around the corner. All the windows banged shut then. A crowd gathered in the street and started to pray.

"Poor Pappi," Ma says.

He's lovely in the photo on granny's wall, with wavy dark hair. A face like an angel, everyone says. He has his own private grave in Glasnevin Cemetery. All alone up there he is. No company, like the babies in the Holy Angels. The neighbours carved a cross in the ground, on the very spot, where he died.

"You could see it still there, like a sad memory, " Ma says. "If you were to dig down under the tar they pored later on."

46

THE IRON CURTAIN

Everything is different behind the Iron Curtain. It's supposed to be where all the trouble is. The Iron Curtain is trillions of miles away. The Iron Curtain is frozen over.

"A freezin' bitter cold place;" her Da says.

Russians and Poles and Hungarians live behind the iron curtain. They have high boots and cross stony faces.

"Ya wouldn't want t'meet one in a dark alley," Da says.

"Are Hungarians always hungry?" Franey goes.

Is everything made of iron behind the Iron Curtain, like houses and buildings, tables and chairs? Patti wonders. And what about Ma's iron tablets; are they made behind the Iron Curtain?

"The Russians might blow us to kingdom come," her Da says, rubbing his hands together. He says they have special weapons and bombs. These new bombs can make your skin sizzle like a sausage in a pan. One minute we'd be here, the next we'd be gone. The world could end in a flash of lightening. There's this man sitting in a grey shed somewhere behind the Iron Curtain. All he has to do is press a red button and it's all over.

"It's the cold war," Da says, "between the Americans and the Russians."

They have spaceships. Sputnik was the first satellite. A Russian dog called Laika was sent up for experiments. The space ship travelled at 18000 miles per hour, Da said. He read all about it in the newspaper. A monkey was sent up another time. On granny's telly, they saw the monkey with the wires on its head and a knitted jumper to keep it warm. It put its hands up to try to pull off the wires.

"The Russians might start a war any day," Da says

He marches up and down the kitchen, like a soldier in his pretend boots. The kids try to imitate him, lifting their legs up high and marching beside him.

"The Wushians the Wushians," they say.

Da says if they attack America, then we're in for it. We'll get it next. A cloud of dust will come across the Atlantic Ocean, then across Ireland. We might see the gynormous cloud in the sky, like a big mushroom and Hey Presto! It's all over. We won't have time to bless ourselves. We won't have time to blink. Hot ashes will cover everything, cities and mountains, trees and rivers. Roche's Stores, Arnott's, the Dasiy Market. All gone! It'll be World War Three.

Ma says: "Shut up about the bloody Russians."

She's sick of the Russians and world wars. She's sick of hearing about atom bombs and H bombs and the iron curtain. She says she'll go melancholy if he doesn't shut up.

"Maybe we could all hide," Patti says, in the coalhole, or down the sewers or up the forty steps.

"The banshee is up there," Bernie says.

"Better the banshee than the bloody Russians," Ma goes.

"There's no use hiding," Da says. Then he's on about the Communists.

"The Communists will take over. It'll be the end of civilisation as we know it. Sure we'd be better off dead."

"The Wussians! The Wussians! The Wussians! The kids go.

In *Voyage to the Bottom of the Sea,* the submarine called Seaview makes an underwater sound, like a bloyink! Bloyink! It's supposed to be a nuclear spy mission by the Americans to stop World War Three. Jimmy's friend Kinger says it's Espionage. In the TV programme, Get Smart, a thing called a Cone of Silence comes down over Maxwell Smart and Ninety Nine. It's supposed to stop everyone hearing what they're saying, but they can't even hear themselves, so that's dead dopey, Patti thinks. Maxwell Smart has a phone in his shoe, but mostly it never works. Her granny says: "Spy this and spy that and sure, that talking horse Mister Ed on the telly'd make a better spy than Maxwell Smart."

A bit of outer space landed in someone's back yard in Duck Lane. They say it's a bit of a falling star. From the balconies, they saw it falling. Everyone was out searching. The woman in the house in Duck Lane showed them a jaggedy thing, like a big cinder, about the same size as a football. She's keeping it as a souvenir from space. Someone says it might be worth money some day, when them spaceships land on the moon. Then they're talking about the strange lights in the sky, before the star fell. It might be aliens from space, or maybe it's the bloody Russians on a spy mission. They might be planning an attack.

47

A SCRATCHED SUITCASE

It has creases and scratches like a spider web on the dingey lid. It looks old and worn out, like it's been all over the world. It smells cardboardy and musty. Outside it's tan with brass catches; inside it's green plaid. That first time she saw the suitcase, it was after they moved. It came out of the van with the table and chairs. She remembers it was full of stuff, when her Da opened it out; delf wrapped in newspapers, knives and forks, holy pictures, tools, fuses, a ball of twine, Da's shaving stuff. It's Da's going away case, in case he's going away. He keeps it ready under the bed. Just in case. He says he might go out foreign one of these days. It might be any day now. It could be tomorrow. He has plenty of ideas. He might go to England. He might join the Foreign Legion or the French navy. He might go to Africa and join the missions. And there's always the Congo. Sometimes he drags the suitcase out and leaves it in the hall and that's supposed to mean he's going away for deffo. One day, he must've forgot to lock it, so they opened it up and had a little peep inside. Someone had to stand on the bath board and keep watch from the lookout glass in the scullery, in case he was coming. There's Ma down on her honkers with the lid up. Here's all the kids, with their heads stuck in the suitcase.

Her Ma is flabbergasted. There's no clothes or shoes or going away stuff. There's nothing really, only little brown leather diaries, bundles of receipts, a few holy pictures, stacks of Sacred Heart Messengers, rolls of sticky tape, twine, a tin of three in one oil, and an old-fashioned biscuit box with a picture of a girl with curly hair like Shirley Temple.

"Where's all his luggage and goin' away stuff? " Patti says.

"He must be travellin' light. I suppose ya wouldn't want much on your back out in the Congo and sure the Foreign Legion'd give him the free uniform."

So they close the suitcase and stand it back where it was, against the wall beside the hall door. Then she warns them: There's to be no tattle tales, about open suitcases. That case was never touched. That's the rule.

"One of these days, I'll dump that battered yoke down the chute, along with all them Holy Messengers and that'll serve him right," she says.

Then she sings the drunken sailor song:

What would you do with the drunken sailor, what would you do with the drunken sailor, what would you do with the drunken sailor, early in the morning.

Then she says maybe it might be a good thing if their Da went on a slow boat to China. Patti knows her Da was meant to be a sailor, before he got hooked up into holy wedlock. He might've been a big shot in the navy, maybe even a captain.

Ma says: "The Navy is right."

But Da always says, it's never too late and he'll be gone from this place soon enough and that'll be the last they'll see of him. But soon never comes. He bangs the table with his fist. He says he's had enough of bloody Ireland and crying babbies.

"Go on so. Make sure and send us a post card," Ma says.

He gives out hell about the suitcase. He keeps on about it. He knew it was opened. There was stuff inside moved and the babby kept pointing at it and Franey kept staring at it. There's banging through the wall from next door.

"Some people has to be up early for work," the muffled voice shouts.

"The walls have ears," her Ma says, "and some people can't mind their own bloody business."

Soon means never and Da never goes away, so the scratched suitcase stays under the bed. It might be an antique some day, like the army medals in granny's drawer and the piece of outer space that fell into the yard in Duck Lane.

They see these lovely looking suntanned sailors in town, dressed like the one on the Players box, in their white bellbottoms and their cute little hats. Sometimes they have their arm around a girl. Sometimes they're in a bunch. Some of the girls go mad for sailors, but her Ma always says: "Never trust a sailor on leave. A sailor on leave can leave you in the halfpenny place. A sailor on leave can leave you in the lurch."

She's not sure what that means, but Patti wouldn't mind if her Da was a real sailor. She can imagine him, done up in the sailor suit on a huge ship. Maybe he's captain. She could tell them in school. They'd all be mad jealous. He'd send home stacks of money. Bring home fab presents from all over the world. And he'd hardly ever be home, only for about two weeks on leave. They'd have cake in the morning and cake in the evening and fish and chips for their supper every night.

48

SMELLY PHEASANTS

Her Da brings him home from the pub, this strange looking man with a funny hat. Ma clears a chair for him and makes him sit down. Da has bottles of stout under his arm in a brown bag. The man holds up two pheasants by the necks and throws them across the table.

"There Misses," he says.

Ma says: "Thanks very much. But you might want them for yourself."

No answer.

She picks up the pheasants by the necks, holds them away from her. She leaves them on the bath board on newspapers, with the heads hanging upside-down. In the scullery, she holds her nose with one hand and her stomach with the other. She tries not to look at the eyes.

The kids watch the upside-down eyes. The babby goes down on his hunkers, touches the head with his finger.

"Guckee duckee," he says.

"He'll bite ya," Anna says.

Her Ma pulls him out by the arms and straps him into the go-car. He kicks her in the belly.

"Guckeeey duckeeey!" he bawls. She sticks the soother in his mouth.

Then they're all around the man. He has on a tan suede coat with a sheepskin collar and a hat with hanging-down ears. He pats Franey's head and says: "That's a grand lad." Franey smiles up at him, with his big blue eyes and pushes his fringe out of his eyes.

"Hello Misdor," he says. Anna pushes in closer with her elbows, then Bernie behind her. All they do is stare, especially at his funny hat.

"Have manners," Ma says, "and stop gawkin' at the man."

The man smells like Carton's chicken factory and Powers Gold Label. He might give them money or he mightn't. Da opens the stout with a corkscrew. Then they drink out of the bottles.

"That man is a bit of a quare hawk," Ma says in the scullery. She means he's a bit nutskies. Maybe she's right. He's very peculiar looking. Patti saw him before in the pub; he's one of her Da's culchie pals. Her Da told them he has a real hunting rifle. He goes on a shoot in the woods. He shoots pheasants and rabbits and sells them around the pubs. At the table, they talk man stuff. Ma offers him tea, but he says: "No thanks Misses." He drinks up fast, says he has a bit of business on the southside. Then he starts to bang his pockets. The kids keep watching. He roots down deep. He takes out coins and silver and throws them on the table.

"For the childer," he says and they all start to grab. Then they start to fight over who gets what, so Ma says she'll share it out after. Patti sees one half crown, two sixpences and loads of coppers.

Her Da makes a big fuss of the man going out the door. He opens the kitchen door wide for him, and then the hall door and you'd think he was a lord. The man does a salute at the hall door. All the kids wave after him.

In the scullery, Da starts on the pheasants. He rubs his hands together, rolls up his sleeves. He starts to pluck them first. They all want to help. Here they are, all plucking feathers, until it's a feathery heap on the floor. Off come the orangey brown feathers, until it's only bare skin. Then the heads: Chop! Chop! He goes with the sharp carving knife.

Ma says: "Sacred Heart!"

Then the legs. Chop! Chop! Chop! Chop! He cuts open the first pheasant. He pulls skin apart at the bum. He sticks his hand in and reefs out the guts. Inside the pheasant, it's all dark and bony. Here they are, all watching from the scullery door with pinched noses, their hands half over their eyes.

Oh the smell! There's a terrible smell all over the place: it's worse than Carton's Chicken factory, it's worse than rotten fish. Ma holds her stomach. She says: "Jesus!" Da gives her a look. Then she opens down the scullery window and takes deep breaths. Anna grabs the heads off the bath board.

"Smelly, Smelly," she says holding her nose.

Franey grabs the feet. "Stinky, Stinky," he says. They chase each other round the table: "Cluckety cluck! Cluckety cluck!"

"Guckee duckee! " the babby shouts.

In the scullery, there's blood all over the place. The guts are on newspaper on the bath board; it's Ma's job to roll them up in the newspapers and throw them down the chute. She looks away. She rolls them up real quick and runs out the door. Da steeps the pheasants in cold water in the basin. They'll make lovely pheasant stew tomorrow he says. Granny Connor says: "There's no nicer meat than pheasant and you wouldn't get the like in the Gresham Hotel."

Everyone wants to see the pheasants. Goo Chaney comes in to have a look. She says, she never tasted pheasant herself, but she'd like to and isn't it well for them, with a tasty feast like that for their dinner.

49

A CANARY

This day, Patti answers the door and there's these two young fellas standing there with a canary in a cage. Her Ma comes rushing out to see.

"Misses, d'ya wanta buy a canary?"

He holds up the cage and pulls back a check teacloth. There's the yellow canary, swinging on a little wood perch.

"A wha'?"

"A real canary, all the way from the Canary Islands."

"What would I want with a bloody canary? Have I not enough on me plate with this lot? "

"It tweets and it whistles. Misses."

"It can tweet all it wants."

The kids are all out. The babby tries to grab at the cage.

"Birdy birdy."

"Have youse anthin' more useful for sale; like plastic knickers or Vim or Dettol?"

"No. Only a canary. Misses, we don't want much for the canary. It'll sing songs for yeah. It knows tunes."

"What tunes?"

"Loads a tunes. It's very harmonious."

"Well make it sing a song then."

He covers up the cage with the teacloth.

"It only sings at night, before it goes to sleep. Like a nightin'gale."

"Do I look thick? Are youse coddin' me or what? "

"No."

"I'll give youse harmonious. Now get away with that yella thing in the name a God."

"Two and six is all we want for the Canary. Four bob for the cage as well and we'll throw in bird seed for nothin'."

"If I had two and six, it's not a bloody canary I'd spend it on."

243

She shoos them away. They watch them knock on every door in the flats. They see every door closing with a bang.

It's always the same on Fridays with sellers at the door. It might be jumpers or socks or lampshades or toilet rolls. There's knocks every minute. The Royal Liver, the Mater Hospital pools, the picture-frame man. Sometimes they pretend not to be in and hide in the back bedroom.

50

SHAN MOHANGI

It's a big story around town. They're all talking about it at the washlines and on the balconies. They're miming and making sign language. After mass, at the chapel gates, they're standing around in clusters, the men on one side, the women on the other. The women bless themselves over and over with holy water. They keep kissing the crosses of their rosary beads.

They say: "God between us and all harm."

They're saying it's the worst crime Dublin ever saw. It's on the front of all the newspapers, about this black man who chopped up a woman. Somewhere in a flat in Harcourt Street, this lovely young girl was murdered. The police are supposed to know who it was.

"He's a black forener, with a big long foren name."

Her Ma with her head stuck in the Herald.

"He's called Shan Mohangi. God protect us, but there's a name!"

The look on Ma's face, you'd think she saw a ghost. She bites her thumb nail. Says:

"Another tragedy. What's the world comin' to at all?"

She reads out a line from the Herald:

"A woman passing smelt a strange odour and raised the alarm. The dis mem bered re mains were discovered soon after."

"Oh Sacred Heart, protect us!" she keeps saying. She reads the whole article, every single word.

The black man cut the girl's body up after he murdered her and dumped it into a barrel. Then he tried to burn the body in a furnace in a basement shed.

"That's a dangerous place in-anyway," she says. "Over be Baggot Street Bridge. The ladies of the night frequent that vicinity. The unfortunates and the men in the cars who stop for them."

Patti heard them talking about the unfortunates before. The unfortunates are out there, on the quays and up laneways. They go in cars with men for money. They wear black knickers and red lipstick. They're saying that maybe she was one of the unfortunates, the poor girl in Harcourt Street who got sliced up. It's not just her Ma who's afraid. Everyone is. They keep saying:

"That blackie is some butcher, chopped her up, like meat, cut her up into ribbons, the place must've been a blood bath!"

Some are saying: maybe that girl might've been in trouble or in the family way, but she didn't deserve a death like that. The men prefer to talk about it in the pub. The pubs fill up with their noisy talk: how the black man had the opportunity and the motive to carry out the crime, how he had access to the instruments of torture, like saws and knives and hatchets, how he was well used to cuttin' up bodies, him being a medical student. How these black fellas in high places are getting educated in that posh College of Surgeons, at the expense of the Irish taxpayers; they might as well take the money out of their pockets as they're at it. How he'll get away with it, because of his connections to government and royalty. And what was that girl doing anyway, with a black man? Could she not've found herself a nice Dublin fella for Godsake?

Uncle Willie says: "If he wasn't a black man, there wouldn't be such an uproar," but granda says: "black man or white man, he should be hanged."

After dark the courtyard is empty, except for the Ma's out on the balconies watching. The red glow of their cigarette butts moving in the dark. They're talking in whispers. It's dead quiet, the skaters, the trolley pushers, the skippers, all gone in early. Everyone is grounded. They can't go outside the gates or into town or near the quays. They can't play in the handball alley or the Mary Street Park. All of a sudden, the streets are spooky and everywhere they keep seeing dark shadows. People say the town is gone to hell and Dublin will never be the same again after a tragedy like that. The black man is supposed to be locked up, but there might be more like him out there.

"Hang Mohangi! Hang Mohangi! " everyone is chanting.

They say he'll get off, because he's in the know. He's supposed to be a respectable medical student at the College of Surgeons with plenty of money. His family are well to do, connected to Government people and Royalty. Her Ma can't get over it.

"To think a thing like that could happen in Dublin town. It's like somethin' that'd happen out in the Congo."

Her nerves are gone. Every day she drowns them with holy water and says their guardian angel prayer in case they forget. She tells them to keep an eye out for dark shadows and dark strangers.

"That Mo Hangi should be hanged!" she says.

"He'll walk," Da says. "He'll get a pardon or something; then they'll send him back to wherever he came from and that'll be the end of that."

He straightens the Herald out, rolls it up tight and stuffs it into his pocket.

"There's more important things happenin' in the world," he says.

"Like what?" Ma says, but he doesn't answer.

Patti knows what her Ma means. She joins in and sings the Hang Mohangi song, with the others. She thinks Shan Mohangi should be hanged, even if he is a medical student, even if he's well to do. It's hard, but she tries to imagine the murdered girl in the basement. Poor Hazel. All the bits of her, in the barrel, all that blood and bone and stuff! She was supposed to be his girlfriend. How could he do it? He must've had saws and knives and hatchets, like a butcher. She wonders what was she wearing. Had she got on a mini-skirt, or high heels? Was she nice-looking? Why did he kill her in-anyway?

Everyone wants to see the house where it happened. They want to sing the Hang Mohangi song in Harcourt Street. So they go for a ramble, her and Vera and this other girl. It's not that far. They know the way from Stephen's Green to Harcourt Street. There's a small crowd gathered further up the street. Some of them look like newspaper reporters. There's tape tied around a part of the street, with this policemen on guard duty with his hands behind his back. A woman tells them, the scene has been closed off. Something to do with a new lead that the police have. They can't go any further. Patti gets a shivery feeling down her back. It's only down the street, on the other side of the road. Number 95, it said in the Herald. There's a pub and a café beside the house. Vera says, she can smell something peculiar and there might still be blood, maybe even pieces of her body still in the barrel. They might as well go home. She doesn't like the look of that street in-anyway. It's dead spooky. And the unfortunates and the men in the cars might be here.

Her Ma doesn't know she went to Harcourt Street, or she'd have blue murder. Her Ma says there's evil in the world and the devil is never far away. You'd have to watch your back all the time. You'd never know when he might appear out of nowhere. Since it happened, it's like there's this dark shadow of the black man everywhere. In the dark you wouldn't see him, except for his teeth and the whites of his eyes, he'd have his arm around your neck before you knew it. Then he might cut off your head and your arms and legs and you might end up like poor Hazel in the barrel.

51

THE DAIRY

"No cigarettes, or cakes or sweets," Mary shouts over the counter. "Until all your slates are cleared."

Her deep voice comes out of the dairy door, like a loudspeaker and you can hear it all along the queue. It's Friday and the queue for the Dairy is out the door, past the post office and around the corner. Most of them have messagebags, a few have empty go-cars and one or two have wood pull trolleys. Someone behind says:

"For Godsake, she must be in one of her humours again. It's a pity about her."

The queue moves up a bit. Patti holds tight onto Anna's hand.

"Ma'll go mad with no smokes."

"Can we get chocla sweets?" Anna says.

"No, or biscuits either."

"Why-i?"

"That's the why. Now don't start!"

Anna does a little girly dance on her tippy-toes. She has on her bold cheeky face.

"I'll run away."

"No ya won't."

"Was that Mary from the dairy shoutin'?"

"Who else dya think it was? Didn't ya hear what she said? No sweets!"

The Dairy is on the southside, near the Liffey, around the corner from granny's. Her Ma has a bill there. Her own special page in the brown bill-book that sits on the counter beside the weighing scales. The book is as wide as the counter when it's opened. The customers' names are in the margin, with the messages they bought and the prices scribbled beside them. The sum is done under the blue line for the balance. People are supposed to settle up on Friday, or Saturday or even Sunday. Some people never settle up and that's when a red biro mark goes under their name. After a few weeks, the shopkeeper has to make house calls. House calls means trouble.

House calls means, Miss Lidon scouting around the streets looking for your address. House calls means Miss Lidon banging down your door with her huge fists. House calls means Miss Lidon with her sleeves rolled up, with her hairy arms showing. House calls means Miss Lidon, with the brown bill book under her other arm. She opens it. She points to the red line. She talks about overheads and undercharging and bad debts and rent. She talks legal stuff, like a solicitor, that no one understands.

"She's like the Collector General," her Ma says, hiding behind the scullery curtain.

"Shopkeepers are rotten with money, but they'd follow ya to Timbuktu for a halfpenny. That's how they have all their money."

Sometimes, you can smell everything from outside: fresh cakes, ham, Sunlight- soap, Mary's dinners cooking in the parlour. Today, the tide is out, and all you can smell is the rotten-egg smell of the Liffey. It's cold. A snippy breeze up the quays.

"Mary Mary from the Dairy, " Anna sings, with her face stuck up to the window.

"Shut up or she'll hear ya."

There's boxes of Black Magic and Milk Tray in the window, tins of Bachelors beans, stacked high on top of one another, bags of Flahavan's oatlets. Oxos. Around the edges, Mary has placed jars of sweets, tins of Picnic salmon and sardines. The slide door in the window goes across and you can see the hefty shape of Miss Lidon, her long arm, reaching for a tin of beans. There's two of them serving, a tall horsey one and a small blocky one with a sideways walk. Miss Lidon has wiry brown hair in a side split. On one side, it falls into her eyes and she keeps pushing it back with the back of her hand.

"She has big hands for a woman," her Ma says. "Very big feet too, God bless the mark."

She wears a brown flowery, crossed-over smock and brown sandals. She's wide as well as tall. In the Dairy, when she turns around, her back is like a brown flowery wall.

Through the brown glass in the parlour door, you can see the shapes of the two of them. Back there, they sit at the fire if the shop is empty. Sometimes they have the radio on loud, listening to Dear Frankie letters. The door makes a jangle sound when someone comes into the shop, but they don't always hear it. They drink tea out of white enamel mugs while they serve. They always have their mouths full of something. Miss Lidon always has half a sandwich in one hand and a pencil in the other. Mary eats chunks of cheese.

The queue moves up and at last they're inside. They're up to their eyes; Miss Lidon especially, who's adding up a bill. She keeps getting it wrong and starting again. The bill book is open on the counter. Mary says, "YES?" Patti hasn't got a list, so she tells her what her Ma wants: Butter and sugar and tea, slices or corned beef and cheese, a tinna peas, ten players, fruit slices, a halfa pounda Marietta.

"Wait a minute." Mary says. Over Miss Lidon's shoulder, she has a look in the bill-book. She wets her finger and turns pages. She squints down at her Ma's special page. She looks up from the book.

She says: "Tell your mammy no cigarettes or biscuits or cakes."

Patti shrugs her shoulders.

Anna says: "We want Chocla sweets! "

Mary gives her a look.

Patti gives Anna a dig in the arm.

"Ma says she'll pay on the double next week."

Miss Lidon looks up from the book.

"She didn't settle last week either."

"Well treble then."

Mary scrunches her eyebrows and gives Patti a long look. She whispers something to Miss Lidon. Miss Lidon is up to her eyes with the bills. She's lost her track now, she says, wetting her thumb and turning back the pages. Mary thinks for a minute. She turns and goes to the butter churn. She starts on the country butter first. She twists the wooden handle. She scoops up the butter into a messy mush between the paddles. She slaps it and bashes it and wallops it. She's trying to smooth it now. She's looking for a neat little quarter shape. After forever, she puts it in the greaseproof paper. She weighs it. Takes a bit back. Wallops it back into shape again. Wraps it. The sugar is loose in a big cardboard box on the floor. She scoops out the sugar into a brown paper bag. She weighs it and closes the bag like an envelope at the top. She cuts slices of tin beef from the block under the glass cover. There's a good few people in the shop behind them, waiting to get served. Anna grabs a fistful of sugar from the box, licks it off her hand like fizz. Spills the rest on the floor and makes a sugar-slide. She rubs her foot back and forth until it crackles.

"I'll swing for you in a minute," Patti says, pulling her over by the sleeve, through the queue of people. Anna pulls away, starts to climb on the counter. She tries to reach her hand into a jar of chocolate sweets beside the cash register.

"Gimme them!" she says.

Miss Lidon says: "Get her down off that counter quick!"

"Stop messin' I said. You're a little demon."

She won't listen. She keeps swinging out of the counter. All she wants are chocolate sweets.

There's a glass cabinet of cakes on one side. The biscuits are under the counter in boxes with glass lids. They can see mikado, custard creams, kimberly and chocolate gold grain.

Miss Lidon scratches her head, blows out hard and closes the book with a snap. She climbs up the stepladder to get the peas.

"Looka her big feet," Anna says. "Looka her sangals."

"Shut up. She'll hear ya."

Huge feet, in brown leather sandals, on the fourth step. Miss Lidon is not wearing stockings. Her Ma says Miss Lidon's feet are like canal barges and she should be working for Guinness's, instead of the Dairy.

Anna sees the biscuits. She keeps looking at the chocolate gold grain. She squats down on her hunkers, puts her nose near the glass lid.

"Get back up here. Now!"

"I'm on'y lookin'."

Patti knows, in half a second, she'd have that box raided, be out the door and halfway down the quays with her arms full of chocolate gold grain. She hauls her over and holds her by the arm. Mary is cutting Craft cheese at the top counter, with the wire cutter; she keeps breaking bits off and nibbling like a big white mouse. Mary has purplish veins on her cheeks, her hair is silvery white, with a grown out perm. It's dead neat, when there's only one of them serving, if the other one has to go out the back for briquettes. That's when they can sneak fingers of cream from the cakes in the cabinet, or lumps of chocolate from the éclairs. It's dead easy. The mad kids take things sometimes, when their backs are turned. They put stuff up their jumpers and down their trousers.

Miss Lidon steps back down with the peas. Takes her pencil from behind her ear. She bangs the tin down on the counter. They see the light brown hairs on the front of her arms. She writes everything down in the bill book: the butter, the sugar the cheese and the corned beef. She puts it all in a bag then.

She says: "Tell your Mammy to come over herself during the week. Or I might have to make a house call."

Her Ma is disgusted when Patti tells her there's no smokes or cakes. She says it's about time she took her business elsewhere. The Dairy is not the only shop in town and there's plenty of shopkeepers on the look out for new business.

52

MARY'S QUALITY DRAPERS

Her Ma stares in the window of Mary's shop. You'd know by her that she wants something. It's that want look in her eyes: kind of lonely, kind of sad. First she looks at the babies' stuff: bonnets and matinee coats, romper suits and frilly dresses. Then the other stuff for the boys: shorts and sloppy joes and S belts.

"Plenty of style," she says, her eye moving up to a confirmation dress on a hanger in the doorway.

"Will we go in?" Patti says, but she keeps staring at the dress. There's confirmation stuff for boys and girls hanging at both sides of the doorway, flannel grey suits with short trousers, a pink nylon dress with a white underskirt. It won't be that long now till Patti's confo.

"That's a very showy shade of pink," she says.

"Yeah. It's not that nice."

"Very plain too. Your Aunt Jinny'd make nicer with a few yards of nylon."

Mary's Quality Drapers is across the road from the Father Matthew Hall, around the corner from the Richmond Hospital. Mary sells everything, Ma says, from knicker elastic to hair ribbon. In summer, the shop has a cellophane blind inside the two small windows, so that everything is turned yellow. Her windows are always decked out with bonnets, matinee coats, booties, vests, rugs, frocks, blouses, nylons, bras, corsets, confirmation clothes, hats and gloves.

They can see Mary's tall shape in there through the window, a measuring tape around her neck. She's always chatting away in her nice soft voice to customers:

"Oh that's very nice indeed, fits you to a T Misses. Maybe a bit off the hem. Yes. Could do with taking in an inch as well."

She's always busy busy busy, on the ladder, at the drawers, in the stock room.

Outside and in the doorway, it's crammed with stuff hanging up: coats, dresses, two-piece costumes, shop smocks, bibs. Up a step, inside the door and the nice new- clothesy smell, the place full of more stuff hanging up, on rails, behind the counter, from the ceiling. And you have to go in between them, like washing on the clotheslines. There's rows of wooden drawers behind the counter. In them, nappies, knickers, suspenders, socks, slips, S belts, petticoats and socks. Under the counter, a glass case showing the very latest in lace and satin christening robes. There's romper suits for boys, frilly dresses for girls. Nylon. Seersucker. Poplin. Gingham. Cotton. Shower of Hail.

There's a line of more drawers along the walls, with little knobs on them, small ones and big ones and middling ones. Mary is always opening them, pulling things out, and looking for sizes. She roots and upends the drawer if she can't find your size. She wouldn't let it get the better of her.

"Wait! I might have it in stock. I'm sure I have."

Then, up she climbs on the stepladder to the higher drawers. You can see the ladder wobbling and Mary's long legs, with her good court shoes.

"Would you mind holding that ladder for me Misses, only, it's a bit shaky? What size was that you wanted Misses?"

"Size forty two Mary, with wide elastic."

The shop fills up while she's on the ladder.

"A half a dozen good terry nappies. Greenhills if you have them."

"Misses, I'll be with you in two ticks."

"Wouldja have a man's vest, size forty- two, and a pair of Interlock long john's for the oulfella?"

"Strong workin' socks?"

"Four pairs of plastic knickers?"

"A binder for a new baby? Two inch satin hair ribbon, powder blue, enough for plaits?"

"An elastic stocking for varicose veins."

Mary's face, all red from the heat of the shop, climbing down the ladder, folding and wrapping, opening up her book, making up the bill on the counter.

In at the back, there's a swing-mirror behind a screen. More racks of clothes hanging along the wall under plastic covers. You can pick something out and try it on behind the screen. She takes deposits. She has weekly rates on very easy terms. Her Ma says Mary is refined; she's tall and thin, with long arms and legs, she has brown wavy hair she gets done in the hairdressers.

On Saturdays, the shop gets crowded and smoky and you can hardly move in there. It's mostly nylons and white ankle socks she sells for mass. Patti goes to Mary's for the nylons. The nylons are loose in the stocking drawer. Mary holds one up to demonstrate and it's like a real leg flattened out: toe, heel, leg, knee, fat dark bit at the top where the suspenders go. She goes through the shades then, dark brown and mid brown, tan and light tan. Patti tells her, it's the light shade her Ma wants, not the dark bulletproof tan.

"Oh that's right. Flesh Tone. Yes, I should've remembered."

She takes out another stocking, measures the leg with her tape measure.

"Yes that's about your Mammy's size all right."

She folds two nylons and wraps them in white tissue paper.

"Does she need anything else, ribbon or elastic or shoe-laces?"

"No. That's all."

"How's your Mammy?"

"All right."

"Well, is she?"

"Yeah. I s'pose so."

"And your granny?"

"Ok. A bit wheezy."

"Oh. Tell her to mind herself."

"Ok."

"Right so. There's a good girl."

It cost's one and eleven for the nylons. They're from the very best hosiery factory in Blackhall Place. Made from the finest nylon. They won't ladder if her mammy minds them. Patti knows her Ma won't mind them. They'll probably ladder after the first wear; go to smithereens, with the babby always climbing up her legs. She's allowed to browse if she wants. She likes to look around, smell the lovely new clothes smell. Mary doesn't mind, as long as she doesn't pull the stuff off the rails or mess. She sells wedding outfits for the mother of the bride, the dresses and coats to match, in a lovely new crease proof material called crimplene, and the loose floaty flowery dresses for the grannies. You see them in there, trying on stuff in front of the swing mirror, behind the screen and the laughs of them in there. Mary shouting over the screen:

"Are youse girls all right for sizes?"

Her Ma likes Mary. She likes the way you can pay her by degrees and the way she wouldn't follow you to Timbuktu for payment, not like some shopkeepers she knows. Throw her a few bob every week to keep her happy. It's lovely stuff she sells. And not too dear either.

At communion or confirmation time, you wouldn't get in the door with the queue. Mary going running in and out the back, up and down the ladder, measuring and cutting and opening and closing drawers with her hip.

"I'll get to everyone eventually, no panic girls."

"Mary. Is that confirmation dress from America?"

"Is that lace hand stitched?"

"I don't want common stuff on my young one."

"Did ya get in the cancan knickers in a nine to ten?

"Is there wool in them vests?"

"I want boys wool knee socks."

"I need a dark red dicky bow for my Johnny's confo."

"Mary. I want somethin' very uncommon for my Concepta. Maybe, a bit of embroidery anglaise."

"Would you have a camel hair travelling coat, for a young one with cork buttons and a belt?"

"Now ladies ladies, we mightn't have the Paris fashions, but we have the very next best thing. I've lovely wool coats just after coming in from the Highlands in Scotland. I say, you won't get the likes in the Gay Child."

She turns the go-car around, has one more look at the baby stuff, says:

"We better go."

257

"Will we go in for a while Ma, have a little look. Mary won't mind?"

"No. It's gettin' late. Your Da'll be in for his tea."

They go the long way home. They stop at Stokes to get cigarettes. It's dark inside the shop, a blind half pulled down the window like there's a funeral on. Miss Stoke wears her hair in a bun, a high fat black bun her Ma calls a topknot. She has cheekbones. A long chin. Wears a blue check nylon shop smock with a zip up the front. There's nothing in the window, except dinged empty cornflakes boxes, stacked on top of one another, and a few dead flies. Inside, there's blue and white lino on the floor, a smell of soap and sugar. It's the same with the shelves; hardly anything on them. People don't go in there much, except to buy cigarettes. Miss Stoke is nervy. She has a high shaky voice. Her Ma says she's flighty. On the counter, there's a glass cake cover, with a few stale looking cakes; outside the counter, there's half-empty biscuit tins.

A tall thin man looks out through the parlour door. He's supposed to be her brother, but some people say brother is right. The kids from the flats throw stones and the window got broke a few times. She says she'll tell the guards. Poor Miss Stoke has a little cry behind the counter. She says they have her heart broke and her nerves on edge. She stands at the half open door. She holds her face.

"Goway!" She says in her shaky voice and the kids put on the culchie voice:

"GOWAY GOWAY!"

She might or she mightn't be the whole shillin. Her Ma says that it's the bloody kids has her demented, God help her. She warns them, before she goes in, not to scourge that woman.

"She might suffer with her nerves. She might have a steel plate in her head."

"Stokey stokey stokey!" Anna shouts when she's outside the shop, but Miss Stoke doesn't hear her.

53

THE SHOP WITH
NO COUNTERS

This cheeky young fella with a fat jumper is selling around the doors.

"D'ya want any Rinso, Brillo or soap Misses?"

First she says no, then she changes her mind.

He holds up his jumper.

"Let's see that soap. Is that Sunlight?"

She sniffs the soap, holds it up to her nose to make sure it's Sunlight.

"Two packs for a shillin' Misses."

"I hope that's not hot stuff?"

"Nope."

He pulls down his jumper again.

"Ok. If youse come back after six, I'll take two."

That's when they see them, all the other young fellas with the fat jumpers. Here they are coming in the gate. They start knocking at the first few flats, number one, two and three. They're taking things out of their jumpers: Jacobs biscuits, Lyons tea, packets of Knorr soup.

"Where'd they get all that stuff?" Ma says to the young fella.

"Oh Missus, there's this new shop downtown."

"A new shop. Where?"

"Down past Mary Street. It's called Powers."

"Powers. Never heard of it. Is it a cu' price?"

"No. You can take things, there's no counter."

"Mother of God."

She blesses herself.

"I swear t'God Misses."

He crosses his neck with his thumb.

"We got loads of stuff free. No one stops you. Honest."

People are saying it might be some gimmick to attract new customers. Everyone wants to see the shop with no counters.

Her Ma sends Patti down to investigate with Anna and Bernie. They cross at Capel Street through slow traffic. They pass the Dolls Hospital and Mary Street Park. They were right. There it is. A brand new shop. It's huge. She can't remember what was there before. She thinks it was a pram shop that was closed down for ages. Now it has plate glass windows and doors. There's signs up, with all the special opening offers marked in red: knorr soup, Lyons tea, Kellogg's cornflakes. Two packets of Marietta biscuits for the price of one. Inside, it's huge. There's wire baskets in a stack at the door, shelves full of stuff, with prices sticking up on white cards. A little market garden full of vegetables in a corner. A long lying down fridge full of ice cream and fish fingers and peas. A long strip of lights along the ceiling. There's a girl at a cash register down the back and a small queue of people waiting with baskets. There's music coming out of the ceiling or the wall. It's true what that young fella said. You could take anything and walk out easy peasy. It'd be a cinch.

They have a walk around. The bread is on the left, on a long wood shelf: sliced pans and turnovers and batch loaves. There's loose cakes on square trays underneath. Anna's eyes are like marbles. Patti warns the two of them not to touch anything. In the next aisle, there's tins of beans and peas, jars of beetroot and bottles of vinegar. A smaller fridge holds butter and cheese. There's soap, shaving stuff, toilet rolls, bleach and pine. There's a few kids looking around. The word is spreading fast. They're coming up from the other side of town, from East Wall and Sheriff Street.

"Them young fellas must've robbed the place blind," Ma says when they tell her about Powers. She's flabbergasted when she sees it for herself the next day. She can't get over the open shelves and the low prices and the special offers.

"Who'd believe it? Everything in the one shop. A shop where you could get all your messages at once if you had the money."

Her Da says it won't last. People don't want to buy everything in the one shop? But Ma thinks they might. It'd save on shoe leather and time and money. The market dealers say this kind of place could do them out of business and they might have to protest to Dublin Corporation. Have they not enough competition with Moore Street, without new inventions like supermarkets?

54

MADE IN CHINA

Uncle Willie says it's a g sign of the times, but the old days are finished. The whole concept of shopping, as we know it, is changing before our very eyes. He says the supermarket is one thing, but the walkaround store is the next big thing. It will take over from places like Woolworth's and Hector Grey's, where they still have old-fashioned counters. Granda ruffles his newspaper. Says it's all cheap imports and it will probably do away with the street traders at Christmas. Granny says it won't; not in her lifetime. The street dealers in Henry Street would never stand for it, no more than the dealers in the Daisy Market would, without putting up a fight. Da says Hector Grey has the toy market cornered and there'd be no competition from walkaround stores. Willie says Hector Grey is finished.

Since it opened, it's always packed. The new walkaround store is every ones favourite shop. It's near the Dolls Hospital, next to the handbag and umbrella shop. You can buy anything in there: pot scrubbers, toilet rolls, soap, candles, plastic tablecloths, toys, delf, tumblers, picture frames, mousetraps and ornaments. You go in. You walk around. The owner will only allow them in one at a time. They're not supposed to touch anything. You'll get put out if you do. If you break something, you have to pay. The first time they go in, the owner follows them and watches them in case they try to rob something. There's wire baskets full of stuff outside the door, there's buckets and spades and swimming tubes hanging up. They see this young fella getting chased out the door with something under his coat. He turns down a side lane into Wolfe Tone Street and drops whatever he robbed. It crashes into smithereens on the ground. It's a flowerpot or a vase, made of white delf with red flowers.

There's plastic figures that are supposed to be Action Man.

Jimmy says: "No way is that Action Man. The real Action Man costs a bomb in Clery's. The real Action Man has a wood box under his foot to store his army kit."

There's skinny dolls that are all the fashion. There's one called Wendy, with a brown flick and fringe. The store salesman says she's every bit as good as that Sindy doll they're all raving about. Wendy is very big in England, he says. He has her at a knock down price; he has everything at a knock down price. How many paydays would it take to buy Wendy, Patti wonders? No Trigger bars or Macaroon bars or Smarties for how many months to save up?

Uncle Willie says: "They're all cheap imitations, mass produced, for a mass market, imported from China for a quick profit."

Everything in the store has "Made in China" on the cardboard box. Made in China means cheap.

There's a long queue down Mary Street for the Mary Poppins umbrellas. The walk- around store has them before everyone else.

"More cheap imitations from China," Willie says, "And an umbrella factory only around the corner." Granda says it's disgraceful and no wonder the country is backward. Everyone thinks they're Mary Poppins. Everyone is running round with their umbrellas up like they might take off and fly. They're all tripping and falling over. In her Ma's place they're jumping off the backs of the beds with the black umbrella she calls a gamp.

"Put down that gamp quick, before we're all struck down with years of bad luck!" she says. She grabs the umbrella and hides it. No umbrellas up in the house. That's the rule on the northside and the southside. In the flats, they're jumping off the stairs with their umbrellas up. They heard that this young one in Pimlico broke her two legs when she jumped off a high wall, because she thought she was Mary Poppins.

"That Mary Poppins has all the kids gone mad," Ma says.

"That Mary Poppins has a lot to answer for," granny Connor says.

"That Mary Poppins is makin' that walk around salesman in Mary Street a small fortune," granda says.

It's all because of the film that was on in the Adelphi. In the film, Julie Andrews was playing Mary Poppins. Mary had special powers. Mary went flying over the chimneys with her magic umbrella. The boys think she's thick, but the girls think she's dead brill. Up Thomas Street, the dealers are selling the Mary Poppins umbrellas but they're supposed to be fake. The dealers in the Daisy market are doing a roaring trade selling plastic coloured umbrellas and all the kids are buying them.

55

THE BIG CHOP

The needlework nun pulls her hair back into an elastic band, her fringe into a clip at the side and she looks like a little culchie.

"You're a dis greyace, with that untidy mane of shaggy hair! Tell your mother that hair needs to be cut."

She writes out a note for her to bring home. The envelope is sealed, but she knows it's about her long hair. Nuns hate long hair. They want everyone to be scalped, like themselves. They want everyone to have pear heads and egg heads. Outside the school, she takes out the clip and the elastic band, fixes her hair back the way it was, with her fringe down over her eyebrows. She takes off her glasses. Her Ma is in one of her panicky moods, when she goes home. She reads the note to herself at the window light.

"Oh sweet Jesus, not them bloody nuns complainin' again."

"She says I'm a disgrace."

"Does she now?"

She folds her arms tight. She thinks for a minute.

She calls in the kids, lines them all up near the grate. She gets the big scissors out of the drawer. She tests it out by cutting a piece of cardboard.

"Ah Ma," Patti says, but it's no use. She's in her haircutting mood and that means trouble. Franey goes first. She lifts him up on the chair and puts the towel around his shoulders. She starts at the front, snip, snip snip, until all his lovely curls are gone. Anna goes next; but she won't stay easy. She jiggles about.

"Stand easy!" Ma says.

She starts on her fringe first. Then the sides, then the back. Anna's brown hair mixed with Franey's blonde hair on the floor. Ma works fast; snip, snip, snip, until it's a crooked, sideways fringe, with lumpy bits that stick out. After Bernie, it's

Patti's turn. She needn't think she's cutting her hair. She will in her eye!

"Next!" she goes like she was a real hairdresser.

"C'mon, I said, it's your turn next. I haven't all day."

"No. I don't want my hair cut, so leave me alone."

She tries to run away, but her Ma catches her by the hair, starts combing out the knotty bits first.

"Go way!"

"It's all tangles and rats tails."

She starts at the front, snips big slices off her fringe.

"Maybe that nun'll keep her mouth shut now," she says, with a big piece of hair in her hand.

Patti has the waterworks, when she looks in the mirror. It's a holy show. Her fringe is well too short, nearly up to her scalp. There's tons of her dark hair on the floor. It's like in a real hair-dressers, with all the hair piled up: blonde and brown and dark brown. They all look the same with all their fringes going side-ways in a crooked line. They're all whinging, except the babby who didn't get his curls cut yet and Jimmy who always goes to the barbers.

When she sees them granny says: "God protect us, but that's some knife and fork job. They're like little orphans."

But Ma says: "It's grand and tidy and sure short hair is all the fashion now anyway."

PART 3

56

HER CONFO

It took ages, but she's glad her hair grew back. She had to wear a stupid Alice band for weeks after the big chop. Now, she has her fringe again and a little ponytail. It's just as well, because she's making her confo. There's choir practice and tons of catechism and special confirmation prayers. They have to pick a special confirmation name so she picks Maria Goretti. Then they have to write a composition about the saint. In the book of saints, it said Maria was a very brave girl. She was the eldest of six children. They lived up the mountains in Italy where they shared a barn with a friend and his son Allessandro. Maria was in charge of the kids, like Patti is sometimes. Her Da died when she was nine. Maria couldn't read or write, but she was very holy and she prayed all the time. This day, Allessandro sharpened his knife and dragged her into the kitchen. She had the babby in her arms. He'd stab her if she didn't let him touch her, he said. She didn't let him near her so he stabbed her fourteen times. Before she died she said:

"I forgive Allessandro with all my heart."

It's a very good choice because Maria Goretti is a fine example to all young girls, Sister says, when she reads the composition. She forgave the boy who attacked and stabbed her and that's true forgiveness. It's hard to believe how a little young one could forgive someone who stabbed her fourteen times. Vera picks this posh Saint, with plenty of money, called Saint Catherine of Bologna. She's the patron saint of artists, another very holy girl who died in the fifteenth century. Catherine's Da was loaded. She had a vision of Our Lady and the baby Jesus, after which she recited one thousand Hail Marys. She wrote tons of poems to Jesus.

Before their confo, they have to take the pledge. Patti makes the promise to the Sacred Heart not to touch drink until she's eighteen. Not a drop! No sneaks of Alfredo's red wine. No sups of stout in the pub. The priest gives her the special blessing.

Granny looks out the window. She says it's not a bad day for the Holy Ghost, and please God, them dirty clouds might break up after. Patti is glad and she's not glad. She has the knotty nerves in her belly. She was only allowed a half cup of tea with no milk or sugar, before half seven. It's the nerves and the sour tea mixed up in there. She has the shivers as well. She hopes she doesn't get sick all over her new confo dress. One good thing: she's allowed not to wear her glasses. She has them in her new black patent handbag. She has blue lace gloves to match her dress. She puts one on and carries the other one. Granny put the rags in her hair last night after she got bathed. They pinched her head all night, the old nylons and bits of cloth that make your hair curly. Now she has the corkscrew curls, but she doesn't like them. They're like the stupid Irish dancing ringlets that they wear at the Feis Ceoil. They're bashed down under her blue straw hat, like fat fried sausages. Her hair is hard and smelly from the Colet hair lacquer they sprayed in. The curls bounce a bit, when she jumps. Outside the flats, she pulls at them to loosen them out.

They have to meet in the schoolyard. Sister gives them instructions. She tells them to go over their catechism questions in their heads. She tells them how important this day is for the rest of their lives. She tells them to prepare themselves for the Holy Ghost and his seven gifts. At the back of the chapel they wait in a line. Sister gives the hand signal and they walk real slow up the aisle. The organ starts with one note. Then the choir. With their hands joined and their heads bowed they start to sing.

Holy God we praise thy name Lord of God we bow before thee.

The whole chapel is full of the sound of the hymn. The boys walk beside them in a separate line. They're dressed nearly the same; it's either grey suits, or brown suits, V neck jumpers and white shirts. It's all crew cuts and sharp side splits. Clean washed faces. She's glad she's not a boy. Some of the messers have smirky faces behind their joined hands. Everyone is watching them, all their heads turned: even the tramps in the back seats are gawking. It feels a bit like Holy Communion, but she feels more grownup now. Patti has the jitters. The Holy Ghost is here. Somewhere in the chapel, maybe up in the Gods where the choir sings. She thinks he's all white, with a soft holy light around him, like the moon has sometimes on frosty nights. He'll go into her. He'll stay there. Forever. He'll make her holy. She'll be a soldier of Christ.

As long as she doesn't break the pledge.

They have to stay standing until the hymn is finished. First, there's this big silence. Then the side door opens and creaks. Two priests walk out first. Then the bishop comes out then with a procession behind him. There's two altar boys holding up his robe; two more priests, then more altar boys. He kind of floats in all the heavy robes across the red carpet, his tall hat sticking up in two pointy bits like a house in a storybook. He's carrying something, like a fairy's wand, only bigger. He bows in front of the tabernacle. A babby starts crying somewhere down the back. One of the priests goes: Ahem! Ahem! He looks down the aisle real cranky like. Someone gets up. Footsteps. The chapel door opens and closes. They start the Latin prayers. There's loads of gorgeous flowers on the altar, red and yellow and purple and she thinks they might be tulips. A big swanky throne, on one side of the altar. After tons of prayers, after standing and kneeling, kneeling and standing, the altar boy swings the chain for the holy incense. Everyone bows their heads.

Oh God! Oh No! All of a sudden it's there; a sharp pain in the bottom of her belly. Maybe it's just that she's hungry. She's dying for a cuppa tea. Her belly feels empty. It rumbles. She hopes . . . No. She can't be. She went twice before she came out. Granny made sure. Oh God! She hopes she's not asked a hard question. She learned all her catechism questions off by heart; she knows nearly the whole green catechism, but she's afraid she won't remember.

She has the shakes.

She asks herself the questions in her head.

Then she tells herself the answers.

She knows them.

But she might forget.

She says them again.

Vera is at the other end of the pew in a stand out pink dress with millions of underskirts. She thinks she's gorgeous. She told everyone her dress came all the way from America. Catherine is all in lemon; lemon dress, lemon coat, lemon hat. Her Ma had to get a cheque for Mc Donnell's Children's Fashions in Parnell Street. Lemon is fab. Patti wanted lemon, but Aunt Jinny insisted; blue was her colour, she said. It took her weeks to make the dress on her Singer sewing machine. A bit every night after work. It's nice. It stands out a bit, but not too much, with two stiff underskirts. There's lace around the collar and lace at the hem. Very uncommon, Aunt Jinny said, not like what's in the shops. Her fawn coat was made to measure. It cost a small fortune from the tailors in Strand Street. Granny had to sell tons of fruit to pay for that coat. She looks down at her Clark's black patent shoes. Lovely. And her snow-white crimp ankle socks.

She has new cancan knickers over her cotton ones. If she wets them she'll be a holy show.

Her dress!

Her coat!

Her socks!

She's bursting. She crosses her legs tight. She twirls her ankles. Sometimes in school, if she doesn't think about it, it goes away.

It won't.

It will so.

There'll be holy murder if she wets all her new stuff. She wishes she had proper kidneys like other kids. Kidneys that don't make you want to piddle all the time, kidneys that don't make you wet the bed sometimes.

She tries to think of her Ma. She's at home washing the babby. Then she'll rock him on her knee and sing to him and Franey'll get mad jealous. She hopes she likes her dress, she didn't see it yet, because she's sleeping in granny's. It's a pity she can't see her here in the chapel getting her seven gifts from the Holy Ghost. She'll see her after, she supposes. All the places Patti has to go after chapel. Around the doors to Ma's friends, across the bridge to granny Connor's, the Daisy market, the fish market, Aunt Lilly's, the chipper woman in Duck Lane, the woman in the fruit shop in Capel Street, Misses whatsername the habit woman on the quays. She looks down again at her new shoes. Oh God! Someone wet the floor already, she can see a trickly pool, like a slithery snake, under the kneeling rung. It must be that young one in front, in the royal blue coat and white hat. If she jiggles her feet around, like in Irish dancing it's not that bad. There's lovely coloured light coming through the stain glass windows, blue, purple, red and green. The saints and the angels are looking up to heaven.

The bell rings. They have to kneel down. She squeezes and squeezes. Then it's time to sing another hymn. They stand up. Sister gives the note with her ruler. Patti opens her mouth and pretends to sing: O Salutaris Hostia.

More prayers and then it's time.

For questions.

Oh no!

Oh God!

There's muttering down the line and all the feet start to shuffle.

Here he comes. Oh gosh! The size of him! He's huge. Like a big moving statue. They can't see his feet with all the robes. He walks real slow and careful, like a bride going up the aisle. Catherine looks over. Her face is like the colour of white tissue paper. The altar boys are holding up his cloak; she knows one of them from the flats. He has this real holy face on, his hair done in a sharp side-split, bashed down flat with hair oil. He's wearing white runners. The bishop stops. He has something in his hand, a prayer book, or a catechism. Maybe he won't ask her a question. Maybe she'll be one of the lucky ones. One row in front and he starts at the first girl. He moves on, picks out some and skips others. He turns pages with his thumb, like he's picking out questions. It's her row then. He's four girls away. She can't breath. It's like her chest is bursting behind her confo medal. He stops at Patti. She hopes he can't see her crossed legs.

"Who is the father of Jesus Christ?"

Thank God and the Holy Ghost. She knows that one.

"God is the Father of Jesus Christ . . ."

He gives a little nod. He waits. Looks in his book. Looks at her again. What's he lookin' at? She has a little think. Oh right. There's more.

"Saint Joseph was his foster father or guardian."

He nods.

Patti nearly chokes.

She must've got it right.

She won't be made a show of now.

She's delighted. She's nearly a full member of the Holy Catholic Church now. Smarty pants Vera doesn't get asked a question. She has on her holy face. He goes to the boys' side and skips loads of boys. He stops at a few and then he walks back up the red carpet. The altar boys are swinging the chain again. The incense goes up her nose. She likes that.

After Holy Communion, they go to the throne to be confirmed, one girl and one boy at a time. The bishop sits down and the altar boys arrange the robes around his feet. He makes the sign of the cross on Patti's forehead.

He says: "I sign thee with the sign of the cross and I confirm thee with the chrism of salvation."

Then he touches her cheek with his thumb. She knows. That means she's a Soldier of Christ. She knows what she has to do next. She genuflects and kisses the holy ring. Barely! She goes back to her seat. It feels good to be confirmed, but she doesn't feel like a soldier. She feels special though, like the Holy Ghost is in her and she's a bit holier than she was. There's one more hymn and then it's over. AT LAST! She's jaded. She's wall falling. Thank God the pain in her belly went away and she didn't make a show of herself. Maybe it was the Holy Ghost that helped her out.

Outside, everyone is saying: Thank God it's not raining. It's packed out in the porch. They're all admiring the bishop, saying isn't he like a Saint and wouldn't he bring tears to your eyes. Some of them are waiting to kiss his ring. The boys are in a bunch at the gate rubbing their hands together. They're talking about all the money they'll make. All of a sudden, Patti has to run into the schoolyard toilet. There's a queue outside and they're all doing a little dance in their new confo shoes.

In Geromes in Henry Street, she'll get her photo taken.

The photographer will ask her to smile.

Say cheese, he'll say.

She doesn't like getting her photo taken. She feels dead gawky in front of a camera.

She has a fried egg, sausage and white pudding and gillions of tea in granny's. She's like a babby, with the check tea towel around her neck like a dribbler.

"Leave the flowers on the plate," Aunt Dinah says.

In the market, Biddy gives her a big tight hug. Then she gives her a wet sloppy kiss on the cheek.

"There chicken. You're a little smasher," she says. Patti wipes off the lipstick when she's not looking. Biddy is all soft and fleshy under the white crossover smock. She has on her high heels and black velvet hat. She opens Patti's hand. She presses in a half crown and closes it again.

"Put that in your bag chicken and don't lose it," she whispers.

Patti says: thanks very much. She puts the half crown in her bag. She rattles it. The sound of the first money rattling. It's dead brill. Biddy lights a cigarette, starts to chop the leaves off her cauliflowers.

"Did the bishop ask ya a question?"

"Yeah. It was a bit hard, but I got it right."

Granny nods her head at Biddy.

"She's a right little scholar, that one."

"So she is. She looks a picture in that blue dress. A credit to yourself and her Ma, God bless her."

Catty has a face on. She hopes she doesn't kiss her. She has a ronny and little beardy bits on her chin. And she smells of old potatoes.

She says: "You're a lovely girl," and gives her a brown thropenny bit.

Patti says: "Thanks very much."

Catty's hat is bashed down on her forehead, as usual, so you can only see half of her face. Her brown coat is open, showing off her clean white market-smock. She has a cranky face, but she's not really cranky. She's making a hill of onions on her stall. First, she peels off the loose skins, then she builds the onions up into a pyramid shape. Patti sees her potatoes have eyes, her caulies have dirty faces, with brown spots on them like moles and they must be weeks old.

The chicken women all stand back from their stalls when she goes down the steps.

"Will ya look a her! Do a twirl for us."

Patti does a twirl.

"Another one. Go on, lets see that lovely tulle underskirt."

So she does a quicker twirl. Then they pull up her skirt. They look underneath.

"That's a very unusual rig-out. Was it bought in the Gay Child?"

"No. Aunty Jinny made it. She makes French clothes for kids in Paris."

"Is that so? She's lovely hands."

"Are them Clark's shoes you've on? "

"Yes they are!" Granny shouts from up the steps. "I Bought them in Arnott's. And that crocodile handbag cost a small fortune!"

She can see the sicky chicken guts in the big tin drum. The smell! There's heads and beaks and feet. There's blood dripping down the side of the drum. The chicken women are well to do, and some of them live out far in houses. She hopes they won't feel her dress again; she doesn't want to smell like a chicken on her confirmation day. She has to go, she says. She has to visit Bridie and Molly and loads of other people.

"Ah go on, give us one more twirl."

She has to do another bloody twirl before they give her the money.

Up to the clothes stalls then.

"Nice nylon in that dress," Molly says and gives her a shilling out of her money pocket.

There's a crowd around her stall. They're all rooting through a big bundle of clothes that's for sale. Molly holds them up, one at a time: there's dresses, coats, a corset, a huge pair of Long Johns. She's doing an auction.

"C'mon now ladies. I'm clearing out t'day. I'm nearly givin' them away at these prices, selling bargains galore."

She stands up on her upside-down box. She winks at Patti. Someone buys the corset for one and six. Molly says it was hardly worn and that all her merchandise is made of the very best material, ladies stuff from the suburbs out in Harold's Cross and Terenure and Dalkey. The corset is pink, like granny's one, with bones and laces and hooks and eyes. She wraps it up in newspaper, stuffs it into the woman's straw messagebag. The women start to laugh and titter when she holds up the Long Johns.

"Sacred heart! the size of them Long Johns," Biddy says.

"Ya could fit my fella and your fella inta them yokes no bother."

"I say, Men's best under garments for cold frosty nights. Who'll start me off at one and six?" Molly shouts out.

Around the corner, Bride sells delf and holy water founts, hair-clips and clothes hangers. Bridie is wrapping up a teapot in newspaper for a customer. She's singing *Black Magic* in a slow lazy voice. When she sees Patti she stops singing with her mouth open. She says:

"Well I never . . . You'd travel a long way for a frock the like of that."

Here we go.

"Do a twirl for your Aunty Bridie like a good girl."

One twirl. Two twirls.

"That's a smashin underskirt, the way it goes up when you twirl."

"Here love."

Bridie hands her a shiny florin out of her market pocket.

Two whole shillings!

"Tell your Ma I said you're only gorgeous."

Blue suits her, she says. Blue is her colour all right. Then she finishes wrapping the teapot and goes on with her song like she never stopped singing.

Two Americans walk by with tartan trousers and raincoats. The woman is wearing a plastic rain hat with red dots over a beehive of blonde hair. Granny puts on her smile and fixes her fruit into a neat pyramid. The Americas stop to look at her apples.

"Nice apples lady?"

Granny's nice friendly voice.

"Beauty of Bath, or nice Jaffa oranges, only just off the boat? "

She polishes an apple with her apron, cuts it in two with her penknife, then she tears open an orange and squeezes out the juice.

"Here, taste that," she says.

The woman with the beehive takes a big bite of the apple.

"That's good," she says. "That's so good!"

They'll take six, they say. Then they see Patti behind the stall.

"Oh my Gaawd!" the woman says. "Isn't she WONDER-FUL!"

"It's her confirmation day," granny says opening out a bag.

"Isn't that just swell," the man says.

They keep looking at her. They smile with their whole faces. They have on cream Aran jumpers, under the raincoats. It's the blackberry and diamond pattern that's all the fashion. They're dressed exactly the same. Nearly. Except the man has tan boots on and the woman has grey Hush Puppies. The man is fat. The woman is thin. Biddy tries to catch their attention. She says she has lovely Spanish plums and she's letting them go very cheap today. In her low voice Catty says she has nice juicy William pears, freshly picked from the orchard. She opens a paper bag, before they have time to answer. She counts in four brown pears real quick. Granny gives her a look. The Americans pay granny for the fruit and give Patti the change.

"Here Honey. Have a nice day."

It's pennies and twopences and a throppence.

Biddy grabs the American's arm all of a sudden.

"Here, c'mover here me oul secosha," she goes.

She puts down her cigarette. She rolls up her sleeves. She starts to clap her hands. She pulls him out into the aisle. The American's face goes red. A big stain up to his forehead.

"Oh gosh! She's going to do the three hand reel," Patti says.

"Oh Biddy, you're a howl," granny says.

Biddy pulls her skirt out at the sides like an Irish dancer. She goes in and out on her tippy toes. She lifts her knee up high and they can see pink garters where her stocking's end. Patti hopes the American can't see them as well.

She takes his hand. Holds it up and sort of guides him along.

The American says: "Oh G Lady, but I'm no dancer."

"You'll get the hang of it in a minute."

Biddy pretends not to hear. She keeps up the dance. The woman with the beehive watches from granny's stall. She has her hands to her face. She's half laughing, half crying.

"Oh golly G!" she says.

Her husband's feet are all over the place. He nearly trips on the rough ground.

Biddy's face is pinky red. Granny takes out her mouth organ, wipes it across her apron. First she gets her note. She has to blow real hard.

Everyone claps.

The chicken women come up the steps.

"Yoo hoo!"

Biddy thumps her hips like a cowboy on a horse. They're all out now in the middle of the aisle, the chicken women and the clothes sellers and a few customers from Molly's stall. Biddy always does this with the Americans. It's only a bit of gas, she says. She winks over at Patti. She holds out one hand. Oh no! She wants her to join in. Patti feels her face; it's hot. She doesn't want to.

"No!"

"C'mon now, chicken, dance for your Aunty Biddy."

Granny gives her a look that says she'd better.

First she puts her handbag in the press under the stall. Next, she takes off her hat and her glove. She can do a reel, but her new shoes are a bit stiff and they're'll be holy murder if she scuffs the toes.

She holds out her dress. They all clap. She feels dead dopey.

Now it's two rows of them dancing in and out, in and out. It's Patti in the middle trying not to scuff her shoes. It's granny, blowing hard into her mouth organ. It's everyone dancing together. It's the three-hand reel, turned into the ten-hand reel. Biddy is breathless all of a sudden. So is the American. They keep up the dance as long as they can. They dance a bit more. It's like the American is starting to like it, just when it stops. Biddy stops. She bends over and takes big breaths.

"I'm jacked," she says. Everyone slows down. The American says he's deadbeat. Thank God the dance is over, Patti thinks. She puts back on her hat. Then her right hand glove. Biddy holds the American's face in her hands, gives him a big kiss on the cheek. Then real quick, she weighs a bag of plumbs, adds one for good measure.

"Enjoy them," she says. "I'll leave them the one and six."

The American roots in his pockets, turns them inside out. His wife takes out a ten-shilling note. Biddy has the change ready. She hopes they'll come back to the Daisy if they ever visit Ireland again. Then it's all goodbyes and handshakes. The Americans leave with their bags of fruit piled in their arms, everyone waving them out the gate. Granny says Biddy is a ticket. Biddy say's it's only a bit of sport and wouldn't it be the sad day, if they couldn't have a laugh. Then it's break time. Granny gets out her cream crackers and cheese. Gertie the canteen woman brings in a pot of fresh tea.

They'll go to Dignams after the market. Her Granny might go or she mightn't. She's not a drinker. But she might have a ginger ale after all the commotion. The woman who sells holy stuff and toilet rolls give her a tanner on the way out. Patti can buy a hot doughnut. Loads of hot doughnuts if she wants. Trillions of Trigger bars. A Toblerone. Yes. One of the big fat ones you buy in Woolworth's. Maybe a packet of Rolo's. Two packets.

In the bakery in Mary Street, she gets five hot jam doughnuts. In Miss Stokes's shop, she gets a pot of Fruitfield blackcurrant jam. Miss Stokes looks over the counter at her dress. Miss Stoke says nothing, only takes the money and throws it in the drawer under the counter.

There's her Ma, at the hall door with the babby in her arms. The babby with a Liga in his hand. Bits of gooey biscuit stuck to his chin.

"Come in quick. It's after two. I thought you'd never come."

She takes the jam and the doughnuts. She puts on the kettle. She lifts up her handbag by the handle.

"My God that bag is heavy!" she says, when she feels the weight of it. They all want to touch her dress, but her Ma says: "maulers off!"

Anna keeps touching the lace at the bottom.

"Leave it. Don't pull that dress," Ma says, but she won't stop. Bernie keeps staring at her new shoes. They all want to shake her handbag.

"It wont be long till youse make yours," she says. "Only a couple a more years."

They're all around the table. Her Ma cuts up the doughnuts, takes the lid off the jam jar with a knife. She pours tea. There's jam in the doughnuts, but only a bit. Patti spoons in more jam. She likes jam when it's straight out of the pot. She has a few spoonfuls. They all have jammy faces.

"Mind that dress!" Her Ma covers her up with a towel while she eats.

"Was he nice? The bishop?"

"Yeah he was all right."

"I heard he was a lovely man."

"You should've seen his robes and his hat and his throne."

"Who done you hair?"

"Granny. With the rags."

"I don't like them sausage curls."

"Neither do I."

"Your granny doesn't know what suits ya."

Patti takes off her hat. Rests it in her lap

"C'mere till I try an fix them proper."

They're all pulling at her hair then. They're all jeering her hat. Franey thinks it's a poe poe, so they're all in stitches then.

"The po po, the po po," he says.

"That hat is all the fashion. The latest in confirmation style," her Ma says.

With her fingers she pulls down the sausage ringlets into a loose corkscrew shape and fixes the hat back on.

"That's better. Them tight curls are very hickey. Not right for your face. She looks at her underskirts and examines the seams.

"Jinny did a nice job. There's nice stuff in that dress. You wouldn't see the likes of that downtown. It's very uncommon."

Then she asks her, would she be all right for a little loan? Just a few bob until children's allowance day.

"Well all right," Patti says, after thinking about it for a while.

In the flats, they're all after her. The kids, who all got the day off school follow her around.

"Giz a shillin'," they keep shouting. It's not just her they're after. Everyone is counting their money to see who got the most. A young fella from the far flats tells everyone he got a five-pound note, but no one believes him. He's only showing off to make them jealous. Everyone says prove it, but he won't show them.

They go downtown, her and Aunt Dinah. It's her special treat. In Cafolla's café, they get Knickerbocker Glories. In Clery's wool department she buys royal blue wool for a new school cardigan. In Woolworth's she buys a packet of hair clips and a torch with batteries. With all her confo money, Aunt Dinah says, she could buy Woolworth's and still have change left over. In the walkaround stores, she finds a present for her Ma. She's not sure at first what it is. Aunt Dinah says it's an egg timer. It has Made in China on the bottom. It's two little glasses with a hole in between. It's full on the bottom with sand. It's for when you want to boil an egg soft or hard. The walkaround store man gives her a demonstration. You turn up the sand part. You wait until the sand is emptied from the top section to the bottom. Half way is for a soft egg, all the way is for a hard boiled egg. It's dead neat. The man says it's very practical, a thing no modern kitchen should be without.

Aunt Dinah says, "Your Ma'd love that."

Patti thinks so too, because sometimes her Ma forgets about the egg and the shell gets all stuck to the pot.

"I'll take it," she says.

The man puts it into a cardboard box, wraps it up nice in blue shiny paper and sticks it with sticky tape at the corners.

"There. A grand little pressie for your Mammy," he says.

57

PLAYING BUNGALOW

After your confo, it's like, you're a grown-up all of a sudden. Young fellas start to give you funny looks, even when you have your glasses on. They start to whisper to each other when you pass. It was only a couple of weeks after her confo, when her brother's friend tried to put his arm around her. It sneaked around real slow in granny's hall, so she had to push him away. The eejit! It was when they were playing house with her tin bungalow, the one that santy gave her for Christmas. They were parking their car in the garage, the plastic man and woman figures who live in the bungalow called Ambleside. Then they were in the kitchen. They were going to have dinner in the dining room. She was supposed to be the woman and he was supposed to be the man. They were doing voices. He had on the deep Da kind of voice. She had on the soft Ma voice.

"What would you like for dinner, chops or liver?" she goes.

"Oh chops I think."

"Chops it is so. Pork chop with kidney?"

"Oh all right so. Pork chop but no kidney."

"I'll put up the pan."

"And what about after dinner?" He says.

"What about it?"

He says nothing. He moves the woman figure out of the tin kitchen and into the tin dining room. He sits her down for a minute to eat her dinner. Then he moves her again into the tin bedroom. He puts her on the brown plastic four-poster bed. He lies her down. All of a sudden he has this stupid looking grin on his face.

He goes: "Well?"

She goes: "Well what?"

And that's when the arm started to move.

"I thought we'd watch Quicksilver on the telly," she says.

"We don't have a telly, stupid," he says.

He was right there; they didn't have a telly, the couple in the tin bungalow called Ambleside. They only have a pretend radio that's made into the kitchen wall. He makes a stupid face then and that's when she feels the arm, the fingers, creepy crawly at her neck. He says something real peculiar then, as if he was a cowboy and she was a horse, and she tells him to get lost pronto.

"Get lost you!" She says.

"I will not get lost," he says back.

"Hump off, I said and don't come back."

So the face of him, all pink and stupid. Out he gallops from granny's hall in his short trousers.

"Nincompoop!" She goes after him. Her face is hot. She's not sure why. She just knows she's annoyed with him. So that's the end of him playing bungalows in granny's hall. He can stay up there on that balcony; he needn't think he's playing bungalows again with her. She tells Vera. Vera says, so what? Vera thinks young fellas are brill.

58

KISSIN

Vera fancies the man in The Man From Uncle. She thinks he's dead neat.

"Did ya see whatsisname, blondie last night?" She goes.

"Ya mean Ilya Kuryakin?"

"Yeah. Your man who talks French."

"Yeah, but it's not French, it's Russian."

"Russian?"

"Yeah. He's a bit girly isn't he?"

"He *is* not girly. Blondie is bleedin' massive; specially his fringe and his polo neck."

"He's not that nice."

"He *is* so. Nicer than Napoleon Solo in-anyway."

"I suppose so. I don't like Napoleon Solo's eyes or his greasy hair."

"Imagine," Vera goes.

"What?"

"Kissin' Napoleon Solo."

No she can't imagine.

"Go way you. I wouldn't kiss anyone, especially Napoleon Solo."

"Cowardy cowardy custard, stick your head in mustard."

Vera is thick sometimes. Napoleon Solo has shifty eyes. He looks at people sort of sideways with what her Ma calls the sly eye. You'd know he was thinking something evil. And the way he talks like he has fizz caught in his throat. It's different with blondie; all the girls are after him. Even the young fellas think he's great.

Vera always gets caught at kiss chasing.

"You can't catch me," she says and runs too slow so she'll get caught easy. A snotty-nosed young fella always catches her and has to kiss her up against the fish market wall. She puts her right foot up to the wall with her knee sticking out.

"What's it like?"

"Wha'?"

"The kissin'."

"Oh it's dead brillo," she goes with her eyes rolling round like she was mental.

"Oh yeah, brillo me eye."

"You have to do it right; you have to close your eyes," she says.

"Why?"

"You just have. You know the way they do it around the markets or up the ice lane or in the films."

"That's stupid."

Even if they hadn't got snotty noses, she wouldn't kiss them. And for deffo she wouldn't close her eyes.

Vera says it's not that bad, so when it gets dark, they go round the gates to see the kissin'. All these fellas and girls in doorways and the market gates and up the ice lane. At every single gate and every single doorway, they're kissin'. It's pitch dark, but up real close, they can see the backs and heads of the fella's. There's the kissin' noises in the dark. The sound of their breaths. Then more kissin. It's dead dopey, Patti thinks. A bloody waste of time.

"I'm goin', someone might see us."

"Wait. We might see more."

On the way home, she thinks about all the kissing in the pitch dark. She tries to imagine it. It's Disgusting! It's balderdash!"

"Vera. You know the way young fellas have spits and snots?"

"Jaysus. You're a hickey Mary, like them old maids in the Legion of Mary."

"I am not hickey!"

The worst thing in the whole world is to get called hickey. A Hickey Mary is as bad as a culchie.

"Hickey Hickey Mary!"

"Fuck off!" Patti says.

Oh Jaysus. Now she's a big curser.

"Go an' bolox!" Vera goes with her hands on her hips.

Vera will have to tell that in confession.

"That's a mortal sin."

"Bleedin right it is."

She hates her now. She'd like to tell her straight to her face.

"Poxy Poxy," Vera goes and runs up the stairs.

Vera is nutskies, a Cadbury's Fruit and Nut. She'd want to wash her mouth out with Sunlight soap. Then she'd want to swallow a bottle of Dettol.

59

MUHAMMAD ALI

They watched the Cassius Clay fight on granny's telly. They sat on the floor up close to the screen. Here's Cassius coming up the aisle, in his long satin dressing gown.

"I'm the greatest," he says, punching the air.

He gives the audience the big smile with his pearly white teeth.

"I'm the champion'," he says.

In the ring he takes off his gown. He looks all shiny and muscley in his loose silky trunks.

Granda says, "Be God, he'll massacree tha' fella."

He dances around and gives his opponent the look. The referee puts in his gum shield and his whole face changes. Now he looks mean and dangerous.

Jimmy does shadow punches along with Cassius.

"He's the greatest fighter in the universe," he says.

"He's a bit full of himself for a boxer," Aunt Dinah says.

"He's nice lookin' though for a black man." Granny says.

Granda says: "Shutup and let us listen for Godsake."

The fight ends with a knockout and the referee counting, but Cassius wins easy peasy. Everyone cheers. The place goes nuts. A girl walks round in a mini skirt, holding up a card. Granda says, "Tha' fella is out for the count. There was no contest and that Cassius Clay has fists like rocks. That fella has a body made of iron."

He looks over at Jimmy. He makes a fist. He says: "That's a champ and no doubt. That's the fella to watch." Jimmy puts on his red boxing gloves he got off Santi and takes off his glasses. He dances around the kitchen table with his gloves up to his face. He tries to look real mean like Cassius. Granda tells him he has to keep his head tucked in and his face protected. The way he does the dance thing, he looks like a real pro. Granny says that he'll be ready for the Stadium in no time, but he'd want to mind his nose or it might spoil his chances later on with the girls. Jimmy goes scarlet. Granda shows him how to spar and save his nose. How to punch and dive and duck at the right time.

"It's all in the feet," granda says. "You have to keep on the move and never give the other fella a chance."

Jimmy practices every day. Some day he might be world champion like Cassius Clay. Some day he might even be on telly.

"It's all ahead of him," granda says. "It's all in the future."

60

GRANNY'S PERM

Over on the southside, they're all on about Aunt Annie's wedding. Aunt Jinny is up all hours sewing on her sewing machine with her head down and her feet going a mile a minute on the foot pedal. There's yards of dress material all over the kitchen, half made coats and dresses hanging up on the walls and it's like a factory in there. Aunt Annie is in and out of the kitchen for fittings. She's standing up on a chair, holding in her stomach, stretching this way and that, breathing in and breathing out. Is it nearly finished she wants to know? There's Jinny with pins between her teeth and tailors chalk. She wishes it was, she says, and then maybe she might get a rest. Will she ever get to bed? Will she ever get to sleep? She wants to know. This wedding has her demented. This wedding will be the death of her. The uncles mooch around with cranky faces. They say they're bloody well fed up with all this weddin' carry on, that Singer sewing machine going all hours of the night, and the whole place covered in half made frocks. Granny says that if they don't whisht up complainin' she'll put them flyin'. She's not too ould to throw a few clatters. Aunt Annie said granny has to get her hair done for the wedding. That's the rule. She needn't think she's going to her wedding with that shockin' long hair down over her shoulders. She needn't think she's making a show of her on the most important day of her life.

They're arguing all the time; they're all talking fast at one another without looking at one another. They're eating their words. Around the table the words get mixed up and swallowed with their dinner. They're grabbing at pieces of air with their fingers. They're clutching onto pieces of skirt. It's the way they talk when they're not talking. Granny calls it *Wool gathering*.

"G'way with yis, youse have me scourged," she says.

Would she not see sense for the love a God? One says to the other. Granny doesn't want to look like all the other grannies who have perms. She doesn't want to look like Al Jolson singing Mammy. That's what she says. She goes all huffy. When she's huffy, she walks in circles, around and around the flat shaking her head and blessing herself and saying, Blessusansavus! She won't take off her scarf. She says it'd take a better woman than Anna Liffey to get her to cut and perm her hair. Aunt Jinny rocks to and fro on her chair. Aunt Annie says that perms are all the go and that Anna Liffey is the best hairdresser on the southside of town. That Anna Liffey could make a new woman out of her with a few snips of her scissors.

Granny doesn't believe her.

"Perms is it? Perms? Who wants perms?" She says.

Aunt Jinny says it'll go gorgeous with the distinctive Austrian style coat and dress she's making her. She looks over at the half made coat hanging on the wall over the sideboard, a row of straight pins holding up the hem.

"That turquoise crimplene wasn't cheap and that turquoise crimplene wouldn't go with long hair," she says. Granny tightens her scarf knot under her chin, drinks a sup of porter from her mug.

"We'll be the talk of the town; they'll be talking about this wedding for centuries. Centuries!" Aunt Jinny says.

* * *

There's Granny a few days after, in front of Anna Liffey's mirror, all her lovely black and grey hair on the floor. Here she is under a roundy hairdryer like a pink motorbike helmet and the face on her. She hates perms, she shouts through the dryer noise. On the chair beside her there's a stack of True Romance magazines. Patti has a root through them; it's all stupid love stories about doctors and nurses, airhostesses and captains. Same as the Banba books in Capel Street.

Anna Liffey takes out one perm curler to test if the hair is dry.

"That's grand," she shouts. "You're nearly done."

"Thanks be to God and his blessed mother, because the head is nearly burnt off me."

Granny makes a face and holds her ears. Anna Liffey turns off the dryer and lifts the hood back.

Granny sits in front of the mirror, with a head of wooly curls, like a golliwog, trying not to look at herself.

"God protect us and watch over us!" She says when she sees it. Anna Liffey shows her the back with a hand-mirror. She says: "A change is as good as a rest and that perm takes ten years off you."

Granny makes a face and sniffs. When it's all done, she puts her scarf back on. She pulls it forward at her forehead like a helmet and makes a big knot under her chin. She bangs the door on the way out and the bell jangles with a blinggg! Her and Patti sneak in the end gate in case anyone sees them. They walk real fast through the courtyard and don't look up in case there's heads over the balcony.

She's mortified when she sees herself in the long wardrobe mirror. Patti holds back the door while she has a good look. Her Ma is already there with the kids; they all want to see the perm.

"God. You're years younger," she says into the mirror, but granny is disgusted. They know by her face.

"Would ya credit it, what a difference that perm makes?" Aunt Jinny says.

"I told ya, Anna Liffey could work wonders with that scissors. It's like a new head on your shoulders," Aunt Annie says. Here they are all in the back bedroom, staring into the wardrobe mirror. Granny puts her scarf back on. She'd prefer her hair the way it was. She doesn't like that ammonia smell either, or the hard feel of her hair or the unmerciful itch in her scalp.

"I mightn't go to this weddin' at all," she says.

Aunt Annie is disgusted. She grabs her trench coat off the back of the bedroom door; she rushes out and slams the hall door after her.

Then they want her to wear a handbag, a white handbag and white shoes to match out of Heathers, if you don't mind. Is it not bad enough she was near scalped alive in Anna Liffey's without handbags?

"I'm not wearin' a handbag! Noshatall!"

"You can't go to a weddin' without a handbag."

There's nothing wrong with her good messagebag she tells them all, but they keep on at her; nag nag nag! Aunt Annie says they'll be a holy show and all the posh Palaces will be at the wedding in oceans of style. Aunt Jinny says people wouldn't forget a thing like that in a hurry, a messagebag at a wedding, a mother of the bride with no handbag. They'll be the laughing stock of Saint Audoen's House and no doubt about it. In the bedroom she kneels and says a rosary that granny will change her mind. Patti is not sure about the handbag idea. It mightn't suit granny. Her Ma says: Handbags are nice enough, but a decent looking purse'd be sufficient at a wedding. And her mother's hand made straw messagebag is very unusual.

It's only for peace sake that granny gives in and agrees to wear a white handbag. It's only to stop them atein' one another alive at the dinner table. But when they ask her to wear white gloves, she says: "That's enough guff outa the lot of youse now."

Then she tells them to get out of her way quick.

"Gloves is it? " she keeps saying. She does the half angry laugh and walks around in circles.

On the morning of the wedding the neighbours come in for glasses of stout. A pack of cheeky kids wait outside the door for a grushy. Gawkers and nosey parkers hanging like turkeys over the balconies. Granny looks funny in her new turquoise rig-out. Her feet look different in the white slip-on shoes with a small blocky heel. Aunt Jinny is in a Paris contrast of red and grey. Aunt Annie looks lovely in a powder blue dress and a little top hat with a veil. The bridesmaids are all in lemon. Aunt Rita is in black and white, a little boxy check jacket and a black tight skirt. Anna Liffey did a lovely job on Rita; her roots are all gone and her blonde hair is up in a beehive with a pearl slide at the back. She looks at the floor. She smokes real fast, one Woodbine after another.

In the kitchen there's songs about goodbye and songs about Ireland. There's one about a mother's love. A woman from upstairs holds Aunt Annie's hand and sings to her in a shivery voice. Aunt Annie goes red. She's mortified she whispers, because she's no spring chicken, and you'd think she was going to America instead of the Coombe Cottages up the hill. In the scullery her Ma has a bottle of stout in one hand and a glass in the other. She says to Aunt Rita: "This is it. No more jazz clubs for Annie, no more gallivantin' to dancehalls and picture houses and pubs at the weekend. She'll have to knuckle down and become a widower's wife. To think our Annie could've had any man on this earth, same as our Jinny, but when she was young she only wanted to marry God."

Aunt Rita is not really listening. She's biting her nails and smoking like she's in another world. The uncles mooch around in their good suits and laundered shirts. They have the Sweet Afton boxes out on the top of the sideboard. They're smoking and drinking to Aunt Annie's wedding. Granny keeps watching them. She says they'll smoke their brains out if they're not careful. Aunt Annie leaves first, then everyone behind her. Before granny locks the door, they look back into the empty kitchen. Cigarette smoke swirls up towards the three-tier chandelier, stout bottles cover the table and the fire is low in the grate. There's photos outside the chapel with everyone watching. It's not a big wedding. A few family and friends in a small hotel downtown. Aunt Annie and her new second- hand husband are going to a secret place for their honeymoon.

There's more room in the bed and the kitchen, but the place seems dead empty without Aunt Annie. Her Tea Rose talcum powder smell is gone and her hair-clips and all her stuff. There's loads of space for Rita and Jinny's clothes in the wardrobe. There's room for their soap and toothpaste on the draining board in the scullery. Under the bed, there's tons of room for shoes. Aunt Annie visits on Sundays with Mister Palace and his two lovely daughters who play the piano as a duet. They have a little grey car and a lovely cottage with an upstairs and a back-yard. It's dead posh up there Patti thinks. Her Ma says: Annie has a readymade respectable family all right, but she wouldn't like a second hand husband herself. Aunt Jinny says: "Isn't it well for her with a beaushiful house and a motor car and a pi-ano into the bargain."

Aunt Rita says she wouldn't be a stepmother for all the tea in China. Granny says she has a splittin' headache and it must be that bloody Anna Liffey perm. She tries to comb it out, but it only makes it worse. She sticks her head in a basin of water and rubs out the curls with a towel. She'd take a hot iron to it if it was long enough, but it's too short she says. Next, she plasters it with olive oil and sugar. Now the perm is half in and half out. It's wooly curls on one side, half straight hair on the other side. Aunt Jinny says it's a holy show.

61

THE MESSAGE

"You'd want to be careful down that direction," her Ma says, when she tells her where's she's going.

"I have to get the message for granny."

"Still an all. Bring someone witcha in case. It's rough down there near them docks."

So she asks Vera.

"Is it far?" Vera asks.

"Not that far."

"Not bloody half. Miles away I suppose."

Here they go down the quays. They pass the four bridges and stop at the docks. They see The Lady Patricia boat with Uncle Willie's cabin cruiser next to it.

"That's my uncle's boat."

"That rusty yoke? Ya call that a boat?"

"It's not just any old boat; it's called a cabin cruiser for your information. Our Uncle Willie is a sailor."

"Sailor me arse."

They stand and watch. It's true what Vera says. The boat looks sad and lonely, knocking against the quay wall.

"Let's go," Vera says.

They cross the road. They pass by the Custom House. They turn a corner and keep walking along by the East Wall.

"My feet are only killin' me. I'm goin' straight back home," Vera says.

"It's not much further," Patti says, although she's not sure now. She thought it was nearer the Custom House, a grey block of flats like their own flats, but it's miles past that. So Vera turns back in her huffs.

"I'm bleedin' knackered," she says and sneaks off.

Sleeveen sneak off, Patti calls her in her head.

A bit further on she puts on her glasses. Yes. Now she can see it a good bit away, a dark grey block, a bit like their flats with two high gate pillars.

Near the flats, Patti takes off her glasses again and hides them in her gymslip pocket.

There's kids on the gate pillars and they start to throw stones. Feck! This young fella at the gate gives her stony looks, then he puts out his hands to stop her going past. On the ground this mangy looking Alsatian sits in a raggy heap beside him. She straightens her shoulders and looks straight into his face. She picks up a stone. She waits. She fires it past the Alsatian. The dog lifts it's head, then puts it down again like it couldn't be bothered. It looks dead bony and she's sure it has something wrong with one of its legs. So maybe it can't run after her. The young fella stands aside and lets her go past then. The ones on the gate pillars shout after her, stupid stuff about her gymslip and her German up-plaits. Patti puts the invisible cone of silence over her head like Maxwell Smart and NinetyNine. She pretends not to hear.

The flat is on the top balcony. It's where the woman with the message lives with all her kids. Up there there's a terrific view of the docks and the Alexander Basin. She knocks; two small taps. She waits. She sees a curtain moving back, in the scullery window, and she knows they're watching her from behind. A girl in a long flowery dress answers.

"Me Ma is lyin' down," she says. "She has a pain in her head."

She rubs the back of her hand across her nose. She sniffs like she has a bad cold.

Patti knows the girl. Her big sister is in her class. She says: "Hold on."

She closes over the hall door, goes in and comes back in a minute.

"Me Ma says ya can come in."

It's darkish inside and there's a smell of burnt dinner. The curtains are closed over and there's a slit down the middle with a skinny stripe of light. There's dirty plates and delf on the table. The kids are messing, jumping up on chairs and the bath board and diving back down. They dig one another and chase after each other around the room. It's a bit like her own place sometimes.

Kay's long droopy dress nearly touches the floor. Patti knows they're poor; all the kids with no gymslips and long dresses are poor. The dresses get passed down through the family. They're called hand-me-downs.

The baby in the pram has dribbles down it's chin. There's another smell she recognises; it's nappies that are steeping somewhere in a bucket. The kids look mausey and messy. Their Ma'd want to put a comb through their heads to untangle the knots, Patty thinks. They all have the same eyes that turn into the inside corners. They stare, crossways, like a lion that's on telly in a programme about a zoo.

"Em . . . Could you ask your Ma for the message?" Patti says.

All Kay does is stare across the table with her lion eyes. The little ones have the same look like little baby lions.

"Maaa!" Kay shouts in the bedroom door. "Maaa!"

The woman appears from the room then rubbing her back. She's wearing a black creased dress that looks too tight for her. Her face is squashed up and pale, like the colour of tripe after you boil it. Her eyes are red and puffy, like maybe she had the waterworks. She's a bit fat around the belly. There's a good few kids; Patti counted seven including the baby, and there's more voices coming from the bedroom. She lifts the baby out of the pram. The baby makes a gurgle sound and try's to pull at her nose. She puts it over her shoulder and pats it on the back.

"Tell your granny I've no message; tell her I'll be into the market next week."

"Next week? Right so. But are you sure, only . . . ?"

"First thing Frida' mornin', true as God."

She makes a sign on her throat with her finger and sits down on a chair. She wipes the baby's face with her sleeve. The little ones start to drag out of her skirt. They're jealous of the baby in her arms.

On the way down, the mangy dog is plonked at the bottom of the stairs. As quick as she can she steps past it. The dog barks and growls after her, but it doesn't move so she legs it fast as she can, her heart thumping under her gymslip. Outside the gate she makes a run for it back up the East Wall. She knows granny'll be annoyed about the message. She crosses the bridge and watches the boats for a while. The dockers are busy unloading a huge cargo boat. There's pulleys and cranes to lift the heavy stuff. Down a bit further a man unloading boxes from a banana boat gives her a bunch of green bananas.

"Here kiddo," he says. "Bring these home to your Ma."

She takes the hand of bananas. Says: "Thanks very much."

"Wait till they go ripe." The man says.

Patti nods. She wouldn't eat green bananas. Green bananas give you a pain in your belly like crab apples. The men shout and curse at one another like it's normal. They spit and whistle and make hand gestures. Dockers are big hunky men with crew cuts and tattoos up their arms. They'd drink the Liffey dry and still be thirsty, her granny always says. Sometimes her Ma says that she should've married a docker.

"You could buy all the tea in China if you married a docker. You could live in a mansion," she says.

On the way home she thinks about the woman and the message. Patti knows the woman. Every week she shops in the Daisy market. Granny keeps the soft pears and apples and tomatoes for her. Gives her a load of stuff cheap. Then she might whisper something in granny's ear and granny'll have to do a root in her money pocket. Then she'll pass her the message in her closed fist. Everyone knows what the message is. It's a little loan to tide the woman over until her husband gets paid or until her husband gets sober. It's the first time she went to collect it. The woman always pays back on time so she must be in big trouble, Patti thinks.

62

A LIITLE MIRACLE

Her Ma takes deep breaths: long slow breaths, then short fast breaths. Patti links her up the hill and walks real slow beside her. She stops all of a sudden. She holds onto the railings at John's Lane chapel.

"Jesus Mary and Joseph!"

"Are ya all right Ma?"

"Yeah, wait here for a minute."

They wait. They wait longer. More deep breaths.

Then she says: "C'mon, we better hurry."

She tries her best to walk. Under her leopard skin coat, her smock is stretched tight over her belly, the red roses pulled across and flattened out. Patti knows that the smock is so tight the buttons are open down the back. They had to cross the bridge to granny's place first. They left the other kids there. Granny was mortified when she saw them at the door. Said that her Ma's an awful character. Said she'd put the heart crossways in a body. She gives out loads. She blesses herself. She walks in little circles. There's Ma, on the chair, bent over and holding her stomach, her messagebag full of hospital stuff beside her on the floor.

"For the love of the Mother of Good Council! Will I get t'amblance?" Granny says.

"No! No amblance. I'm grand."

"What's wrong with Ma? Is Ma sick? The kids kept asking, but Patti wasn't sure. It was like this when she got Olive Elizabeth. The long deep breaths. The short fast breaths. All she knew was that her Ma had to go to hospital in a hurry.

"Right so. Get up that hill quick! You go with her," granny says.

The traffic is very heavy in Thomas Street. It's a long, long walk to the hospital. Her Ma says it's good exercise for the legs. They carry the messagebag between them, one handle each.

"That's better," she says. She holds onto a window ledge, bends over and takes more breaths.

"Sweet Jesus!" she says and starts to move again.

"Maybe we should sit down somewhere for a minute Ma."

"No, I said. We have to keep movin'."

They take a short cut through Meath Street, her Ma stopping every few minutes. Her Ma bending over and people staring at the two of them, like they were mad.

"It's not . . . much further." Ma's shaky voice.

At the Coombe porch, she's half bent over, her legs crossed, like she's bursting to go to the toilet. The porter takes in the messagebag first. Then he helps her in the door. She can barely stand now. The porter says there's no children allowed inside. She half turns her head, tells Patti in a breathless quivery voice, to run down the hill quick and to give granny a hand with the kids.

"Ok so. See yeah."

"Watch . . . the cars. Specially crossin' over Thomas Street."

"Right."

Back in granny's place it's all noise and madhouse.

"Did she make it in the door?"

"Yeah. The porter brought her in"

"These childer are stone wild."

The kids have her granny scourged. How her Ma puts up with them, she doesn't know, she says.

"They're like cowboys and Indians."

She has a headache. A splitting headache. She has to make strong tea and drink oceans of it. Oceans!

It's a couple of hours later. Granny whispering to Aunt Jinny in the hall, with the kitchen door closed over. Then Aunt Jinny comes rushing into the kitchen, with a big grin on her face.

"Thanks be to God and his holy blessed mother," she says blessing herself.

"Your Ma has a new baby girl."

"Thanks be ta God!" granny says.

Then the kids are all going nuts. Dancing around the table, doing a war dance and shouting: We have a new baby! We have a new baby! Patti has to check them, but they won't stop.

"Was the baby in the cabbage patch?" Anna says.

"No o. The stork brang it," Bernie says.

"Don't start, youse pair, stork or cabbage patch, it doesn't matter, it's here now and we can't send it back," granny says.

Aunt Jinny is all excited. She takes off her coat and sits down at the table. She says she rang up the Coombe from Murtagh's public telephone on her way home from work.

"Your Ma was only in the door when she got the new baby. A little girl she has, eight pound weight and not a mark on her. 'Mother and baby are doing well, the nurse said on the phone."

Everyone is happy. Granny gives them sugar on bread. Aunt Jinny puts on more tea and they drink tea to the new baby, that she'll be strong and healthy, that she'll make it in this world. Granny says that she knew by the tealeaves it was going to be another girl. Granny says the leaves never lie.

A few days after, when her Ma comes home, there's a bunch of kids around the door. They all want to see the new baby. It's like they never saw a new baby in their lives. She's wrapped up tight in two baby shawls, her hands out at the top. They all want to touch her, but Ma says she's very delicate. They try to touch her face and her head. In the kitchen, Ma loosens her shawls and they see her properly in her long baby gown. They count her fingers and toes. They want to touch her belly button and her face and her head. The baby is lovely. A face like a little angel. But no way is she going to Heaven; not this time, Patti thinks. She's no dimple, like Olive Elizabeth, but she has loads of hair, what Ma calls kinky hair.

The grannies can't agree on who she's like. Granny Connor says she's a Connor all right, the spittin' image of their Ma when she was a new baby; but her other granny says she's a ringer for her Da and you'd think he was after spittin' her out of his mouth. The aunties don't know yet. Patti thinks she's just like a new baby. Her Ma says she's like herself. She says she's a good feeder and you'd want to keep a Jersey cow to keep up with her. She might be an acrobat, with them strong wiry limbs, so everyone is happy again.

The Moses basket is out in the kitchen on two stuck together chairs. All the new baby does is sleep with her eyes shut tight. The kids keep waking her up and they all have their heads stuck in the basket. They keep pinching her face and feeling her hands. Sometimes her eyes open and roll upwards. Her Ma says when a baby's eyes are rolling, it's a very good sign. It means they're dreaming and seeing angels. The angels keep them safe from diseases and devils. Anna and Bernie keep trying to lift the baby up, when Ma's back is turned. Patti has to give out to them. Her Ma watches from the scullery, where she's washing the clothes in the bath. She says the bones at the crown of her head are still open. It'll be weeks before they close and it's very dangerous to touch. The place is full of baby stuff. There's nappies drying in the stone oven over the fire, a feeding bottle and brown tits boiling in the pot on the stove, there's Vaseline and Johnston's baby powder and blue stone on the table. The blue stone is for cleaning the baby's belly button. You put it on cotton wool and dab it around where the cord is. It's the same colour as ink and it smells funny. In a couple of days, the cord will fall off, but it looks horrible, like there's this scabby thing hanging out of her belly. The whole place smells of hospitals and new babies and bluestone. Her Ma is exhausted. She has to take the little red blood tablets for the iron. Franey keeps asking her will she turn into an iron woman from all the iron tablets she's taking? Ma says she'd want to be some iron woman all right and she wishes she was.

Patti can't help looking at her Ma's skinny stomach. The navy smock hangs loose on her now, her legs are white again and the little wiry veins near her knees are gone. Out at the door, she shows off the new baby. People say she's a little miracle and Ma says she's one of God's creatures. And how is she herself after the birth, they ask. She's grand she tells the neighbours, only she's a bit tired. One of them says she's a bit pale looking and she'd want to mind herself. She'll be better after she gets churched, she says.

So that Sunday, they go to the chapel. Patti is allowed to carry the baby some of the way and she's delighted. Then Bernie and Anna want to carry her, but they can't hold her head right. So Ma says: "No. Youse're too small. You'll only let her fall." There's murder then outside the chapel.

"Lemme hold the baby!" Anna screams.

"No lemme lemme hold the baby," Bernie shouts.

They have on the bold cheeky faces.

"The Reverend Mother is watching from that convent window," Patti says to frighten them. Then her Ma says she'll get that cranky nun with the claw fingers and the big stick to teach them a lesson. They're afraid of their lives of her, so they shut up pronto and all of a sudden they're little goody goodie's. In the porch, she warns them.

"Behave in the holy house of God! Or I'll swing for the pair of yiz!"

She called the baby Doris after Doris Day. She said some day she might be a good singer. After the christening she gets churched near the statue of Saint Anne. The priest lights a candle and tells her to hold it. Patti takes the baby, so she can kneel down. The priest says the special prayers that mean she can venture out of the house now that she has the blessing. Then he sprinkles her with holy water from a bowl and says more prayers in Latin. Ma is delighted. Outside the chapel she says she's glad to be able to go out again and breath fresh air into her lungs. On the way home, people stop to have a look at the baby.

"A beaushy." They say.

"A little angel, God bless her."

They put silver coins behind Doris's head, under the christening shawl for hansel and good luck.

Ma says: "Thanks very much, but you shouldn't, you might want that yourself tomorra for the dinner."

"Oh for God's sake will ya stop it, sure it's only a bit of hansel for the child."

She says she feels better already and there's nothing like a good churchin' to give you back your strength.

The cord falls off like a big scab after a few days. The bellybutton looks all right, but her Ma keeps washing it with blue stone just in case. When she's washing her in the basin, she pretends to bite her bum. She says there's nothing like a new baby's skin, it's so soft and perfect. She shakes on powder and pins on the nappy. After she's dressed, she puts Doris down and ties the pram to the drainpipe outside.

"Why can't we keep her in the house? " Patti asks.

"No. She's better off outside in the fresh air. She'll thrive out there. A baby needs fresh air in its lungs. "

She doesn't believe in molly coddling; she always says you should never over handle a baby or it'll start to think you've nothing better to do. It'll cry for attention at every hands turn. So it's the drainpipe for Doris until the next feed. The pram looks lovely, all decked out in soft new rugs and a frilly quilt. The sacred heart picture and two miraculous medals hang from the hood on pink satin ribbon. Everyone passing stops to look into the pram. They say:

"God bless the baby, isn't she only massive? Looka that head of hair, and the cute eyes of her, next thing ya know she'll be sittin' up and talkin'."

The little young ones think she's a dolly; they all want to wheel her around the flats in the pram. They keep knocking at the door:

"Misses, can we wheel your new baby? Please please Misses, go on Misses."

They join their hands like they're praying, but Ma says no, not yet, maybe in a few weeks time, when the baby is bigger.

She's not a new baby anymore. The new baby look is gone off her. The creases are gone out of her face; her head is bigger and the downy baby hair is nearly all gone. She's getting new hair at the front, a kind of brownish colour, what Ma calls auburn.

"She's takin' after our Annie with that auburn hair," she says.

"Does that mean she's a Connor?" Patty says.

"I s'pose so. Isn't she the lucky one. Annie has lovely hair."

Patti knows what she means. When the sun shines, there's these lit up parts in Annie's brown hair, like it's on fire. So that's what her Ma means by auburn.

Doris is drinking gallons of milk and it's a good job they have the two free bottles from the health nurse. She likes Farley's Rusks and goody goody. She likes to grab your hand and bite your fingers. She bites everything and Ma says that's because she's teething. She has a teething ring, but she keeps throwing it out of the pram. They call her the babby now, instead of the baby.

"Why don't ya bring her for a walk," her Ma says.

Yes, it's about time, Patti thinks, she got used to everything in their neighbourhood. She puts on her pink teddy suit and then she covers her up with the rugs. She props her up the pillow, so she can see out. First, they go through the big front gates with the two grey pillars. She tells Doris that that whiskey smell is from Jameson's distillery and that smelly smell is from the fish market and that other peculiar smell is from Guinness's brewery. She crosses the road and turns the corner. She shows her the school on the hill. She tells Doris that's where she goes to school. It's a famous school founded by this woman, called Maria Teresa Mulally, nearly two hundred years ago. In a few years time, she'll be going there herself. First, she'll learn her ABC's, then she'll make her Holy Communion, then she'll learn about the stone age people and the people who died for Ireland, about the sugar factories and the rivers and lakes and mountains. Someday she'll be a little scholar.

Patti turns the pram around. Facing the hill, through the big green gate, there's shouts and loud voices coming out of the market. She tells Doris that's where their granny has her market stall. Granny is roofed-in, not like the Moore Street crowd who have to stand out in the rain all day. She's the one with the silver hair and bright blue eyes. She's the one with the Prize Bonds and the furry fox's tails and the mink stole. She'll know all about her soon enough. Doris'll be out of nappies before she knows it. In no time, she'll be toddling around. Then she'll be walking like everyone else. Later on, she'll be helping granny in the market, lifting and carrying and doing deliveries. She might send her to the bookies with a bet, or to the druggist in King Street for the cough bottle.

She turns left into Little Mary Street. She looks up at the dirty windows, where Betty and her Dad were supposed to open Dixie's Diner. The For-Rent sign is gone, but the place still looks empty. She takes the first turn right at Slattery's pub into

Capel Street. Outside the music shop, she looks in the window at the banjos and guitars and drums.

"That's where you buy the musical instruments. Our Uncle Willie is an accordion and piano player, our granny plays the mouth organ and our Aunt Dinah is a lovely singer. Our Ma sings too, but only sometimes." She stops outside Steins. As usual, there's a queue at the counter. She points out the pigs' feet, the hearts, the kidneys and the tripe. "That's the yukki stuff our Da boils with milk and onions. This is where they'll send you for the rashers and sausages for the coddles. The Banba is across the road; that's where granda gets his cowboy books and that's where you do the swaps with the Bunties and Judies. The walkaround store is around the corner, near the Dolls Hospital."

Doris looks up with her hazel eyes. It's like she's trying to answer. She starts to dribble and blow bubbles. "Agoo," she says.

"Agoo yourself," Patti says. "Agoo agoo, agoo!"

"Ba baa," Doris says, and blows more bubbles. Patti gives her a clap.

"Good girl. The Ba ba ba!"

She's talking babby talk already. Her Ma '11be delighted she said baba. She said agoo weeks ago. It always starts with agoo and then Baba and Dada and Mama.

"The Ba ba ba!" Patti says again.

Doris starts to wriggle around. She can twist herself into knots in the pram. She tries to catch the Sacred Heart picture but she keeps missing. Patti checks her pram straps, fixes her rugs real tight, so she can't loosen them. She lies back on her pillow. Her eyes follow the sky then. She stares at the clouds and maybe she's seeing angels, Patti thinks. It's time to turn back. Them clouds look dark, like there might be rain. She does a big turn with the pram. She doesn't want to tell her, not yet, but it's not that easy around here. After she learns to walk, she'll have to learn to fight. She can never be a yellabelly. Maybe, she'll teach her to do the tonsil pinch. Or maybe Doris'll be lucky and not be lampy like Patti. Maybe she'll have no splits in her teeth.

But one thing's for sure, she'll have to wear the goofy gymslip and go to the convent on the hill.

* * *

They were playing up the balcony. Vera says she has a bit of news. It's about babies, how they get born. She says she heard you get babies out of your belly button.

"It opens up when the belly is huge and, guess wha'?" She says.

"Wha'?"

"Out pops the babby."

"Go way outa that."

"Sure as God!"

"And then what?"

"And then the belly goes back; it closes up again."

"On it's own? Holy mackerel! "

"I'm tellin' ya, I heard it from a big young one. She's brainy. She can do algebra. She said that's how come their bellies go flat again and they don't wear the smocks."

"That's stupid; how could a whole baby fit through a little belly button?"

"It does. Cross my heart and hope to die."

She wets her finger. She closes her eyes and crosses her heart. She thinks she knows everything, that Vera.

"They're tellin' packs a dirty lies. The Ma's and the Da's. There's no stupid stork or cabbage bleedin' patch," she says.

"I'm not stupid. I knew that!"

Patti guessed that already. She knows they don't buy them either; if they had to buy them, they'd want plenty of money. Sometimes her Ma forgets about the cabbage patch and the stork. She says it costs a fortune to buy a new baby. So if it's not the stalk or the cabbage patch or the fortune, what is it?

They have chalk. They start to write. On the lobby wall they draw two bellies, a fat roundy belly and a flat belly.

"There, you see," Vera, says. "It grows. It opens up when it's fat enough."

"No. I don't see."

She never saw the whole lot of a grown- up's belly, only bits of her Ma's sometimes, when she's changing her clothes. She sort of twists her clothes around her, like the girls changing on the beach, so you don't see much of her.

They examine their own belly buttons. They measure them with their fingers. Patti's is far back and deep, like it's in a little bowl. It's touchy. It makes her shiver when she sticks her finger in it. Vera's is like a big fat pimple, the way it sticks out. They draw two more bellies sideways. When she thinks of it, her Ma's belly was like a huge balloon through the smock, before she had Doris, then it was skinny again. It was the same with Vera's Ma, when she got her new baby.

"Isn't it always like that? Skinny then fat. Then skinny again?" Vera says.

"No. It's fat first, then skinny, then fat again."

It sounds dead dopey, but maybe it's true. It's the same with most of the Ma's, they have the huge roundy bellies in the smocks, then the flat bellies and the loose smocks.

They watch out for fat bellies and flat bellies and in-between bellies. They make notes. It's like they're doing a school project, where they write everything down and draw pictures. In school, everyone is talking about babies and bellybuttons. It gets passed around at break time. It spreads. They're whispering with their hands over their mouths. They're holding back hair and whispering into ears. One of the brainy boxes says it might be scientific. She reads her brothers science annuals and she thinks everything is scientific. They have a mission, she says. They have to collect info. They'll call it the Facts of Life Mission.

A few of them hold a meeting under the stairs. Someone keeps ello. It feels real important. There's five of them at the meeting, like in the Famous Five. Together they might solve the mystery. Brainy box says a balloon starts off small before you blow it up.

"It swells. It bursts. It goes back down."

"So what?" Patti says.

"It makes sense."

"No it doesn't; what has a balloon got to do with a baby?"

312

"The baby starts small. It grows. It has to get out, same as air in the balloon."

"That's balderdash," Patti says.

They can't write any notes to each other. It's dicey. They can't mention it to boys either, especially their brothers. They wouldn't understand. Patti thinks there might be something in the library, upstairs in the adult section. They all agree that the best way to find out stuff is to listen out for anything new, near doorways and keyholes, under balconies, in the shops, outside the chapel gates. Make notes in your head and report it back at the next meeting.

It's in her head all the time. A baby in your belly. Sure it'd smother with no air. It doesn't make sense. Patti tries to imagine it; the baby's head, then the whole baby, then the bellybutton bursting open. She keeps thinking of Doris, after she came home from the hospital. Her head. The length of her. Her feet and toes. In the library she searches in the art section first. The nudies in the art pictures have roundy white bellies and small diddies like pimples, so maybe there's a baby in there. It's mostly pictures and there's nothing about babies in the writing at the bottom of the page.

She can't find anything scientific either; in the science section, the books are all about space and planets and atom bombs. There's nothing much in the medical books either, it's all about skeletons, with the names of all the bones marked out in boxes. She never knew she had so many bones in one hand. There's disgusting stuff about skin diseases, like warts and pimples and pustules, whatever they are. There's pictures of pustules under a microscope. It's gross! Scabies are there too, an up close picture of a bunch of them on someone's hand. She heard about scabies all right. It's contagious, like leprosy. There's these little clusters between the fingers, an itchy red rash. If you got the scabies, you'd have to be fumigated. She snaps the book shut. She could ask the librarian, if there's a book about getting babies, but she doesn't want to.

There's nothing much to report at the next meeting. No one has any news, except for brainy box who says she has an idea.

It might be like a seed you plant, the seed grows into a baby, like an apple. It's not clear how the seed gets planted, but she's working on that, she says. Another girl, Therese, says she heard a woman talking in their yard; it was about a neighbour who got sectioned. She couldn't hear everything, but it sounded like she had a new baby and her belly was cut into sections in the Rotunda Hospital. "Sliced!" one woman said to the other. So maybe that's what happens; they make a cut like an operation. Patti heard that word sectioned before. It was in the Daisy Market. The dealers were talking about this new operation. This woman got sectioned. She said they cut her crossways like a hotcross bun.

"It's a start," brainy box says.

"It's better than nothing," Ann Byrne says.

63

A SUNNY DAY

It's summer at last. The sun peeps its sparkly head out from behind the white clouds. It shines and twinkles and the whole block of flats lights up, the grey fish market wall, the balconies, the doors and the windows. They're on their school holidays. Her Ma has a new dress. It's lovely. Bluey greeny shiny stuff with a feathery pattern that's figured-in at the waist. Aunt Jinny made the dress in work from a bit of leftover material, she calls a remnant.

"What colour would you call that?" Patti asks.

"Peacock blue," her Ma says, "like the feathers of a peacock."

She'll swank in that dress, she says. They might go to the seaside if the weather keeps up. Last night, her Ma put the clips in her hair to make it curly, so up pops the curls, when she takes out the clips. She loosens them out with her fingers, so it's all curly around her face. She's rubbing on rouge at the mirror in the back bedroom.

"Make sure there's no one coming," she says.

"Course there isn't. The coast is clear."

She tips at her lips with the lipstick. She pats them together, but not all her lips are filled in.

"There's bits missin' Ma, over there at the edges."

"It'll do. It's not a dancehall I'm goin' to, but I wish it was."

She wiggles into her new peacock dress, pulls it up over her slip and pushes her hands through the armholes.

"Isn't it gorgeous?"

"Oh, it's lovely Ma."

"Zip me up."

Patti tries the zip. She has to pull hard at her waist, where the zip stops and the shiny peacock stuff stretches on each side.

"Hold in your belly."

She takes a deep breath and pulls in her belly.

"Hurry up, or I'll burst."

"The zip is stuck in the middle."

"Pull harder."

She pulls the two dress sides together. Then she pulls harder with the zip. It goes up. Just.

"There, that's better," her Ma says, letting out her breath.

"It fits ya like a glove Ma."

She looks lovely Patti thinks only the dress is a bit tight. In front of the mirror she does a half twirl. She tries to see her back.

"Am I stickin' out at the back?"

"No. Only a bit at the front."

"Aunt Jinny says she can let the dress out, if it's a bit tight. But it's all right for now."

She wets her finger and rubs at her eyebrows. She blinks in the mirror. Her black hair bounces. She puts a clip at the front to hold it off her face.

"There. That'll do," she says to the mirror.

It's like a different Ma in the new dress with her hair done. They put on their new poplin dresses that Aunt Jinny made. They have pleats and puff sleeves and they're not in any of the shops in town.

Patti loves the seaside. They always go to Portmarnock in the summer. The sky was all blue when she woke. She saw a blue square in the windowpane. First it was sunny, then it was cloudy, and then it got sunny again. First they're going, then they're not going, then they're going again. Her Ma keeps checking the sky. She's in and out all the time, her face changing like the sky.

Then she jumps up on the bath board to see out the window.

"Would ya credit it, bloody rain clouds and the sun's gone in again."

They're all out at the door, watching for the sun.

"There it is. It's out again. There's loads of blue sky up there, under them clouds. By the time we get to Portmarnock, it'll be bluer," Patti says.

"All right so. We better get a move on."

Phew! That was close. They could've ended up just going to Stephen's Green or The Phoenix Park, or just hanging around the flats. So her Ma has on her sunny face again. She makes the banana sambos with the small sliced pan. She wraps them up in the yellow greaseproof wrapper. She makes goody goody for the babby with milk and bread. She feeds and changes her. She straps her in the pram and gives her a Farley's Rusk to chew on. Patti puts the sloppy Joes on the boys, and the S belts on their shorts to stop them falling down. They keep kicking and wriggling away from her.

They're nearly ready. The straw messagebag is full up to the brim. Anna wants to carry the bucket and spade. So does Bernie. They have a tug of war and they won't let go. One pulls this way and one pulls that way. Anna grinds her teeth. Her face goes red from all the pulling. The bucket handle breaks off and the bucket goes flying and Bernie falls backwards against the wall.

"It's b'oke! It's b'oke!" she roars.

"Ha Ha. That chuck you!" Anna says and grabs the bucket. They're on the floor then, Anna on top of Bernie, then Bernie on top of Anna. They're pulling hair and trying to bite one another like mad things. Her Ma says she'll give them a good clatter if they don't stop. She tries to separate them, but they're twisted together, like a skipping rope. She grabs Anna's arm. "Let go!" She shouts. She lets go then. Anna sticks her tongue out at Bernie and Bernie sticks her tongue out at Anna.

"Yiz are like fish market cats," Ma says, picking up the bucket.

"There'll be no seaside or buckets and spades if youse pair keep this up."

So, like magic they're good again.

They walk fast out through the end gate; they pass Coalman's rope weavers and the fruit market. At Mary's Abbey, they cut through a cobbly lane onto the quays.

"The noise of your dress Ma."

A swish of the blue shiny cloth, when she walks.

"It's the stuff in it. Jinny said it was something between taffeta and silk, a cloth made for style, a cloth you'd never get in Ireland."

She stops to light a cigarette. She takes a long drag and blows smoke into the air. A sudden breeze from the Liffey grabs the smoke and bends it sideways. The sun is hot again. Her Ma says: "You could fry an egg on that ground." And they all start to laugh.

Jimmy has his Batman cloak on over his striped tee shirt. He's doing Batman stunts everywhere; he's running up steps and jumping back down, he's climbing up poles and lamp posts.

"Sock! Pow!" He goes, punching the air.

"You'll melt in that Batman cloak," Ma says.

Doris has dribbles down her chin. She's still munching on the Farley's Rusk. She has on a white sun bonnet and a lemon cotton dress. She looks dead cute, propped up on her pillow. Franey is trying to pull off Jimmy's Batman cloak.

"Me Baman, me Baman," he keeps shouting.

"I'll swing for the lot of yiz if youse don't quit messin'."

She throws her butt over the Liffey wall. It floats for a bit. Then it sinks. They all watch it go under the water.

There's sparkles in the Liffey like diamonds. Anna says the sky is turned upside- down.

"It's only a reflection," Patti says.

"What's a reflection? "

"Like, when you look in the mirror and see your face."

At O'Connell Bridge, they cross at the traffic lights.

"Them kids are as crabby and peevish, I shudda stayed at home."

"We're jaded from all this walkin'," Anna says.

"It's on'y around the next corner, so shut your mouth," Ma says.

The queue is half way down Abbey Street and it must be a mile long.

"Look at the length of that queue Ma," Patti says.

"We'll be hours here."

They stop near the top of the queue. She turns the pram around.

"There's no sign of a bus yet, so sit down on them steps like good children and stay easy. "

"Them steps are wostin' hot Ma," Anna says.

Instead of sitting down, they start running up and down the steps.

"Try an get us a good place on that queue. Squeeze up near the front. No one'll see ya."

"I will not. That's skippin'," Patti says.

"Oh for Gods sake. We'll be here for the duration so."

"I told ya it was long."

"No way can we skip the queue. See the looks they're givin' us already? "

"Let them look all they want. I'm jacked. This heat's a killer and I'm meltin' in this peacock dress."

"So am I."

"Listen, I'm goin' over here for a smoke. Keep us a place on that queue. I won't be a minute."

"Don't be long Ma."

Near the steps, she asks a woman for a light. Patti joins the back of the queue. The queue is thick with prams and go-cars and bags, there's gangs of kids messing and pushing and shouting. They're hours waiting. It's murder trying to get on when the bus comes. The queue pushes forward and gets fatter. There's a big shove to the front; skippers from the back push and dig and kick through the queue. Screaming kids are dragged on the bus by the arms and fold-up prams are thrown under the stairs. It's whoever can push their way onto the bus first. It's whoever has the strongest shoulders. Just when they're near the front, the bus conductor puts out his arm to stop them.

"That's it!" he shouts and rings the bell. There's curses and jeers from some of them who didn't get on. This young fella spits a big gollier at the platform. The conductor waves his fist at him as the bus moves away. Everyone mooches back onto the queue that's not really a queue anymore. Doris is strapped back into her pram. They stay put near the bus stop. The pole is hot. There's stacks of butts at the base.

"We'll have ta go home if a bus doesn't come soon."

"This time we'll get on for deffo Ma, so lets wait for another while," Patti says.

"We better make sure no one skips us."

The kids start to jump on the steps again. It's another long wait for the next bus. It's another big crush when it comes. Everyone pushes from behind. They nearly get pushed off the queue this time, but they push their way through all the shoulders and jump on first. Patti takes Doris.

"Get in there quick, before we're all squashed ta death," her Ma says.

The bus conductor gives out hell about all the prams and go-cars.

"THIS IS NOT A KINTERGARTEN!" He shouts.

"Aul crank," Ma says, folding up the pram.

Patti jumps into a side-seat and holds a place. There's a big scatter for the upstairs seats.

When her Ma gets on, she tells Jimmy to bring Bernie and Anna upstairs and come back down when the conductor goes up, but the bus is so full up they can hardly move. They all squeeze into the side seat. It's mostly women with babbies in their arms. Ma squeezes over and makes more room for this fat woman holding a baby. Patti is nearly smothered with her arms.

"Thanks Misses," the woman says and takes out a hankie and wipes her forehead.

"This heat's shockin! It'd boil ya alive."

"You're tellin' me Mam? I'm near roasted waitin' for this bus."

The conductor goes along to take the fares with his ticket machine. He winds the dial with the handle and the ticket slides out. There's murder over the fares. They won't pay for the kids. They give out hell.

They say, "He's on'y two" or, "She's only three," but you'd know to look at them they were about six or seven.

Her Ma says: "One and a half to Portmarnock beach please."

The conductor looks at Ma, then looks at the kids bunched around her. She opens her purse. She tells him they're only babbies, and little Batman there, is under five.

The conductor says: "Are ya coddin me Misses?"

"No! All my kid's are big for their ages."

"D'ya want to get off at the next stop then?" He says, real cranky.

Ma says, no. She would not! It took her hours to get them all ready and hours more to get on this bus. He scratches his head and asks God to give him patience. He does a head count with his finger.

He says: "One adult and four half's."

Ma gives him a look. Then she takes out the money, the pennies and twopences. She counts it real slow into his hand. The machine rolls out the brand new bus tickets in a white curl.

"Good job it's children's allowance week."

"CIE. Bloody robbery!" the fat woman says. "It's bloody scandalous what they can charge for little chisslers."

They're all kneeling on the seat with their faces stuck to the window. They pass a big park with low railings.

"What's that called?" Patti asks.

"That's Fairview Park," her Ma says.

They pass rows of posh houses with front gardens and stripy covers over the hall doors. They're all jaded. It's hot and sweaty on the bus. Thick with cigarette smoke, like in a pub on a Sunday. It's a good job Patti is not wearing her glasses, because they'd be like dirty windows with all the smoke. She has them in her dress pocket. The babby screams with the heat; she's like a squirmy snake on Ma's lap.

Anna and Bernie are still in sulks over the bucket and spade. Jimmy runs up and down the stairs, reporting on what's going on up there. The conductor shouts a warning to keep Batman under control.

"Musta got up the wrong side of the bed this mornin'," the cranky aul so and so," the fat woman says.

He rings the bell. He warns the messers they'll get put off at the next stop.

"Keep them bloody kids under control!"

Her Ma gives him a look.

"Cheeky get. Musta never been a child 'imself."

It's always like this on the seaside bus. There's a smell of dirty nappies all of a sudden, and Patti hopes it's not their babby. After miles and miles there's a thin blue line of sea somewhere up ahead. They hear them all cheering upstairs.

Her Ma says: "Thanks be ta God, we're here. I'm baked alive. It's like an oven in this bus."

When the bus stops, there's a scatter to get off. It's more pushing and shoving with elbows and shoulders. The bus conductor throws the prams and go-cars onto the path.

"Mind that pram, that's a pure Silver Cross," Ma says.

Outside the bus. A lovely smell of the sea. The screams of the kids, when they see the packed beach and the white sudsy waves. Ma is strangled trying to open out the pram. The fat woman puts down her babby and gives her a hand. Patti straps the babby in. There's a roundy shop with a cornet roof that has beach balls and buckets and spades hanging up. Ma says it's a kiosk. Franey wants a beach ball. The others all want sweeties. They see steps to the beach. Ma bumps the pram down real slow with Patti holding the back. Three of them make a run for it across the sand with their arms out. They kick sand up in the air as they run.

"Get back here now," Ma shouts after them, but they keep going. They stop a bit back from the edge and do a kind of paddle-dance when the water comes in. All of a sudden, a big wave comes and they run back.

"Jesus Mary, I'll batter them," her Ma goes.

The sea is real blue with curly rows of white waves. The sand is warm and soft, through Patti's plastic sandals. They find a place to sit. They're allowed to take off their shoes. The beach is packed, there's stalls for tea and hot water and ice cream. There's coloured rocking boats swinging back and forth with screaming children. A brown fat-bellied donkey, walking and stopping, walking and stopping. A boy with a red face and a straw hat trying to pull it along by the reins. Women spread out on stripy deckchairs, asleep, or making fans out of newspapers, their veiny legs like boiled sausages.

"I'm half dead after that bloody endless journey," Ma says.

Doris wants to get out; she starts to bawl and kick so Ma tightens her straps. Then she tries to grab a bunch of her hair.

"Baba," she says in a gurgle.

"The ba ba! Now say Ma ma!"

Ma sucks her rubber soother first and stuffs it into her mouth.

"That'll keep her gob shut for a while."

She spreads out the towel; they all try to get a bit, but it's not big enough. Patti has bathing togs, flowery elasticy yokes in a sort of browny green material. Her granny bought them brand new in the Daisy Market off Molly. She hates them. They're too tight and they're horrible, but she doesn't care because she wants to get in the water. They're bunched up when she takes them out of the bag, with a musty bleachy smell from the Iveagh Baths. She sits down under the towel. She wriggles out of her clothes. She pulls the tight togs up under her dress. Her Ma ties the strings at her neck. She says she could do with a bit of sun on her skin. Jimmy has fancy blue and red swim trunks; he puts back on his Batman cloak and Ma says it's a show.

"Gimme that bloody cloak for Godsake."

She grabs at the cloak and folds it up.

Franey is in red poplin shorts. Ma says he's like a little German with his head of blonde curls. There's kids running around the beach in their knickers and vests. Bernie doesn't like the sun. She crosses her arms high and puts on a face.

"Don' like the seaside," she says.

"Don't start you," Ma warns her.

She sits down in a huff and starts to bite her nails. She grabs the bucket and starts to fill it with sand. Anna reefs it back off her. Here they go again.

"Gimme tha' bucka! " Anna shouts.

"Get that bloody bucket off them," Ma shouts. There's murder over the bucket. Patti starts to make a pie. They all get chances at filling the bucket. Then they're fighting over who's sand pie is the biggest.

The babby starts to cry for her bottle. Ma roots in the messagebag. It's wrapped in a baby vest, so the milk is still warm. She shakes the bottle first. She props her up on the pillow and feeds her in the pram, with the bottle resting on a bunched blanket. Then she lifts her up and puts her over her shoulder to break her wind. After a while she asks the woman sitting beside them, would she throw an eye to their stuff while they're in the water. The woman says:

"Certainly. Don't worry. I'll keep an eye missus."

Here they go like mad things running through the sand.

"Geronimo!" Jimmy shouts. He runs in S's, around the people sitting on the sand. The others follow him.

"Geronimo! Geronimo!"

Patti dips her toes in first, then her feet, until the water is up to her ankles. Ohhh! It's for eee zin'! For ee zin! Her teeth are chattering all on their own.

"It's lovely," she shouts back to the others, even though it's like ice.

They all go for a paddle then. Her Ma kicks off her shoes, tucks her peacock dress into her knickers. She looks funny with her legs bare and white without stockings.

"Yusha! Yusha Mary Ellen!"

She dips the babby's feet in the water. Then she sits her down. After a while, her plastic knickers fill up with water so it squirts out the sides, like a waterspout. Doris loves the water. Ma says she's a water baby. She's kicking and splashing and laughing at the same time. The others love it too. They're all in now, except Bernie who's standing well back on the sand.

"C'mon it's brillo," Patti shouts, but she won't budge. It's like her feet are stuck in the sand.

It's all screaming voices in the air and the crashing noise of the sea against the sand. Further out there's a few good swimmers, with their heads bobbing up and down. The big wide sky is like the blue nylon of her confo dress, she thinks.

The water feels heavy when you go out a bit. Under the water, it's all shells and sea stones and bunches of slimy brown seaweed. Her Ma shouts at them to stay in the shallow part near the edge.

"Not too far now!"

Anna is splashing everyone, kicking water up and running back out.

Ma says: "Look out!"

A big wave coming fast, up to Patti's shoulders.

"Holy Nightmare," Jimmy shouts.

They jump up at the same time, but the wave is too strong. It trips them up and knocks them over. Tons of salty water into her mouth. Yuk! Patti coughs and tries to spit it out. They're all in stitches. Jimmy says it was deadly, when he comes up. He dives into the next wave headfirst. He's able to swim. A bit. The water is getting warmer. They all hold hands near the edge. They do a ringa ringa rosy. They all fall down in the shallow water at the edge. Ma looks dead happy, like she belongs to the sea. With one hand, she throws water onto her arms and face.

"That's smashin'," she says. "The longer you're in, the warmer it gets."

Her new peacock dress is all wet at the bottom. Her lovely springy curls are out and her hair is gone straight again. There's no rouge left on her cheeks either. And her nose is getting sunburnt. All their noses are.

Then she says: "That's enough for now. We'll go back and have a banana sambo."

She dips the babby's feet in the water one last time, and starts to walk back.

They see a motorboat with it's pointy front sticking up out of the water. It's doing fancy turns and loops and skids. It leaves a line of white foam behind it.

"Ba'man's boat," Franey shouts.

It looks like the one in Batman all right, only it's a different colour. On the way back up the beach, all their teeth are chattering. All their knees are knocking.

Everyone wants the towel.

"MAA THE T TOWEL!"

"It's only seawater and yiz'll dry off in the sun, " she says. So there's murder over the towel.

She dries the babby first, then changes her nappy on her lap. She squeezes out her vest and spreads it out to dry on the sand. The woman beside them says she has her hands full, but they're lovely children God bless them. Ma nods like she knows that already. Says thanks very much. Then she roots in the messagebag for the banana sambos.

"Here, run over an' get a large bottle of orange from that stall over there."

She counts out money, but it's not enough. The stall woman says she needs another tuppence. Ma gives out.

She says: "The bloody price of minerals out here!"

They get chances at drinking from the bottle. The orange is a bit warm, but it's lovely with real bits of orange. The banana sambos are gone brown and squashy, but still they gobble them up; it's gobble gobble gobble, munch munch munch.

"Eat proper and take your time. It's not little savages I'm rearin'," Ma says.

It's always the same after you're in water, like after the Iveagh Baths. You're always starving. Bernie wants more. So does Anna.

"Is there any more sambitches Ma?"

"No. Now go and play and no more fights over buckets."

She gets out the box of Farley's rusks for the babby, but they all want one. All the hands in the long box, with the babby's smiley face on the front.

All the munching and the crunching and you'd think they were babbies themselves.

There's a light snippy breeze. Then there's this gorgeous smell of chips all of a sudden. Like what you get passing a chipper.

"D'ya get it Ma?" Patti says.

"What?"

"The smell."

"Don't start you. Aren't I only after changing that babby."

"No. Not the nappy. I smell chips. Can we get chips?"

"Chips? Chips is it? "

"Get chips Ma," Bernie says. "G'on, pleeeese!"

"Ch eps! Ch eps!" Anna bawls.

And then Franey: "Chipy's Chipy's!"

They all want chips, but chips are too dear, Ma tells them. They cost a small fortune off the stalls. She heard it's a shilling for a single out here and they're only nine pence in the chipper at home.

"They'd rob the eye out of your head, these seaside dealers and come back for the eyelashes."

The woman beside them nods.

"That's right Misses. Bloody robbery out here. Everything marked up sky high just cause it's a sunny day."

"A Rothschild, you'd want to be for them."

The woman laughs.

"What's a Rothschild?" Franey asks.

"A very rich man. A millionaire. I shudda married a millionaire and then we could buy our own chip shop and Tailor Keith's lemonade factory as we're at it."

The woman says the seaside dealers make more money than the Moore Street dealers. They charge for boiling water too.

"Imagine, chargin' for water! Have they no shame?"

She opens her purse. She roots around in there with her fingers. She opens flaps and zips.

"Ok so, anthin' to keep youse all happy."

She takes out a shilling. She gives it to Patti.

She says, "Get a single and tell that woman, to throw in a few extra chips for good measure. Say they're for the babby. And don't forget plenty of salt and vinegar."

Jimmy says he'll help her to carry the chips. Anna says, so will she. Then Bernie.

"I can carry the chips meself. They're not that heavy."

They're all behind her then, Jimmy in his Batcloak, Anna with her wet hair in her eyes, Bernie behind her, with her arms folded, Franey behind Bernie. Here they are, all following her up the sandy hill. There's a queue. They wait in line. There's a deadly smell of grease and vinegar. It's a kind of caravan thing up the steps. A big open hatch at the front with a stripy canopy overhead. A blackboard sign reads: Long ray and chips for two and six. They hear the chips sizzling in the fryer. There's not much in the little white bag when they get it. It looks smaller than the bags in their own chipper and they're small enough. The woman has on a blue bib with a money pocket, like the ones in the Daisy. She has blonde hair with black roots at her scalp. She gives Patti a look when she asks for a few extra chips for the babby. Then she turns all of a sudden. She scoops up a few more chips and drops one back down. Anna tries to climb up and grab a chip. Patti gives her a slap on the hand.

"Go back to Ma, I said."

"NO O! I want cheps!"

The salt and vinegar are in big white plastic bottles. You're allowed to shake it on yourself, so Patti pours on loads. There's tomato ketchup as well, but her Ma doesn't like it.

"The smell of them chips!" she says. She looks in the bag. She shakes it. She counts the chips.

"Begod that's the smallest single I ever saw. You'd get more chips outa two potatoes."

The kids are all around the bag. Patti tells them to wait. Her Ma shares them out, one at a time.

She sucks a chip to soften it for the Babby. Then she blows on it.

"Chippi for Dorie."

The babby scrunches up her nose, makes a face and spits out the chip.

Franey grabs at the bag. They have a few more chips and then there's only a little pool of vinegar left in the end of the bag.

"They were massive," Ma says licking the paper bag, "only they'd make ya go mad for more. I shudda brought more bread for chip sambos."

She twists the bag into a knot and tells Patti to throw it in the wire bin. Then she has a smoke and rocks the babby until she falls asleep.

They play for a while in the sand with the bucket and spade. They get chances at filling the bucket and turning it over. Anna knocks Bernie's pie over and Bernie knocks Anna's pie over. Ma says she'll be taken for the two of them if they start again. They all get dressed then, because it's starting to get chilly. They go shell picking. Patti puts on her glasses. She fills her dress pocket with shells. She'll make a shell box when she gets home, like the one in granny's glass case. Franey finds the biggest shell. He

won't let it go, but Patti says, "Put your ear to it." So they all
have a listen in the big white twisted shell that looks like an ear.
The sea sound is in the shell and they can hear it roaring. Ma
says there's nothing wrong with their ears, thank God, whatever about their eyes. When the tide goes out, they move further down the beach. Patti wants to go winkle picking. Her Ma
says, "Cheerio Misses," to the woman beside them. The woman
smiles. She says, "So long and God bless." She waves. They all
wave back. It's only the bigger ones that are allowed to pick
winkles. The rocks are slippery and slimy so they have to be
careful. They see small pinky crabs and things like tadpoles in
the rock pools. The black shiny winkles are stuck to the rocks.
They make a sucky sound when they lift them, like they don't
want to get picked. Patti tells them not to pick the whitey-pink
Albino winkles or the pale brown ones. They might be poison.
Between them, they fill a plastic bag with good black winkles.
Ma takes a nappy pin out of her bag. She shows them how to
take out the winkle. You have to root out the winkle with the
pin. First you take off the scab. You put the winkle in your mouth.
You bite into it. It's warm and cold at the same time. It's a bit slimy,
but it tastes lovely, and it smells like the sea.

They're lucky with the bus. This time they get the first bus that
comes. This time they get good seats. The conductor is nice and
smiley. He helps with the pram. He asks them did they go for a
swim.

"The water was only out of this world," Ma says all friendly.

He doesn't take a fare for Anna and Bernie and Ma says
he's a gentleman. Everyone is tired and sunburnt. They'll turn
brown tomorrow and they'll all be like little Italians. She forgot
to bring the olive oil and vinegar. The olive oil and vinegar is
only marvellous for making you go brown. Everyone on the bus
has red faces and red arms and red necks. They all get chances
with the pin at eating the winkles. It's quieter on the bus back
to town. The babby sleeps all the way. The boys are exhausted,
stretched out on a side seat beside Ma. Patti sits in another seat
between Anna and Bernie. She has to watch them in case they
start to mess. Jimmy is upstairs in the front seat in his Batman

cloak. They're all happy and tired walking back through town. It's still sunny. The sky has pinky bits and her Ma says it'll be another scorcher tomorrow. She looks happy. She says it was a grand day, but she's parching with the drouth and what she'd give for a creamy glass of stout.

There's Da sitting at the table, all grumpy, like a bear with a sore head.

"Where were youse?" He says to Ma.

"Nowhere."

"Nowhere? Nowhere?"

She lifts the babby out of the pram. Doris starts to rub her eyes and wake up.

"Where d'ya think we were? It was massive out, the sun splittin' the trees so we went to the seaside."

"Yeah, to Por'marnick an we got chips and orange and winkles . . ."

Anna's big mouth. Ma digs her in the elbow.

"Isn't it well for yiz now. Chips and orange and winkles and me here, with nothin' but, but . . ."

"There's coddle in the pot." Ma says.

"Coddle is it? Coddle is right."

He gets up. He goes in the scullery. He lifts the lid off the coddle pot. He holds it up real high like a shield.

He says: "Is that what you'd call a coddle?"

Ma's face has the guilty look, the look that means she's done something wrong, but she doesn't know what. She bites her thumbnail. She sucks her jaws in like a film star.

"It's all right," she says. "Sausages an' all. I on'y made it this mornin'."

"Sausages? Sausages?" he says and roots around in the pot with a fork.

"And rashers," Ma says back. "Steins' best collar rashers."

Da plonks the lid down with a bang. He comes out from the scullery with big fast footsteps, then he bangs the kitchen door after him. Then they hear the hall door slam and the glass shake. Da's footsteps like lightening down the courtyard.

It's all quiet then; a shivery kind of quiet. Her Ma puts the babby down in her pram and lights the gas jet under the coddle. The kids want to play out for a little while.

Outside, they all look up. There's a huge ball of sun over the Liffey, like a giant blood orange. Inside, Ma's face goes dark, kind of lonely, kind of sad and a little bit nervy. She shakes her Players box and counts what's left. She lights up from the gas jet. At the table she sits down and takes long deep drags. Cigarette smoke covers her face like a dusty picture.

"It was a good day wasn't it?"

"Yeah. It was dead brill."

"I'm glad we went."

"So am I."

"We'll go again next year if God spares us."

64

A BIT OF CULTURE

That Portmarnock day was the best day of the summer. After that it rained and sometimes it poured out of the heavens. They're already back in school. It's the day of their school tour and they're all excited. It's a long walk through town, across the Halfpenny Bridge, though the stone archway, up past the ESB, past Trinity College. This year, it's a special treat. They're going to the National Art Gallery. It's about time they learned a bit of culture, Sister said. There's Sister up ahead with her arms wagging and her habit flapping behind her. She stops every few minutes to check the line. She counts heads. She warns them about school policy in a public place, about conducting themselves in a decent manner. She checks mouths for chewing gum. Uniforms and shoes and hair. She makes them straighten their ties and sashes. She says the building they are about to enter is a national treasure trove, a place of learning and culture with sculptures and paintings by famous artists. There will be consequences for those who don't behave themselves.

They queue near the stone pillars, while sister has a word with the porter. Then she gives the signal for them to follow. Inside, it's packed with students with backpacks and yellow raincoats. They're all talking real fast in foreign accents. They look like they might be Spanish with their brown eyes and black hair. Their voices are so loud, they echo around the walls. The queue starts to move along. The porter sits behind a big mahogany desk. He has on a navy blazer. He looks a bit cranky. He gives them stony looks. He comes over, real bossy with his hands behind his back. He tells Sister she must keep her class under control. There's to be no shouting or loud talking or bad language and they can't touch any of the paintings. Sister assures him, there's no need to worry, and that her girls are very respectable and well behaved. She has on her nice smiley face, the one she has for visitors.

"Come come girls," she goes and does a clap clap with her hands.

"Follow me and no talking."

She puts one finger to her lips and you'd think they were in low babies. They try to keep in line, but the line keeps breaking up. There's a statue of a nudey man on a stand in the hallway. Sister keeps her head in the air and pretends not to see. They all hurry past. A tour guide is standing back in front of a picture with the students all around her. She's talking fast and pointing out parts of the painting with a pointer.

The floors are slippy and shiny in the big room. Sister tells them to go easy. That they're like a herd of elephants. It's the holy paintings she wants them to see, the big huge ones that are nearly as big as the wall. They're all about Jesus and the saints and angels. There's one about Adam and Eve in the garden. Another one about John the Baptist. They pass by some nudey pictures. Girls in their skin, with chubby faced angels flying above them. They're like the ones in the library book. They try to keep in the laughing.

Vera gives Patti a dig.

"Looka the size of her belly."

Everyone starts to titter. Sister turns around quick on her heels. She looks down the line. She tells them to behave themselves in this important place of culture! She's vexed, she says and there'll be extra homework for the troublemakers when they get back to class. Her face goes bright pink. She pulls down her head veil at the back. She turns and walks fast, past the big paintings, past the portraits of old men with funny broad hats, past the landscapes. She keeps going through another doorway.

In another room the paintings are smaller. Sister stops in front of one of them. She says it's the Liffey Swim by Jack B Yeats. It's people watching the Liffey Swim, only it's years ago when people wore old fashioned clothes. There's a few swimmers in the water with their heads turned sideways. Sister says the artist is a famous painter, the brother of W B Yeats the poet. There's more paintings with colours they never saw before. A purple so deep it's nearly black. A yellow so bright it nearly blinds you.

"It's the painting style of the artist," sister says. "You have to stand back to appreciate it."

They all stand back in a bunch. Vera says, "That's crap," under her breath. Lucky Sister doesn't hear her. She looks at all their faces. She says it's not every day you come face to face with the work of great artists. Some of them make a face, like they couldn't care less and some pretend to listen. The porter watches them from the doorway.

65

THE BIG MITCH

They were talking about mitching in school. It was after drill, when Miss Dredge went for a smoke. Vera said it was a cinch, and they were all doing it in sixth class. Here's how it goes. First you have to hide your schoolbag. Then you figure out a place to hang around. There's all different places you can hide out. There's The Temple or the Forty Steps, there's Stephen's Green or the Phoenix Park. There's town. You could mooch around downtown for hours. You could go up Thomas Street or Meath Street. Most important thing is, you have to watch out for the school inspector. But if you do it right, you'd never get caught. Patti was thinking she might go on a mitch herself, to see what it's like. It'd be like an experiment, but it'd be better on her own. She'll hide her schoolbag in granny's coalhole. She hates school and there's no more hiding in the wardrobe. If her Da found out, there'd be blue murder. Her Ma thinks he knows, because he's always looking in the wardrobe at dinner hour. She has to make a plan. She writes it in code at the back of her jotter: P B in C; put bag in coalhole. H I K B: Hide in Kevin Barry flats. W O F D R: watch out for Daddy Ryan.

It's Friday already, the day she picked out. After granny goes out to the market, she hides her bag behind the coalhole. She pushes it well in, behind the lift-up door, under a stack of grape trays. It's a cinch. You'd never guess it was there. She walks normal out the gate like she was going to school. First, she goes to Kevin Barry flats. She goes the long way up Church Street in case anyone sees her. No one knows her in Kevin Barry flats. She sneaks up to the top balcony. There's no one around. She can see everything from up here; the two blocks of flats like big L's, the rows of cottages, the Liffey, the markets, the Four Courts, Nelson's Pillar, all the church steeples, the Temple, her school on the hill. Oh God! When she thinks of it, she feels dead nervous. In class, they'll be doing Irish, reading out loud from their Irish readers. Sean and bloody Máire, two skinny little kids who speak Irish. Sean and Máire with a madra, or a liathroid. She's glad she's not there. It's not that she doesn't like Irish, but the stupid book they learn out of is crap. The Ma and the Da all nicey nicey to one another all the time. It's always the same. Ta Mami sa chistin. Ta Daidi sa gairdín. And that babby they have is a dead ringer for Mister Magoo.

Next it'll be needlework. That's worse. Thanks be to God she went on a mitch. A radio is playing in one of the flats, the clattering sound of delf being washed. There's a lovely smell of a fry. She'd love a cuppa sweet tea, with a slice of fresh bread. A crusty black heel from a loaf out of Johnston Mooney's. Loads of butter. Yum! One of her Ma's crispy black fried sausages. In her granny's place, she had tea and bread. Granny went out early. Good job. They'll never find her schoolbag. Not in a million years.

It's nice up in Kevin Barry flats, except there's a bit of a pissy smell on the stairs. Over the balcony, it's all traffic noise. She can see there's still a queue of lorries and carts lined up outside the fruit market. They're stacked up, with cauliflowers, cabbage, carrots and potatoes. The farmers queue from early morning. Friday is always a busy day. She has rubber bouncing balls in her cardigan pockets. She plays for a while on the lobby with her gymslip tucked sideways into a knot. She throws the balls against the wall and sings to herself: Plainey package a Rinso, over package a Rinso, upy, downy, dashie, archie, backie. It's no good on your own; you need a partner to play against. A woman wearing slippers and holding a big purse passes and gives her a look.

"Should you not be in school? " she says real snotty.

"No"

"Is it a holy day of obligation?"

"No. I have the measles."

"The measles? Should you not be in bed then?"

"No. I'm not contagious."

The woman gives her another look and hurry's down the stairs. She must be one of the nosey parkers, Patti thinks. She better be careful.

She's here ages. It must be real late now. It's dead dopey playing on your own. She has a Nugget polish tin, stuffed with newspapers for playing piggy beds. She has chalk. She'd write on the wall, but you can't rub off the chalk, unless you get a scrubbing brush and bread soda. Someone might see her. Oulones who know her granny. There's the mass bell: DONNGG! DONNGG! DONNGG! Oh no! That means it's only ten to ten. She was thinking it must be about eleven or half eleven. It's only the first mass bell. Here's the second mass bell from Church Street chapel. It's not as loud. Adam and Eves is a bit too far away. But yes, there it is, a different further away sound: Dw ong! Dw ong! And it sounds like a bell with a stutter. They'll be rushing out to Halston Street and Church Street and Adam and Eves, with rosary beads in their pockets. Some of them have different chapels for different days. Patti sits down on a step. It's getting cold. Good job she has her blue school cardigan on over her gymslip. She pulls it tight around her and pulls down the sleeves. This one is a bit short in the sleeves; her granny always makes the sleeves too short or too long. Her blue school tie is rolled in a ball up one of those sleeves. She looks up. The sky is mostly grey, with low soggy clouds, that seem to be moving. She hopes it won't rain. She moves up a step. The ground is cold and hard. It goes up through her gymslip. That's how you get a cold on the kidneys. That means hospital, needles, an operation maybe.

She can't stay here all day. She'll have to move on. A dog barks somewhere in one of the flats. She skips down the steps and jumps the last four. A man is leaning over the first balcony, his trouser braces down over his hips. He looks around at Patti and starts a fit of coughing. He spits phlegm out over the balcony and wipes his mouth with the back of his hand. He turns and looks at her again as if he's seen a ghost. Sneaking along King Street. In at the wall. Her glasses in her pocket. Her fringe over her eyes. She heads into town by Bolton Street and Dominick Street. She's burstin' all of a sudden.

In Roches stores, she legs it up the stairs quick to the toilet. Just in time. She looks in the mirror. She takes out her ponytail, combs her hair with her fingers. The face in the mirror looks peculiar; it's the same Patti, but it's a different Patti too. At the cosmetic counter, she tries on makeup in front of the swing mirror. There's tissues on the counter. It's allowed. You can try out testers to see if a colour suits you. Then you're supposed to rub it off. The Max Factor girls with the white blouses and black skirts look at her looking in the mirror. The blondie one digs the other one in the arm. They say nothing, so it must be ok. She pretends not to notice. Patti likes makeup. Lipstick and eye shadow, mascara and powder. Coral Rose is a nice shade of lipstick. She rubs her lips together. Using a sponge tip, she rubs Aquamarine eye shadow onto her eyelids. It suits her brown eyes. Makes them look bigger. The Pan sticks are in a line with plastic lids in five different shades. She tries out Deep Olive, rubs it all over her face. Yes. That's nice and you'd think she had a tan now. Those dark shades are lovely, for when she'll be going out to dances, only she can't let her Da see her done up. He'll have another canary or blue murder. Her Da thinks makeup is common, but what he doesn't know doesn't kill him. Before leaving the counter, she sprays her neck and wrists with Coty L'aimant perfume. That's Aunt Dinah's favourite. When she's out working, she'll have loads of makeup. The Max Factor girls watch her walking away.

Upstairs, in at the back, she tries on hats. There's funny looking half ball shaped hats covered in flower petals; there's flat ones called pillboxes. She tries on a pillbox in a deep shade of red. No. It doesn't suit her. A bit hickey looking, like a strawberry cream sponge cake. Here's another one made of straw. It has a wide floppy brim with a blue ribbon. She tries it on. Yes. That's nice, only it's too big for her head. It suits her fringe and her new makeup. It'd be nice for a bride, as a going away hat, she thinks. On the stairs, there's a new spy eye security camera. It's a square black yoke with a red flashing eye. It's supposed to catch robbers in the act. It blinks and takes a picture of you when you pass. It sees you everywhere. It follows you around the store, like eyes in a holy picture. On the stairs, Patti stands in front of it. The red eye looks straight back at her. So what? Look all you want, she says in her head. She's not going to rob something, is she? She's not that stupid. On the ground floor, she gets in the lift. The liftman with the grey shop coat presses the down button and starts to whistle. The lift makes a sound like the ham cutter in the Dairy. Then it stops and the door goes back. Patti steps out, says thanks to the liftman. He gives her a salute like a soldier. Downstairs, it's all household stuff; there's ornaments, delf, mirrors, pictures, bedclothes. She has a ramble around. It's lovely and warm with heat coming out of a grill in the ceiling. There's low jazzy music playing somewhere. She sees a tall man in a dark suit. He's walking around with his hands behind his back, like he has nothing to do. Down near the back, there's a bed all made up, with a mauve quilted nylon bedspread. It has pillowcases to match. She's jaded and she'd like to lie down, but the man in the suit is watching her. She sees him in a mirror behind her. She walks back up the steps, makes a funny face at the camera.

There's hardly anyone in Dunnes Stores. She walks around. She looks at all the stuff out on the wood counters. She picks up a wine polo neck jumper and holds it up to her. It's size thirty-four, a bit long for her, but not that long. Polo necks are all the fashion. She'd love one. Maybe next year, when she gets a summer job. Here's a counter of nylon panties in white, blue, lemon and pink. And plainer cotton ones, with millions of tiny air holes. Nice and soft when she feels them. There's outsize bloomers for oulones in blue and pink and white, like what her granny wears. Granny gets hers in Clery's. She'd never buy in Dunnes Stores. It's a bit dark and gloomy in Dunnes, so she doesn't stay long.

Hickeys has nice dress material. It's in behind the counter on wooden shelves, up at the back of the shop. The woman serving is old, with pinky-grey hair up in a bun. She's wearing a white georgette blouse with a high lace collar.

"Yes?" She says. "Can I help you?"

"I was just looking," Patti says.

"At anything in particular?"

"Oh. Em . . . At the dress material. I might have a dress made to measure; my aunty is a dress designer; she makes dresses for the French market."

"Is that right? Should you not be in school?"

"No. It's a day off."

The woman has pearl pink nail varnish, the backs of her hands are spotty and wrinkly.

"You from that convent uptown?"

"Yeah."

A woman comes in wheeling a go-car. She wants four yards of white poplin and four yards of satin lining to match. The old woman stands on a stool. She nearly breaks her neck pulling out the roll of poplin. Patti looks at the embroidery threads on a swivel stand at the side of the counter. The colours! All the different shades of purple. All the sunny yellows and the darker yellows; all the greens, like down the country. She'd love one. She could easily take one. The woman is rolling out the poplin on the counter; the other woman is looking at zips and buttons on another stand. The coast is clear. Her Ma says the devil is never far away. She says he's always on the watch out for weak souls.

In Moore Street, she sees a fish dealer her granny knows. There's a queue waiting around her stall. Patti stands well back and hides in between the queue. She hopes the woman doesn't recognise her. The woman is cutting the heads and tails off a big fish. It's a ray, with huge wings and a long tail. It's grey and slimy with orange spots. She makes a long cut first with her sharp knife. She rips open the belly. She puts in her big red hand and starts to reef out the guts. They're horrible, dark red and purple ringlets, like slimy snakes. She flings them into a steel bin. She does it a few times, before she looks into the fish's belly to make sure it's all clean. Then she hoses it down, inside and out. The woman's face is red and sweaty, her grey hair coming out at the sides of her scarf. She tries to push it back, but it won't stay. She takes a deep drag of her cigarette. She taps ash on the ground. Now, she opens a whole newspaper and wraps up the ray in the pages. A man pays for the fish and the woman says: "Next!"

It's chilly in Moore Street, so Patti moves off. It smells like the Daisy Market and the fish market and Smithfield Market mixed up. There's horses and carts in the middle of the road, there's fruit boxes stacked up all over the place. The horse drivers are unloading boxes of stuff; some of them are standing around smoking. The dealers are calling out the prices in singsongy voices, trying to outdo one another. One of them might see her. Everyone down here knows her granny, so she better leg it quick, she thinks. She twists around the corner into Parnell Street. Pete's pet shop has goldfish in the window. She likes it in there, but she doesn't like the smell. There's hamsters and white mice, budgies and canaries and rabbits. Is she looking for anything in particular, a rabbit or a hamster? Pete asks her. He stands in the doorway in his brown shop-coat.

"Em . . . not really, but we might buy a goldfish in a few weeks. Me brother likes goldfishes."

"Look around so if you want. Them white mice make good little pets. Easy to keep too."

There's loads of them in one cage. She doesn't like them, their skinny tails and pinky eyes. A furry hamster on a wheel is nicer, but they're not allowed to keep pets. The canaries are nice too. You could teach them to sing. Catherine in school has a tortoise. That'd be lovely, if you had a house with a garden, Patti thinks.

"Would you have any tortoises?"

Pete is scooping birdseed from a sack into brown bags. He shakes his head.

"No sale for tortoises in the city. I couldn't sell them round here with no gardens."

"Is that so? Well ok."

It's nice to be outside again in the fresh air. Passing her old house in Wolfe Tone Street, she stops for a minute. It's still the same, the rooms with the old flowery wallpaper and the fireplaces on top of one another. The black fireplace, where they used to sit, at the very top of the room. The plants with the mauve flowers are tangled and spread out now, so they cover the whole patch of ground where the house stood. She thinks about the smelly toilets and the yard rats with the long tails. The all night hoolies and the drunken spunkers on the stairs. The runaway bull in the backyard. She feels a shiver. She hurries past. In Brereton's window, a man is arranging trays of jewellery. With no queue outside the pawn, it looks very posh. There's all the fancy jewellery and silver cutlery sparkling under a spotlight in the window. She'd love to go into the library, but the librarian will only ask her nosy parker questions about school. She might even tell one of the nuns.

In the Banba there's a nice dusty smell of second-hand books. The shelves are packed tight along the wall. A long table in the centre is stacked with comics and magazines. Down at the back, a few men are reading in the thriller section. The paperback books have girls on the covers in their slips, some are in black baby doll nighties. There's a whole shelf of skinny books with doctors and nurses kissing on the covers. There's more with airhostesses and pilots in the same pose. On a chair, there's a stack of True Romances. Aunty Dinah likes those. Patti roots through a stack of comics. They're well used, with doggy ear pages and tea stains. It's mostly Beanos and a few Bunties. They do swaps in the Banba. Pity she hasn't got a comic to swap; she wouldn't mind having a Bunty to read. On the back page, there's Bunty's cut out wardrobe of lovely clothes, with a cut out Bunty to put the clothes on. They have these little tabs to fix them on. There's loads of different Bunty outfits: there's Bunty in her ballet dress, Bunty in her horse-riding costume, Bunty going to a party, Bunty in a bathing suit with a frill. She has winter and summer clothes, with fur mufflers and gloves and boots. Bunty goes to dancing and music lessons. When Bunty wants something she just has to ask.

"Oh Mummy, could I have a new tutu? Oh Mummy, would you get me a new bicycle? Oh mummy, I would really like a new piano."

"Of course darling, anything you want darling."

Bunty has a fab time; she wouldn't mind being Bunty for a day, except for chums. Bunty has chums instead of pals. Patti picks up a comic. There's her cut out wardrobe at the back. It's for summer, a red swimsuit, a red straw hat, red flip-flops, and a red sundress with yellow daisies. Bunty is going to spend the summer with her aunty in her Spanish villa.

Outside, there's a wire bin full of cowboy books. A sign says: Three Westerns for one and six. Granda buys his books here. He likes the Westerns. He says you can't pass the Banba for good value and good reading. She better be careful. Capel Street is busy. Passing Louis Copeland's window, she pulls her hair a bit over the side of her face. She hopes he doesn't see her passing. He knows granny. Outside Boland's bakery, the gorgeous smell of baking bread! She's starving all of a sudden. She hurries past Steins. It's packed as usual. What time is it? No clock around here. There's one on the wall, over Moran and Flynn's, but it's stopped for years at a quarter to three. It must be after one. In Moran and Flynn's window, the male dummies are dressed in bright coloured nylon shirts and denim jeans. There's Levi's and Wrangler's and skinny polo neck jumpers. Johnston Mooney's has a queue out the door. The window is packed with cakes; there's doughnuts, éclairs and custard slices with oodles of warm custard, soft and squashy so it melts in your mouth. She'd like to smash that window and grab a cake. There's a lovely smell of fish and chips from Cafolla's. There's a queue at the counter; it loops around the shop and twists out the door. The Italian man is busy, shaking salt and vinegar and wrapping up chips in white paper. She'd give anything for a single with gillions and trillions of salt and vinegar. Ooodles of lovely grease. If she only had nine pence.

Out on the quays now. She crosses through heavy traffic. Down by the Liffey wall, cars and lorries, horses trotting along, clippity clopity clop. Clopity clipity clop. The tide is in, the bright green water high and wavy. Her face is in it when she bends over the wall. Her fringe. Her shoulders. The sky behind her. It must be all hours. Maybe she'll meet the Time Woman on her daily walk. No sign though of her funny sideways walk.

343

No sign of her arm stuck up in the air, pretending to look at her watch. Wait. Here' s a woman. She'll ask her.

"Miss, excuse me, would you have the right time please?"

No answer. She walks past her with her chin up. Poshy woshy woshy. Stuck up so- and- so, her high heels going clickity click.

This man coming looks friendly.

"Would ya. Would ya have the right time please?"

"Certainly."

He holds out his arm and pulls up his sleeve.

"Nearly half past twelve," he says and off he walks with his umbrella swinging on his arm.

"Thanks very much," Patti says after him.

Nearly half twelve. They'll be going home for lunch. Granny won't know she wasn't home. She's in the market until after four today, stocktaking. Then maybe a few bets after in Arran Street bookies. She likes them cute little sea horses on Capel Street Bridge. At Christ Church, she turns right and passes Corn Market dispensary. There's a smell of hospitals and she hates it. It's where her Ma got all her teeth out under gas. She had to wait months for the new set of teeth and then they looked horsey and too big for her face and the kids were all afraid of her.

In Frawley's Patti looks at the new stock just in. There's Doctor Zhivago boots for girls with laces up the front. She wouldn't mind a pair of those. They have them in black or white. There's duffel coats in charcoal grey and navy blue with wood toggles. Her own red one is nicer. She has to be careful; her granny Connor likes shopping in Frawley's for the curtain nets and tablecloths. There's only a few people in here and no one seems to be buying anything. The shop assistants look fed up with nothing to do. They stand behind the counters with their arms folded. Over in the curtain department, there's rolls of curtain nets with different designs, heavy flowery material for side curtains and bales of coloured oilcloth standing in rows. Her granny has an oilcloth tablecloth in a blue check design. Up the back, a sign says: Foundation Garments for Larger Ladies. There's rows of them on hangers, outsize corsets and bras. She lifts up a Ballet bra in a size forty-two. She holds it up to her in front of the long mirror. A woman behind her in a white blouse is looking at her in the mirror with creased eyebrows.

"Would you like to try that on?" she goes, real smart-alecky.

Patti puts the bra back on the rail.

"No. I was just lookin'."

"Look all you want, but just don't touch. Right?"

"Right."

She gives her a sour look. Patti gives her a look back. She wasn't going to rob it or anything. It was just a bit of gas. Outside, it's raining. There's dark wet dots on the ground. It makes a pattering sound on the shop canopies and stall covers. It's still well too early to go home. No use going into Woolworth's across the road; they watch you like hawks over there. A packet of spangles'd be nice though, if only she had money. Woolworth's sells all kinds of delicious sweets you can't buy anywhere else.

Meath Street is busy. Lovely meat in Kearn's window: big lean lumps of pork and bacon, back rashers and rings of black and white pudding. She'd eat a whole ring of that white pudding. She likes it raw with the skin off. The black pudding has fatty bits through it, but it's supposed to be good for your blood. In the porch on a wood slab, there's a few skinned rabbits, with their heads hanging. The flesh is pinky and shiny. It looks disgusting. Her Da likes rabbit stew. It's supposed to taste like chicken, but it doesn't. She only tasted it once and that was enough. Horrible it was! Up further, she finds a pear on the ground near the stalls, a brown William pear. It's not rotten or dirty so she picks it up. She checks it first for bruises. She wipes it with her cardigan. It's full of lovely juice. There's a nice holy picture shop near a corner at the end of the street. The window is packed with statues: Our Lady of Fatima, Saint Francis, Saint Joseph, The Little Flower, and that one called child of something, with the big hat on like a bishop's. The window is all done in white satin like an altar. There's glass rosary beads in different colours, wood crucifix's for over your bed, Sacred Heart lamps and holy water founts for the hall. At the back of the window, a woman with a beehive pulls back a curtain. It's way too high for her head, like it might topple over any minute. Patti moves off. The dealers up here sell toilet rolls and bleach and Vim. A woman sells Aran jumpers she knits herself; another one sells Fair-Isle cardigans. The smells and sounds are different on the southside and it's like you're in a different city.

It's nice and quiet in John's Lane Chapel. It's darkish. Candles flicker near the altar and along the side on brass stands. All the whispery voices send echoes around the walls. There's a lot of rough looking men with overcoats wrapped with twine. A different smell in here too. Here's a man in a long black cassock. He's called a Sacristan. He stops in front of the altar and genuflects with his head bowed. He goes out a side door and it squeaks all over the chapel. So many statues up here, you'd never run out of saints to pray to. She says a few prayers and sits back.

A man nudges her in the arm. A man with a dirty face and torn clothes. He must've sneaked up on her. There's a drunken smell. It's red biddy or meths. He must be a spunker. He starts to babble something. He's locked. She gets up fast and legs it out the door into the light. It's still raining. Quickity quick around the corner, back down John's Lane and the steep hill makes her run. She cuts through a street with redbrick houses and waits for ages before crossing Church Street Bridge. Her hair and shoulders are wet. She pulls her hair back into a ponytail. The tide is lower now. It's raining hard into the Liffey, seagulls are squealing out in the middle. It's nice to see the rain making holes in the water. Anything is better than being stuck in that smelly classroom. Anything is better than needlework and Irish. There's Ikey the newspaperman with the one eye. He has a bundle under his left arm. Early Herald's and Press's. He calls out HERALOPRESS! HERALOPRESS! He sticks out newspapers at people passing, even if they don't want one.

So. Nearly there. She's glad she done it. The big mitch. She feels different. A bit more grown-up. Her legs are killing her. She has to get back before granny comes home. She'll sneak in to get out her schoolbag. It'll be a cinch. The key is hanging on a string inside the letterbox. She'll write a letter to say she was sick. It was her kidneys or her throat; she's not sure yet. She'll give it to Sister. It'll be easy peasy lemon squeasy. She knows how to do the handwriting like her Da's, the capital D's with the loops and curls, the S's leaning a bit sideways, like they're drunk.

Dear Sister, please excuse Patti being absent . . . Inside the gate now. They'll be on their way home from school. But . . . but what's that outside the door?

Oh No! Oh gosh! Oh Saint Jude of hopeless cases. It's granny's pram tied to the drainpipe. There she is standing on the step. It's granny, with her arms folded. A big face on her. She's in early. She wasn't supposed to be home till after four. Where's her schoolbag, she'll want to know. She paid a fortune for that schoolbag. Only ten steps to the door.

Oh, I forgot it, or I left it in my pal's place, she'll say.

"In school were ya?"

"Yeah."

"Home early so?"

"Em. Not really. We got off a bit early."

"Did ya now. And did ya be any chance see Misses Moloney at all?"

"Misses Moloney? No."

She rolls up her sleeves.

"Well she saw you skivin' and gallivantin' in Moore Street."

Patti looks at the ground. Her feet in her black shoes look dead dopey all of a sudden. She stays where she is.

"Did she?"

"Yis! Around quarter to twelve, she thinks it was."

Oh God. She's in for it. Big time. Her feet won't budge. It's like she's stuck to the concrete.

"And what's this may I ask?"

Granny reaches behind her and grabs something out from the hall. It's her school bag, the tan leather yoke with the baldy straps. She holds it up with her good arm. She's shouting now, so people on the balconies can hear her.

"I suppose this school bag walked into the coalhole by itself!"

She's shaking it now in the air. She goes to belt her with it, but Patti ducks out of the way just in time. It misses. She tries again. It misses again.

"I'll I'll . . . Wait. Just wait till I see your Da! He'll scald ya! He'll send ya ta Artane!"

She throws the bag into the middle of the courtyard. It lands with a bump near a puddle.

"Always up ta somethin'. Like your Ma."

She grabs a newspaper out of the hall. She runs at her again. This time she catches her on the shoulder with her good arm.

Twhuck! Twhack! She goes with the Herald to the side of her skull.

"I'll bite ya. Get back to your Ma's. Get outa here before I . . ."

Granny's face is bright red, the colour it goes when she has an asthma attack. She's starting to wheeze, her eyes going watery at the edges. In a minute she'll be gasping. She tells her not to cross her door again. She goes inside and bangs the hall door. Hard.

Moloney the aul bitch. Must've saw her. There she is at her hall door, with her hunched shoulders. There she is with her big flowery scarf and furry slippers.

Beardy beardy, weirdy weirdy, Moloney the Baloney, the big fat moany.

She'd like to shout it out, all over the flats, so everyone will hear.

She picks up her school bag. There's a few watching on the balconies. She passes Misses Moloney like she doesn't care, slings her bag over her back and walks real slow through the flats. She says a decade of the rosary, a Hail Holy Queen. Hail Holy Queen, Mother of Mercy, please don't send me to Letterfrack or Daingean or Artane.

Outside their door, the babby is lying awake in her pram. She's kicking her legs and trying to catch the Sacred Heart picture. She says ba ba when Patti touches her chin. Inside her Ma is on her knees, scrubbing the kitchen floor with her scarf still on. She looks up.

"What has you home? I thought you were helping your granny after school."

Patti takes giant steps across the wet floor. Throws down her bag on a chair.

"Mind that floor. I'm only after washin' it. You'll go skatin'."

"D'ya want a cuppa tea?"

Ma looks at her queer like.

"Wha'? What did ya say?"

"Tea. D'ya want a cup?"

"Em all right so, the teapot's on a glimmer. Pour us a half cup."

"Ok."

She rubs Sunlight soap into the scrubbing brush, scrubs hard in a circle at a patch of oilcloth.

"Oh me bloody back. I'm half dead with this floor."

She grips a chair and stands up. She rubs at her back.

"Hope I have milk left, you'd want a Jersey cow for them kids."

There's a smell of stewed tea in the scullery. Patti pours strong black tea. It splutters into the cup.

"That tea is very strong Ma."

"It's grand."

She spoons in three sugars, pours in milk.

"That's nearly the last of that milk. A bottle was taken this mornin' from the step. Bloody robbers. They're worse than seagulls."

She shakes her cigarette box, opens the top and counts what's left. It's all noise coming from the bedroom, with the kids jumping on the bed like it's a trampoline.

"The noise. Ma, they're wreckin' that bed in there."

"Oh let them. They're only kids once. They're only playin' cowboys."

"They're messin' with the curtains too. They'll reef them off the windows."

"For God's sake, shut up. You're like your Da, always watchin everything."

Right. Let them wreck the place so. See if I care. Patti moves back the curtain and looks out. Outside it's all heavy traffic and beeping horns. She thinks it was a good day. It was good until she saw granny standing there on the step. Felt like she was free. A bit in-anyway. Better than hiding in the wardrobe. She never saw Moloney Baloney in Moore Street. She's barred now for good from granny's. That's the rule. She's not to cross her door. She said that. Not to put a foot near her door ever again. It was before she slammed the door in her face.

"I say, never mind the kids messin', what has you home?"

"Oh eh . . . granny said I had to come home to get my hair washed."

"Did she? I hope you're not walkin' alive in that head."

"No. Course I'm not."

"Are ya itchy?"

"NO!"

"I don't want joeboys in any of your heads. Come over till I see."

"No. Leave me alone. Don't start at my hair."

She roots in a drawer for the fine comb, but she can't find it. Or the yellow smelly stuff either. Her head is not itchy she tells her again.

At the table, her Da is as quiet as a church mouse, with his head stuck into the Herald. Patti is dead quiet, her own head stuck in her English book. He says nothing about granny and school. He mustn't know, not yet in-anyway. In school, she's marked absent. She didn't write the note from Da, so she has to stand out at the wall until breaktime. She gets tons of eccer. Sister says she wants to see her mother as soon as possible.

"Tell your mother to call to the convent tomorrow, any time after four."

As if. As if her Ma had the time for nuns and convents. Her Ma hasn't time to bless herself she wants to say.

"Yes Sister."

66

A LITTLE ROBBER

There's murder in granny's place. A big commotion. There's money gone missing and they're blaming it on Patti. They say it must've been her who took money from her aunty's bag. It was under the telly table in a brown envelope in the black patent handbag. A whole weeks wages. Gone! It vanished. Into thin air. There's a big investigation.

"You took it didn't you?"

No. She didn't, she says.

"You did so. Tell the truth and shame the devil. You'll have to tell it in confession."

"I DIDN'T. DID NOT!"

"Little ginnett."

"No. No."

"Little cheeky face."

"Little liar."

"Poor Dinah slaving all week in that sewin' factory and no wages."

She won't believe her. She really thinks it was her. She's trying not to cry, but she can't stop the stupid little girly tears, streaking down her face at the table. Here's granny sitting across from her, with her broken glasses on. Here's granny with her face all hard looking.

She's a Villain.

A Gnat.

A Rossy.

It's no use. She just won't listen. She has her mind already made up. Imagine them thinking she's a robber, and from Aunt Dinah. Aunt Dinah, her favourite aunty, the one who buys her orange sodas in the Rainbow Café.

Maybe someone did rob the wages, but it wasn't her. They must've taken them during the night. It could be anyone. Someone was telling lies. Big fat mortalers. All the questions she's asked. It's like she's in court and granny is the judge. She needn't think she's going nowhere till she owns up.

Did she hide it?

NO!

Did she spend it?

NO!

Did she give it to her Ma for the rent money?

NO!

For the Royal Liver Friendly Society?

NO!

For Sloan's?

For Sloan's? NO CHANCE!

A bit of her wants to say she took it, just to shut her up, but then she'd have to give back the money that she never took in the first place. It's a big mess.

Granny searches her clothes and empties out her school bag. They might have to get the police. They might have to take her fingerprints.

It'll be like when the nun's watch went missing in school. The detective came out from the Bridewell with his leather bag. He asked tons of questions they didn't understand. He wrote in his notebook. He dusted for prints first with brushes and sticky tape. There was talk about expulsion and places of correction for the culprit. It was a crime to withhold information. Anyone who knew anything must speak up or risk being punished. At the time, Patti thought it'd be dead neat to be expelled from school. One of the Four Marys in the comic was expelled from boarding school and she thought it was funny. A young one in sixth class was expelled, but she doesn't care. They see her round town smoking and talking to fellas, like she's having a brill time. The nuns think it's punishment. They don't know it's dead neat. In- anyway, they all felt guilty that day. It's like that now; it's like you're guilty even though you're not guilty. Everyone staring at you with cold eyes. Her granny's eyes go a grey stony colour, instead of bright blue. Dinah says it's only money and it'll probably turn up in it's own time. They check

and double-check everywhere. It's like they're looking for buried treasure. They pull the place to smithereens.

"A liar is worse than a robber," granny says. "A liar would
hang you."

She swears to God. She swears on her granda's grave. She's
not lying and it wasn't her. She sticks out her tongue so they can
see there's no sign of a lie there.

"What's up now?" Her Ma says when she sees her at the
door.

She swears again on her prayer book. She swears it wasn't
her.

"Maybe the lost wages will turn up and that'll chuck them,"
She says.

67

A TUBE OF COLGATE

But no. The wages never turned up and maybe that's what started it all. They don't mention the missing wages anymore. It's like it's not important now. All of a sudden, Aunt Dinah is sick. Sometimes she's so weak that she stays in bed all day. She has bad headaches. She takes Andrew's liver salts for her stomach and Misses Cullen's powders for her head. Her hands swell up and the veins stick out like on an old woman's hands. She heard them talking in the kitchen, her granny and her Da. It's something to do with blood pressure and kidneys. It's about blood that doesn't get cleaned out. It's something bad for deffo. She got x-rays in the Richmond Hospital. Granny had the waterworks.

Her Ma said, "It's a shame. She's so pretty and so young."

Aunt Dinah has to take time off work. She has to take capsules, long brown ones from a brown envelope. The doctor says, she has to take it easy, no gallivanting to parties and dancehalls, even though dancing and singing are her favourite things to do.

They're all whispering and you'd know there was something wrong. They're making sign language and miming. Everyone is dead worried. She's in and out of hospital. She got more tests. She's not eating. Not really. Only little picks of food. She's vomiting all the time now. She gets special blood injections. She's very thin. All her clothes are hanging off her. She's on this new kidney machine in Jervis Street Hospital called dialysis. It makes her blood clean. Her kidneys don't work properly, so this machine makes them work better. The machine has tons of wires and tubes hanging out of it. It's a new scientific invention, the first one in Ireland.

Three times a week, her Aunt Dinah goes for dialysis. It takes all the blood out through the tubes. It cleans it and puts it back in again. When she showed Patti the big holes in her arms for the tubes, she nearly died.

"Do they not hurt?"

"At first they did but now they don't really hurt that much."

Her Ma says, "God protect her and spare her, but you'd never see the likes of Dinah again in this world."

They all have to pray real hard that she'll get better. They're talking about a new kidney operation; it's called a transplant. That's another new scientific invention. There was this newspaper article, about a real man who got a kidney from a dead man who died in a road accident. Her Ma blesses herself when she reads it. Says: "Sacred Heart! Blessus and save us! But what's the world comin' to?"

Everyone is saying it's a miracle of science. Here's what they do. They operate on the dead person. They take out the kidney. They pack it in ice cubes to keep it fresh; then they transplant it back into the sick person. It's supposed to be a lifesaver for people who's kidneys don't work properly. They say in a few years time, they'll be doing regular transplants and saving hundreds of lives. They might even be transplanting livers and hearts and lungs one day. Uncle Willie says we're living through amazing times and anything is possible now. Her Da says it might be a breakthrough all right, but it's still very risky. Her Ma says, it's a miracle, because the man would've died without the new kidney.

There's a lot of talk about miracles. There's rosaries and novenas being said for Dinah in churches all over the city. People bring petitions to Knock Shrine and Lourdes for a cure. They bring back relics and miraculous medals and blessed scapulars. The Poor Clares in Harold's Cross are praying for her too, the Friars in Church Street and Adam and Eves and the nice-looking priest out in Mount Argus. All this and poor Dinah is getting worse. Her chap is sad. You'd know by the way he looks at her, his eyes all soft and worried. Dinah can't go out much anymore. She's always too weak after the dialysis. She has to lie down all the time. They say her working days in the sewing factory are over. She's getting thinner and she vomits all the time into a basin beside her bed.

***

They're after bringing granny home from the bingo. They have her by the arms. She can hardly walk. Two stewards from Saint Anthony's hall are linking her in the gate. Her knees are bending like her legs are broke. They're half walking, half dragging her. People in the flats are out on the balconies. The priest comes and the kitchen is full all of a sudden.

She's dead!

God! No! She can't be!

Somebody important says Aunt Dinah died peacefully just before eight this evening. But how can she be dead? There was nothing wrong with her earlier. She sent Patti for toothpaste before she left for the hospital.

"Make sure it's Colgate," she said.

She sees her mouth saying the words. Make sure it's Colgate. She had on her orange mohair coat, the one with the swingy back. Her eyebrows were done lovely and she had on her green eye shadow. Da brought her in the Radio Cabs taxi. She rolled down the window. She said goodbye out through the top. Then she waved. She can see her white hand waving with the black leather glove off. She said it again.

"Make sure its Colgate."

She wasn't allowed in to the dialysis ward, so she gave the Colgate to the nurse at the door. That was about six o'clock. It's all mad in granny's. They take her into the bedroom to lie her down. She's crying bucketloads with her head down. She's sobbing. They want to give her something to calm her down, but she won't take brandy or whiskey. The priest sits on the visitor's chair. The aunties make tea and sandwiches in the scullery. There's bunches of people in the courtyard, blessing themselves and saying Lorda Mercy. Patti kicks the wall, in the alcove between the hot press and the fireplace. She pushes her head hard against the blue flock wallpaper. No one says nothing to her. It's like they're struck dumb all of a sudden. How can she be dead? It's not fair. She's only twenty-one; she only got the key of the hall door. She got stacks of twenty-first birthday cards in the shape of silver keys. She has them in the tallboy drawer in flat cardboard boxes.

Outside the dead house, the porter says they can only have a few minutes with the deceased. He lets them in with his bunch of keys. It's darkish; only a bit of daylight from some high up window. There's a row of dead bodies under the white sheets. The porter thinks Dinah might be the end one, but he's not sure. He stands in the doorway. A long streak of sunlight shines in along the floor. In there, there's a disinfectant smell and another smell like ripe fruit. They walk the line of bodies. Her Ma's hand is shaky. She stops at the foot of the last one. She lifts the sheet back slowly. It's not her. It's this gummy oulfella with a stony face.

"God blessus and save us! Lorda mercy!" Her Ma says blessing herself. They start to move backwards in the dark and light shadows.

"It's dead spooky," Patti says.

"The dead can't harm us. It's the living we need to be afraid of."

"Try that one in the middle."

She lifts the sheet back very slowly. It's her. It's Aunt Dinah. She's smiling. A bit. They bless themselves. They say:

"Lorda mercy."

"God bless 'er but she looks happy," Ma whispers.

She does look happy, like she's having a good dream, but how can you be happy when you're dead? Patti wonders.

"Very peaceful lookin'," her Ma whispers.

They bend and kiss her forehead. Ma first. Then Patti. She's stone cold, like Olive Elizabeth was when she kissed her that terrible day after she died. Her Ma makes a sign of the cross on Dinah's forehead with her thumb. She tells her to rest in peace.

"Isn't she massive?"

Ma's quivery voice.

"Yeah."

"I always said she was like a saint."

"Yeah."

"We'll miss her terrible."

"See she has makeup on. Look. Even her eyelashes are done."

"The length of them eyelashes. I always said she had lovely eyelashes."

They can see, she's wearing her Coty long lash mascara and her cream puff candle glow face powder.

"Would ya look at her hair?"

Her hair is around her shoulders, still in the flick, the way it was when she waved from the taxi yesterday.

Did she get the Colgate toothpaste Patti wonders? Did the nurse give it to her? Her teeth are snow white. They can see a bit of them, where she's kind of half smiling.

"Aren't her teeth nice, Ma?"

"Yeah. Lovely teeth she had. A lovely smile."

"She never missed cleaning her teeth."

"She had lovely clear skin, no pimples, or anything."

"No."

"She was a good sport wasn't she?"

"Yeah."

"A lovely singer too."

"D'ya 'member her singing a Butcher Boy?"

"Yis I do, she loved that song."

Her Ma hums a bit of the tune: *I wish I wish I wish in vain I wish I were a maid again.*

"Remember when she made you that yella check bikini that everyone was mad jealous of?"

"Yeah, it was fab! Pity it was robbed off the washline."

"Remember the Batman and Robin cloaks, she made you and Jimmy out of them old curtains?"

"Yeah."

They bless themselves and say a quick Our Father, a quicker Hail Mary and a Glory Be. They have one last look. Patti sees that her Ma's eyes are shiny with tears; she wipes her hand across her nose and eyes. They pull the sheet back up over Dinah's face. The porter gives them a cranky look and looks at his watch. He locks the door behind them. Outside the gate her Ma says: "That fella wouldn't win any prizes for pleasantness."

Everyone is out. They're all at the funeral. She's supposed to be minding the house. It's dark in granny's place with the blinds down. She knows it's in the cupboard. She'd like a little sup for her nerves. She feels a bit shaky. It's the red stuff Uncle Willie brought home from the restaurant. The one with the man on the label, with rows of grapevines behind him. It's half full. She takes out the cork and pours some into a cup. Not too much. They might know from her breath. She puts water in the bottle and sticks the cork back in. Her brother says she's in for it big time if she gets caught. He makes a slicing action with his hand across his throat.

"So what? It's only a drop and it's only a tonic, like Buckfast Abbey."

She lifts up the cup.

To Aunty Dinah. May she go to Heaven and rest in peace.

It's not as sweet as Buckfast Abbey. It tastes a bit sour like malt vinegar, but that's ok, because she likes vinegar. She goes in the bedroom. She can smell her Yardly lavender talcum powder, mixed with her Coty L'aimant perfume. It's like she's still there. She opens a drawer. There's all her washed clothes, folded in neat squares, her nylons and nightdresses. In another drawer, her tops and twin sets and her mother of pearl hairbrush. Under the bed, there's her black sling backs with the toes turned out, as if she was going to step into them. Her bed is a bit ruffled and creased with the mauve quilt not tucked in. She feels her pillow, where it's still dinged from the shape of her head. Patti sits on the side of the bed and puts up her feet. She's locked. A bit. She has jelly legs all of a sudden. She falls asleep and wakes up suddenly. It's her brother at the bedroom door.

He says, "Ger up quick. Here they all are back from the funeral."

After the funeral, they're up all night. No one can sleep. Patti has a headache. It feels like she's still there in the room, in the flat, behind the door, all over the place. It's the same the next day in the street, or the chapel. Passing the Rainbow Cafe, she sees her at the window seat. She smiles and waves up at her. Dinah waves back. They say rosaries for her soul, that she'll rest in peace. They hope she'll meet up with the babbies and be happy ever after in heaven.

It's a few weeks ago now. Patti misses her terrible. Her singing especially, her jiving, her funny knickerbocker soup and the way she could break her finger and put it back together again.

They're all in black, black shoes and stockings, black skirts and jumpers, black armbands. You can't really talk. You have to whisper. People say to granny: "Sorry for your trouble."

Granny nods like she understands.

"When someone dies, there aren't any proper words," her Ma says:

"When someone belong to you dies, you're never the same, because a part of you dies too. A part of you goes to the grave."

That's how Patti feels. She writes a letter.

Dear Dinah, I hope you got the toothpaste. It was Colgate. I got it in Joe's cut-price stores. The nurse took it off me at the door; she wouldn't let me in to see you. Anyway, we miss you. A lot. We think of you every day. You looked lovely in the coffin, with your hair done and your makeup on. Granny prays every night. We all do. I miss our little chats in the Rainbow Café. I miss your little magic tricks. I hope all your pains are gone. It wasn't me robbed the wages, I swear. Say hello to the babbies if you see them. Say we miss them too. Ma sends them her love. Say we all do. Ma says we'll all be together some day in Heaven. The place is lonely; there's no radio or telly on. There's no dancehalls for the others. We miss the Top Twenties. We miss Radio Caroline and Radio Luxembourg.

Bye-Bye, Patti.

It's dead lonely without Aunt Dinah. Everyone misses her. Patti put the letter in an envelope. First, she wrote Heaven as the address, and then she crossed it out. She knew it was dead dopey. Imagine sending a letter to Heaven? She knew the postman would probably just send it back to the post office. So instead, she keeps it hid in the back of her English copy so no one will find it.

68

SUNSHINE HOUSE

In school some of them are talking about their summer holidays. Butlins Holiday Camp is supposed to be fab, with two swimming pools and amusements and it's own radio station, called Radio Butlins. One of the girls in her class went there twice in the same year. She said she slept in a huge fancy chalet, with bunk beds and all mod cons. She woke up every morning to the sound of Radio Butlins on the loud speaker. Some of the lucky ones go on holidays every year to seaside places in the country. A girl went to Curracloe in County Wexford, and another girl went to Bundoran. Someone else went to Blackpool. Blackpool has a beach called the Golden Mile and a tower that illuminates and loads of amusement arcades. She never went on a real holiday, but there's this terrific place out in North County Dublin in Balbriggan. It's called Sunshine House. It's free and everyone says it's nearly as good as Butlins, except there's no swimming pools or amusements or red coats. The best part is that you get a whole week off school.

This day, a priest came over from the southside and gave them vouchers for Sunshine House. First, he gave them a little test. He asked them an easy catechism question each. Then he gave them a pink ticket. Tickets for Sunshine House are like gold dust, so it's like a dream come through, Patti thinks. Her Ma knows all about Sunshine House. She went there once herself, years and years ago. She told Patti you go swimming every day in the sea and if you can't swim they teach you. You have games on the beach and you get cornflakes every morning for your breakfast instead of porridge. Imagine, a whole week at the beach. A whole week away from the flats.

Her Ma says it's not all plain sailing. You have to pass this medical test first. The office is up the hill, a place in Meath Street beside the dispensary. They only give out the pass if you pass the medical test. Here's this big long queue, all the way down the street, past the stalls. They're all holding the pink tickets. The queue moves real slowly. Inside the door there's this big room, like a dancehall and a woman with black wavy hair is sitting behind a desk near the stage. She's checking their heads and giving them some kind of examination. It must be the medical test, even though she's not a nurse. When it's Patti's turn, the woman looks at the pink ticket and gives it back to her. She examines her hands first; she looks in between her fingers for warts. She makes sure she has no scabies either. She lifts her arms and pokes her fingers in the soft part under her arms. She asks her to take off her shoes and socks and walk up and down in a straight line. Then it's time for questions. She comes out from behind the desk.

"Does your father work?"

"Yeah. Course Da works."

"Is that so?"

Then she tells her to take out her plaits. She pulls her hair back into sections, starts rooting through her head with her poky fingers. Then she looks into her ears and behind her ears.

"So he's in full employment?"

"Yeah, he drives a Radio Cabs taxi. He's might be gettin' his own some day."

"His own taxi. Well well?"

Real snotty like, she tells her to put her shoes back on. She starts to write things down quickly. There's this big form on the desk, with lines and boxes to fill in. She gives Patti the look across the desk. She knows the look; it's a snooty mean look, a look that people give you when they don't like you. It's the kind of look that says, no way are you going to Sunshine House. Ever! After ages, she puts her pen down. She leans back. She says:

"I'm afraid we can't give you a free pass for Sunshine House. Sunshine House is only for poor underprivileged children whose father's are unemployed. The rules are strict with no exceptions. In your case, your father is working and. . . ."

She sucks in her jaws, like she's chewing a Cleeve's toffee.

". . . I can't be certain, but I think you might have nits."

The cheeky bitch. Maybe she has nits herself in that dyed black head of hers.

"I have not nits!"

Patti puts her hands on her hips.

"No one in our family has nits."

She doesn't answer. It's like she's invisible. She looks past her to the queue behind.

"Next!" She goes, and the queue starts to move.

She puts back on her shoes, pulls her hair back into a ponytail. Outside she starts to kick the wall.

Fizz! Feck! Fuck! Three big kicks. More sins to tell in confession. She doesn't care, about mass or confession or benediction, she doesn't care about anything. If she had told lies, instead of telling the truth, it'd be easy peasy. It's always the same, when you tell the truth. You're supposed to tell the truth and shame the devil, but when you do, it all goes wrong. If she said her Da was on the labour, she'd be going to Sunshine House. They'd never find out. She should've told the lie and not shamed the devil. She'd sleep in a dorm with other girls. They'd go swimming and play bat the ball. They'd have dances and concerts at night. She wants to kick that brown brick wall down. She wants to light a match and burn the whole place down. She wants to pull the dyed wavy hair out of that one's head; then she'd like to brain her. It's no use being good, because it gets you nowhere. Most of them back there told lies, most of them on the queue will get the pass. She turns a corner into Thomas Street. A fruit dealer hands her an apple.

"What's wrong witcha?" the dealer says.

"Oh nothin'."

"Did they not give ya the pass for Sunshine House?"

"No"

"Don't mind them. Maybe next year."

"Yeah."

"You're very pale child. Are ya sick?"

"No."

People always say that: "You're very pale." Or: "You're very sallow." It gets on her nerves. She starts to walk away. She takes a bite of the apple.

Here's this young one from her class, skipping along with a big grin on her face.

It's not fair! It's not fair! She got the pass no bother; because she said her Da doesn't work. She holds up the pass real high, like it's a trophy. It's a white card, with her name on the front, like a hospital appointment. She says she can get off school for a whole week. She skips off again. Patti goes down the hill, passes granny's place. She still has the stupid pink voucher the priest gave her. On the quays, she tears it up into little pieces and throws the pieces over the Liffey wall. She watches for a minute until they get sucked into a whirly pool and disappear under the bridge.

Her Ma is raging when she tells her. She's a good mind to go up there to Meath Street herself to that cranky so and so and give her a piece of her mind. She'll give her nits. All her children's heads are spotless clean. The cranky bitch was only looking for any excuse not to send her. Sunshine House is right, she says, but every cloud has a silver lining. Maybe you'd go out there to Sunshine House with a spotless clean head of hair and come back walkin' alive. Worse still, maybe you'd get the scabies or warts. Maybe you'd meet up with hooks and crooks from the rough areas in town. Granny Connor tells her that Sunshine House is no picture postcard place and that Balbriggan is in the back of beyond and didn't she have a lucky escape after all, not getting the pass. They'd give you watery cocoa and stale bread. You'd be better off going to Bray for the day.

So that's the end of Sunshine House.

PART 4

69

UP WENT NELSON

They're asleep in the back bedroom. It's the middle of the night. Jimmy shakes her awake.

"Did you hear that bang?" He goes, his eyes all twinkly from the lamplight outside the window.

"What's up?" Patti says rubbing her eyes.

"It must be a mine, left over from World War Two."

"Go back to sleep and don't be annoyin me." She turns over, but he keeps on shaking her and then she remembers. Yes. It was a big bang. A huge sound, like a million thunder claps all at once. Maybe it's an earthquake.

It must've been a dream, she thinks, sitting up and rubbing her eyes.

"Shut up that racket," her granny shouts through the wall.

They can hear muffled, whispery voices, coming from the upstairs windows. It sounds like the woman from the first floor, talking up to the woman on the second floor. Pulling back the curtain, she can see the empty yellowy street. Then, loud excited voices, a bit in the distance, like when they're coming home from the pub. The echo carries up the street. They get back into bed.

A bit later on she can hear the springs of Jimmy's bed squeaking, as he tosses and turns. She must've fell back asleep, but the next thing she knows, he's shaking the guts out of her again.

Gerrup! Gerrup! Red alert. Red alert!

A pale grey light is peeping through the net curtains, showing up the Sacred Heart picture on the far wall.

"What's up now?"

"Ger up quick."

Then he's pulling on his jumper.

"Somethin's up, the whole flats is out."

"What?"

"We'll have to investigate."

The eyes of the Sacred Heart look across through the half dark. Patti can see his heart inside his open chest, like someone reefed back the skin. The eyes follow them around the room. Outside, the sky is deep grey. There's bunches of heavy cloud moving over from the Liffey. They can hear a terrible racket outside.

Maybe it's World War Three. Maybe it's the Russians. She hopes it's not. She looks up at the Sacred Heart.

Oh Sacred Heart of Jesus I place all my thrust in thee.

In the next room, there's granny, propped up on her pillows saying the rosary.

"Don't venture outside," she says, blessing herself over and over again with the rosary beads. But Jimmy is already gone outside to investigate. Maybe it's the end of the world and any minute the atoms might fall and cover them with burning dust. Outside, they're all standing around yapping.

"Did ya hear it? The big bang in the night. An unmerciful bang!"

The Da's are gathered round in groups, smoking like chimney pots. Some have their lunches wrapped up under their arms. The older ones and the ones who don't work are out in their shirtsleeves. Up on the balconies and around the washlines, the women are bunched together.

"Nelson's gone," they shout.

"Did yis hear? Nelson's gone. Blown ta smithereens!"

They're laughing and tittering. They seem to have the whole story.

The newspaperman is out spreading the news. He shouts so everyone will hear.

"Nelson's been blow'd outa the sky. Blow'd ta kingdom come. God save Ireland!"

He salutes like a soldier and winks with his one eye. The other one tries to wink too, but all you can see is a hollow dark crease where his eye should be.

They all laugh over the balconies. They give him a clap and he takes a bow.

Granny can't believe it. She's flabbergasted.

"Nelson's Pillar gone! Well glory be to God."

She switches on the radio.

"Run down quick and see," she says, hiring up the radio.

Feck Nelson in- anyway, Patti thinks. Poor cranky face Nelson.

First, they go up to the top balcony, but the balcony is packed with people. There's more people on the roof. Someone has binoculars.

"Giz a look," everyone is saying, but there's a queue for the binoculars.

The sky goes darker. It's lashing then. Out of the Heavens. Big huge gusts of wind roaring around corners. It nearly blows them away. All the kids are out now. There's crowds of people, coming out of the laneways and side streets. Dizzy with all the excitement, they walk down Mary's Lane, their feet moving fast over the wet cobbles. They cross over Capel Street easy, because there's no traffic yet. They're hurrying faster down Henry Street and then they see something. Up ahead, there's soldiers on patrol.

"Oh holy nightmare! " Patti says.

They have real rifles. They're stopping the people going any further up the street. One has a big helmet down low on his forehead.

"They're armed and dangerous," Jimmy says.

"At least they're not the Russians."

"Don't give them any information. Keep your traps shut and we'll be all right," Jimmy's friend whispers.

"Don't be so thick," Patti says.

Then one of the soldiers talks through a loud speaker. He says they're to hold back behind the barricades and not to come any further.

It's very foggy all of a sudden. The smoke is all over the top of Henry Street and there's this yukki smell, like the smell from the match factory, only worse. It goes up their noses and down their throats. It makes them cough.

"What's that smell?"

Jimmy's friend is holding his nose.

All of a sudden, they can see something through the smoke.

Everyone looks up. They can barely see it. The broken part of Nelson's Pillar. The pillar part that he used to stand on

"Oh Fuck," Patti goes. "He's gone! He's all gone."

"Holy hallucination!" Jimmy's friend says.

The stump is barely visible through the thick hazy smoke; it's all jaggedy, like a broken arm, with the bone sticking up. All around them the air is heavy with dust and the yukki smell.

"It looks a holy show, the way it's all broken, it'll be real strange to look up and not see Nelson there anymore," Patti says.

Jimmy's friend says when the coast is clear, they'll make a full investigation. It might be a warning and maybe it's the signal for World War Three. They shove their way nearer to the barrier. They push in between the crowds with their elbows. It's all mad in Henry Street. There's shop windows with no glass, all the dummies lying down, like they were shot. Then they can see it. A big mountain of Nelson rubble behind the barrier. Then the soldier tells them to move back with his rifle. The crowd start to give out, but he looks at them real mean from under his helmet. The cops take out their batons then. They hold them up, like they're going to use them, and everyone moves back. Someone in the crowd says: "Yiz big thick culchies," and everyone laughs.

"Good riddance anyway," is all her Ma says.

"Would ya credit it? " says granny.

"Who'd be brazen enough to pull off a stunt like that? Aul Nelson's been lordin' it over our capital city for years. You'd think he owned the place."

"But all he was doing was standing there, where's the harm in that?" Patti says.

Then Granny gets all fiery and snappy:

"I always said it's not our side of the family you come from."

Patti never thought a broken statue could get her going like that. So she's in her bad books again.

Everyone is dead excited about Nelson. Granny Connor shakes her head, like she can't believe it.

"Aul Nelson, blown to smithereens. Oh God t'night!"

It's a pity in a way. She'll miss going up Nelson's Pillar. A few of them went up after school a few times. It was meant to be their new meeting place. It all started when they were outside Nelson's Pillar this day looking up. They could see the long grey pillar poking at the clouds. Patti was mortified at first. She had to pretend not to be afraid of the height. It was only a bit of gas. It was sixpence to go up, but Robby the caretaker let them go up for nothing that first time. One of them kept asking him:

"Ah go on Robby, just this once, we won't tell."

She kept this up for ages and then he gave in.

He warned them: "No messin' or bad language up there."

The first time, they had one cigarette each. Someone had matches. Miles and miles up, round and round a smelly spiral stairway. There was this pissy smell on the steps, so they had to hold their noses. The walls were green mouldy. Patti got a dizzy headache at the top. When she looked down, O'Connell Street goes into a spin, all the buses and cars, the crowds of people, the G P O, the Carlton, Cafolla's, the monuments, the cars and the buses. It was like being in a chairoplane. They could see the sea, like a big grey sash over to the left. They saw the boats on their way to Liverpool and the Isle of Man. They looked like toy boats with a white sudsy squiggle behind them.

Nelson was still miles up with his feet covered in seagull shit. There were a few French students taking photos. They wanted a shot of them in their gymslips. They all stood in a line and linked arms and they all said *Cheese!* Someone took one of their addresses. They smiled and waved up at them from below. They looked down and watched them cross the road, and walk towards O'Connell Bridge. The safety-rail was a bit too low so you could fall over if you weren't careful. On the smelly stairs, they lit up. They made windbreakers out of their hands.

They took drags.

"Infuckinhale!" Vera goes.

They coughed and choked. You have to inhale, or it's not really smoking. They tried to blow smoke out their noses, the way they do in the films. The smoke hurt. It wasn't like she thought it would be. It looks dead modish in the films, but all it did was make Patti feel sick. The breeze was strong up there. It roared like the sea sound in a shell. They talked about the fab new shades of pale pink lipstick and nail varnish in all the shops. Vera kept on about the man in the Man from Uncle. No one had anything much to report on babies and how you get them. Up there they all felt grown up, like they were starting on some important journey. Like it was the first day in the rest of their lives. So that's why she's raging. Why didn't the bombers leave the pillar and just blow up Nelson?

Everyone is talking about another explosion.

"That bloody stump is dangerous and the sooner the better it comes down," her Da says.

"An insult to O'Connell Street," granny says. "Should've been blown up years ago."

The army are to carry out a controlled explosion to blow up the stump. They're using real dynamite. Dublin Corporation workers in white dungarees are pasting up posters all over the place. The notice warns people about the explosion. It says people in the inner city are to keep off balconies and roofs and away from windows. Her Ma says the whole nation is gone Nelson crazy. Downtown, newspaper reporters are nosing around asking stupid questions.

Did you hear the bang?

Can you describe it?

At what time precisely did you hear it?

There's a queue of kids being interviewed for the newspapers. Young fellas and young ones who want their picture in the paper. They push one another out of the way. There's fights between them, over who has the best story. They're all telling the same story, but the reporters wants something new, something different and catchy.

After dark, they're all out with buckets and paint cans and biscuit boxes. Everyone is looking for Nelson's head, or his ear or his finger. All of a sudden, everyone wants a piece of him, even Patti. Her Da says it's like the gold rush down O'Connell Street, with people panning for Nelson dust. Maybe they could make a small fortune, Patti thinks, but they don't find much. When they go searching, all they get are bits of stupid rubble. A man tells them that Nelson's head was removed by a museum expert from Trinity College. Dublin Corporation trucks arrive to clean up. People are saying the rubble could be worth money in years to come, like an antique, so they fill their buckets and boxes.

"Don't attempt," granny warns them, "to bring any of that Nelson rubble into this house!"

She means it. She won't let them near the door. Everyone is hauling up rubble from town. Some have pull trolleys, some have prams and some have box carts. Then they have this idea of selling it to the Yanks. They'll sell it in penny bags. They'll get stickers for labels. They might call it, *Nelson Powder, The Genuine Article*. For the time being, they hide the bit of rubble under the bed in the back bedroom. They push it well under, past Da's going away case, past his toolbox, in at the wall where no one will find it.

All the neighbours gather for the explosion. They're on the roofs and balconies; they're up lampposts and sitting on the fish market wall. On the top balconies, they've barricaded the windows with sheets of heavy cardboard. They wait. They hear the tremor, like before a thunderstorm. Then the big bang. The noise of it all crashing to the ground. In the bedroom, her Ma says a decade of the rosary. After a while when it's safe, they're allowed out. From the top balcony, they see the smoke, a huge grey mushroom shape, like the Atom bomb over O'Connell Street. There's cheering and clapping from all the balconies. The pubs are all packed. Everyone is happy and the smell of dynamite is everywhere. There's rumours about who might've planted the bomb and how it was masterminded. They say it was some stunt all right. They're talking about wires and electrodes and timing devices. It might be someone from their own neighbourhood or some other flats in town. It could be anyone. There's winks and nods. They drink toasts to whoever it was. They keep shouting: Up the Republic! God save Ireland! They're drinking to a new O'Connell Street without Nelson. The men are patting each other on the backs and buying each other drinks. They're laughing about Nelson's head tumbling to the ground, about it being the final blow to the British Empire. They're on about the 1916 rebellion, and all those who lost their lives fighting for Ireland. They're on about Jim Larkin and The 1913 Lockout, when the poor people were on their knees. Everyone is excited; it's like we're all in this together. Her granny has a small sherry. Her Da is doing the rounds of the pubs; he was last seen in Murtagh's bar on the southside where he plays in a darts team. Her Ma has a headache. She can't be bothered with all this Nelson carry on. She has more to worry about than Nelson. She says isn't it well for those who can gallivant and drink like there's no tomorrow. There's some who can't move. There's some who have to stay put. She'd really like to go to the pub with all the others, Patti thinks. She'd like to sing the rebel songs and be a part of all the Nelson excitement.

Instead, she crosses over to granny Connor's place. Granny is very quiet. She makes her a milk stout. She opens out the dresser and gives them all sugar on bread. They lick the sugar off with long tongues. They bite holes out of the middle of the batch loaf. Granny warns them to behave and not to mess and have her place in atoms. She makes onion sambos. She pours on the YR sauce. Loads! She sips black stout from her mug and makes a face. She says: "It doesn't take much around here, to get them all fired up and they'll use any excuse for a hooley and it's tomorrow they'll have ta pay, when there's no rent money or food money or gas money. When they've drank the Liffey dry and the tide's gone out, it's the loan sharks'll benefit."

With Nelson gone everything is different. In school they hold an emergency meeting. It has to be decided where to meet after school. The Nelson bomber blew their cover. The bomber is still out there. Patti imagines him hiding out in the Dublin Mountains in an underground bunker. He has a canteen of water and cans of beans. He's young with a side fringe; he has bombing

376

equipment and a radio. He's probably listening to the radio and hears the newsreader talking about him. He'll move around at night like an animal, he'll hunt for rabbits and he'll eat berries and wild mushrooms when the beans are all gone. They'll never catch up with him; he'll be like the Fugitive, Doctor Richard Kimble who's always on the run.

In class, Sister asks them to write a composition about Nelson's Pillar. She says in years to come, they'll all remember that special day when Nelson was blown up. Patti writes the first sentence.

It was the middle of the night. . . .

70

A VERY PECULIAR OBJECT

Her Da was never out of work in his life. She can remember him when they lived in the old drunken house; he was a deliveryman for a hardware shop in Moore Street called Norton's. He used to drive this white van with boxes of delf in the back. Then he did a special taxi-driving test where he had to drive all over Dublin. He got a certificate to say he passed. Then he became a taxi man for the Radio Cabs company. It's supposed to be a better job, but the hours are cruel and he has to do night work. Everyone thinks they're rich and it's all because of the taxi, the black shiny four door with the black leather seats. It belongs to Radio Cabs. It has a yellow roof sign that lights up at night with loads of seven's.

A lot of men are not working; you see them hanging around the market gates, smoking and messing and pretending to spar with one another like young fellas. They're waiting to be called for unloading lorries. It's called casual work and they get paid by the day. A foreman from the market comes out and picks someone out. First he looks them up and down to make sure they're strong. Then he might smell their breath to see if they have drink on them. Then he taps them on the back if they're lucky. Her granny says, some of them wouldn't work in a blue moon and all they're doing is holding up walls. She calls them wasters and idlers. Her Da might be getting a loan from granny to buy his own taxi, so he won't have to pay interest, like in a bank. He'd rather work days instead of nights he says and some day, they might be rich. Sometimes people he knows will ask him to bring them to the airport, or to Alexander Basin to get the boat. A woman in the flats who was going to America asked him to drive her to Shannon airport. He'll never make money, granny says, because he never charges them enough.

One day this peculiar looking machine appears in the wardrobe all covered with a blanket. It looks like a gas meter, except it's black. It has buttons and knobs. Patti was about to get in the wardrobe with her torch to read a book. She lifts off the blanket and looks it over.

"What's that thing under the blanket Ma?"

"It's a strange lookin' yoke all right. Your Da got it cheap at Reilly's auction rooms. He says it's a taximeter for his new taxi, if he ever gets it. Looks like it's worth money too."

She keeps staring at the meter. She presses buttons but nothing happens. Then she covers it back up with the blanket. The next day it goes missing from the wardrobe and there's blue murder. Her Da empties out the wardrobe. He reefs things from shelves. He pulls everything out, the clothes and the old ties and the shoes, even her Ma's rouge and face powder. He starts to look under the bed and behind the bed.

"Was there anyone in this place? Was that hall door left open? Were there gypsies around?"

"No. The gypsy wasn't around in months," her Ma says.

There's another investigation. Maybe the detectives will be called from the Bridewell. No one knows where the meter is gone. Not even Patti.

"It was there yesterday, under the blanket," she tells her Da. "I saw it with my own eyes."

Then he finds the pawn ticket. Her Ma has her starey face on. She looks at the wall. She asks him if he would like to eat a taxi meter, so Da says, maybe it'd taste better than some of the dinners she makes. The door slams, the glass shakes and it's the Irish earthquake again.

71

THE GAS MAN

In the flats, they have to feed the gas meter with shillings to keep the gas going. Sometimes it runs out and that's the worst thing that can happen. If there's no gas to cook, or if her Ma can't heat milk for the babby's bottle. She has a few tricks up her sleeve for when that happens. She keeps a few old coins handy that fit into the slot meter, like a proper shilling.

"The gas meter doesn't know it's not a real shillin' and what it doesn't know won't kill it," she says.

She knows that old iron gas meter inside and out. It makes a vomiting sound sometimes, when she stuffs it's mouth with her pretend shillings. She has the coin making thing all set up on the bath board in the scullery and it's like a little coin factory in there. What it involves is a sharp knife, her Da's razor blades, and a scissors. She has it all laid out, real neat, like in an operating theatre. Her Ma worked as a tailor before she got married, so she knows all about cutting out with blades and scissors. She has bits of stuff she cuts into shilling shapes. It might be tin or it might be lino or it might be cardboard. She keeps working in a circle until she gets it just right. She finishes it off and holds it up to the light.

"Does that look all right?"

"Yeah, it's grand," Patti says, even though it doesn't look anything like a real shilling.

She tries it out then in the skinny meter mouth. If it spits it back out, she pushes it back in like medicine. Then she might give it a kick.

"Gitdown!" She says, as if the gas meter was a human being. Maybe she says a little prayer then and, Hey Presto! You hear the lovely sliding noise of the coin as it hits the bottom. So here comes the blue gas flame, when her Ma turns on the jet: Putoo! Putoo! Then she gives thanks to the Lord God our Saviour, and it's on with the teapot.

Everyone likes the gasman. He calls every couple of months to empty the meter.

You can hear the voices outside when he's coming:

"Here's the gasman! Here's the gasman!"

Her Ma thinks he's a proper gentleman, especially if he gives her back a few shillings.

"Open the door quick," she says when she hears him.

He knocks on the wood part of the door; two hard raps and you'd know it was him.

He's tall with wide shoulders. He carries a tan leather bag, like a doctor's bag, that opens out like an accordion.

"How're you Missus," he says. She lets him in quick. She has on her happy face.

"Oh come on in out of the cold," she says, opening back the hall door as far as it will go.

"Just as well too. Full up to the brim, that gas meter."

He's not cheeky or forward like some that knock. He has manners. He smiles into the pram at the babby. The table is cleared for his bag. He opens it up. He takes out a torch and a special key for the meter lock. He has to bend down. The meter is in the corner, under the draining board. He reads it first with his torch. He writes it all down on a notepad. He unlocks it then and they hear the tinny sound of the coins spilling into the tray. They all watch him down on his hunkers with his coat-tails spread on the floor. On the table he empties out the tray. They see all the real shillings and the pretend shillings. He picks them up and turns them over. He puts them aside and says nothing. He rolls up his sleeves. He counts the rest. He slides the shillings off the edge of the table into his hand. He puts them back in pound stacks. He might give her back a few shillings or he mightn't. He has a special purse for the money. Her Ma looks out the window while he writes out a docket. You get cut off there and then, if your meter is short and you don't make up the difference. He gives her back the coins and the pretend shillings. He says nothing as he closes up his bag. After he's gone, she slides a coin back into the meter and the sound is hollow and empty. She keeps the rest handy in a drawer in case she needs them.

"You never know. They might come in handy for a rainy day," she says.

72

SPOTTY LINO

It's hard to know what colour it is, sort of red, sort of black with squiggly black spots going through it. Her Ma scrubs it nearly every day.

"It's the bloody pattern," she says. "That lino never looks clean."

What she'd like is a bit of Marley floor with a nice modern pattern and a bit of style. Patti doesn't like it either; the dark colour and the rough feel of it under her feet. It was left over when they were doing the kitchen, so her Da put it down on the scullery floor.

"That's grand," he says, and you'd know it wasn't. For starters, it doesn't fit properly. It doesn't reach the bath and it stops well short before the gas stove and the sink. The end bits stick up and it gets on Ma's nerves. She says it's a holy show.

"You'd break your neck on that bloody lino," she says.

They're always tripping over the edges.

Then this day, when Patti comes in from school, there's the lino rolled up on its side against the wall. There's twine wrapped around the middle.

"That floor's much better without that lino," her Ma says. "It was never the right fit anyway. Run over to Jimmy an' ask him for ten bob."

"What? The lino?"

"Yes. Now here, gimme a hand. It's heavy."

She gets one end; she hauls it over to the pram.

"You grab the other end."

"You must be jokin'. I will not."

"Well d'ya want ta eat it then?"

"No."

"Well go on then. It's no bloody use. I threw out better. Your Da'll never be the wiser."

"Ah Ma."

"Armagh Armagh!" She says and Patti thinks that's funny so she's in stitches.

"What're ya laughin' at?"

"Armagh."

"Yeah I know, now go on and hurry like a good child."

She drags the pram up the steps. The man looks out over the counter, but she can't lift it up.

"It's nearly new. Ma says ten bob."

"Ten bob is it? I'll say this for your Mother, she's a hard ticket."

He scratches his head. He comes out from behind the counter. He has a quick look.

"We don't take lino, not even new lino" he says a bit cranky.

He shakes his head from side to side like he can't believe it.

She has to bring the lino home. She knew it was stupid. She knew they wouldn't take it.

"They don't take lino."

"It's a pity about them. They're gettin' very fussy all of a sudden over there."

They take the lino off the pram. They roll it along the floor into the back bedroom and push it in behind the bed head.

"We'll get a decent bit of Marley that fits right and proper, and throw that bloody stuff out. That scullery floor looks much better without that lino," she says.

Her Da says nothing. He doesn't seem to notice the black stone floor in the scullery. He doesn't mention the missing lino either, so her Ma was right; he's none the wiser.

73

THE CHA CHA CHA

They always know when it's the first Tuesday of the month. The children's allowance book is out on the table and her Ma is singing like a canary in the scullery, her coat on the back of the chair waiting. She dances the Cha Cha Cha around the table. She swings her hips. She wags her elbows. She's always in good humour on children's allowance day. Later, they might get Russian slices or crumpets for tea. Sometimes, they might have a concert with Ma in her singing mood. They all pretend they're in a band. Patti shakes her tambourine. Anna plays the washboard. If her Ma had a hammer she'd hammer in the morning, she'd hammer in the evening, all over this land.

If I had a bell, I'd ring it in the morning, I'd ring it in the evening, all over this land. The babby claps hands in her pram. Franey bangs a pot lid with a wooden spoon, the others bang at an upturned tin bucket with forks and sing along to the chorus.

Sometimes they might go to the pub after the messages. They'll get peanuts or Tayto. Inside, they kind of pretend to hide when the barman brings out the drinks. It's like they're invisible. Her Ma tells them to be quiet and sit in the corner. It's ok in there. A nice little snug, with a hatch, where the women sit away from the men. It's black torn leathery seats and a brass buzzer to ring for your drink. If they mess, they'll be put out. Especially if they keep ringing the bell, or jumping on the seats or banging doors. Her Ma likes a glass of stout with a white creamy head.

"Put a decent head on that Jimmy," she tells the barman, even if his name is not Jimmy. She has a white ronny when she drinks it. She licks the ronny off the top of her lips. She wouldn't drink anything else. She says it's the only alcoholic drink that's good for you. The sign on the wall says: *Guinness is good for you.* It's beside the bearded sailor for the Players Navy Cut advertisement.

They're not supposed to sing in the snug. Some of the women have brown paper parcels on the seat beside them. It's the brown pawn paper with their husband's suit or their young fella's confo clothes wrapped up. Outside there's a line of prams.

Through the square hatch, the barman sticks out his head, when the buzzer sounds and it's like he's in a framed picture. He sticks his finger at the door. He shouts: "No singin'." He has to tell them again and again. He'll have to put them out if they don't stop. They don't care, because it's children's allowance day and everyone is happy. They go sideways in the snug seat, all their shoulders one way, then the other. All their squeaky voices together; *Who's sorry now?* They're on their last chance. There'll be no more glasses of stout, so they better drink up. The women say: It's all right for the men, up at the bar, and no worries. The same men who are always there in the same places.

"Isn't it well for the men, neither chick nor child to mind."

There'll be blue murder if they're late. Her Da. If she hasn't got his tea ready.

74

THE BIG SHOE FIRE

She always says waste not want not, so she'd never throw out anything in case it comes in handy. Old curtains for cat nets, old jumpers for vests, old vests for floor cloths, old newspapers for cleaning windows, old stockings for dusters and old shoes for the fire. It's dead neat when she lights the big roaring fire with the worn out shoes. Sometimes they go shoe hunting under the bed. They pretend they're searching for buried treasure. First they dive off the bed, and then they swim under the bed and behind the wardrobe. They pretend the floor is the sea. Her Ma roots everywhere and it's like the Halloween bonfire with the stack of old shoes in the middle of the floor. She makes a quick inspection, like she's at a market, then she takes out all the shoelaces and puts them in a drawer. The old shoes are always well worn, with holes in the soles and the clicks worn down like an accordion. There's Ma's high heels with the turned up toes, a pair of Da's old black mass shoes, a rockinroll boot, and a bopper boot.

They all have to stand back while she starts the fire with newspapers and a match. She throws on the shoes. She pokes at them with the poker. Next, she pours on grease from the pan. It catches. It makes a roaring sound up the chimney. The shoes start to burn and sizzle. There's a smell of rubber when they start to melt. One shoe bends over and goes into a wrinkly curl. They listen to the hissing sound. They watch the flame turn bluey green and that's when her Ma gets worried. She puts her hands to her face. She says it's a death for sure, when you see that blue flame in the fire, and have they not had enough deaths in the family already? She blesses herself and says a quick prayer. When the blue flame dies, they're allowed to sit around the fire with their legs crossed. They pretend they're cowboys sitting around a campfire. They get hotter and hotter, until they feel the itchy ABC marks starting on their legs.

"We'll roast in this heat," she says.

For a little while the room is like an oven and all their faces are shiny and hot in the firelight. They watch the shadows dance on the wall and then it dies down all of a sudden and the room goes cold again. A big heap of red ash goes pink and then grey and it's like a little volcano. Sometimes, there's voices in the three chimneys above. The voices come down like an echo when the fire goes out and it's like there's this other world over their heads. Her Ma dries the damp clothes in the oven over the fire and they come out like warm baked bread with this nice scorching smell. She puts them to her face to test them. "That's grand. There's nothin' like a shoe fire for heat, better than coal or turf, " she says.

75

THE SOSHITEY MAN

Her Da calls him the German. The kids call him the soshitey man.

"Was the German here today?" her Da asks the kids. "Did the German get paid?"

He means the society man. He calls on Friday's for the insurance money. You'd know it was him, by the sound of his motorbike engine. He parks his Honda Fifty outside near the step. Then he hangs his crash helmet on the handlebars. The society book is always on the table. It's dark beige with black writing. On the cover it says, "Royal Liver Friendly Society." It's a waste of money, Patti thinks, paying out money for years just to bury someone when they die, but her Ma says it's the most important thing after your rent. She has them all insured now, even the grannies. If someone dies it costs a fortune for a funeral; there's the coffin and the grave, there's the black mourning clothes and the black shoes, there's the black and white pudding for the wake, there's stout and ham sandwiches.

The German has a loud cheeky knock, three big bangs on the scullery window. Then he looks through the letterbox and calls her Ma by her first name and Ma says he's as cheeky as a husband. Goo Chaney says that fella has notions beyond his station, and he's awful forward for a society man. Nobody likes him. He wears a leather bomber jacket, like in the war films, and maybe that's why her Da calls him the German. His face is red and blotchy, his teeth are big and yellowy. His Adam's apple sticks out from his open collar; he has what some people call, jujube lips and her Ma says he must've sucked a soother till he was ten.

"Howea love," he says real cheeky to her Ma.

Her face always goes a bit red.

"Oh all right, I s'pose. No use complainin' is there?"

She hands him the book and the money. He takes the money first. He counts it and recounts it to make sure it's all there. Then he takes the book and marks it up.

"Howea lovee dovee," he says if Patty is there. He does this horrible clucking thing with his tongue. He sticks his foot in the hall, it twists around the door and she sees he has these black leather boots with zips at the sides, bright blue socks with diamonds and she hates him. Yuk! His face and his voice. His Adam's apple and his ankle boots.

"Getting very big, that young one. Goodlookin' too like her Ma," he says.

"No she's not. She's more like her Da."

"Oh don't be so modest. She'll be like yourself in another few years."

That's when her Ma closes the hall door over a bit. Then he starts on about all the good looking women in the flats, about all the husbands who don't know how lucky they are. He always asks her Ma does she want a jaunt around the gates on the Honda Fifty. She always laughs it off and says, "Go way you, are ya coddin me or what? I wouldn't get up on that yoke for all the tea in China."

One day she changes her mind all of a sudden. Here's Ma out the door with her slippers and her blue smock on. Here she is with her hair up in clips and her teeth in. They all watch from the step. The society man has a big stupid grin on his face. He revs up the Honda Fifty. He keeps pressing with his boot down as far as it will go and the engine screams louder. Then Ma climbs onto the back saddle and tries to pull down her skirt.

"Are you ready?" He says and she says: "Yeah go on if your goin' for God's sake."

"Are ya steady?"

"Sweet mother of God, will ya go on if you're goin'."

"YA HOOO! Hold on for your life," he goes. Ma holds onto the sides of his bomber jacket.

"Cheerio!" she goes, waving at them on the step and you'd think she was going to America.

"Watch them kids," she shouts back at Patti.

"See youse later alligators," the society man shouts back.

Off they go around the block, slow at first, then faster and faster, around line poles, through washing and sheets hanging out to dry, the society man beeping his horn, doing sharp showy corner turns, Ma screaming for him to stop, her black hair loosening from the clips, her knees out at the sides so you can see the hem of her slip. There's heads hanging over the balconies, kids chasing the motorbike and Fido the dog, barking after them.

"Sweet God! I'll go skatin'," she shouts through the engine noise.

"Hold on tighter! Here we go!"

Up along the bumpy wall then, out the gate, around the markets, back in the other gate. Here's Ma, with a nervy kind of smile. Here's Ma, like she's going to be sick.

"You're a scream," he says, putting on the brake. He leaves the engine running.

"Go on outa that. You're nearly after puttin' the heart crossways in me."

She puts one foot down on the step and climbs off the Honda, holding down her skirt. She tries to fix her hair, where it fell down.

"Give us a kiss. Give us a squeeze," he goes, trying to grab her waist.

"Go way, or I'll give ya a good box for yourself. On your bike now and don't be annoyin' me."

There's a queue for the lifts. The kids all want a go on the motor bike.

"Giz a ja'nt misdor soshitey man. Giz a go on your Honda."

But he's off again, on another jaunt, this time with a woman from upstairs.

Their Da'll have killin if he finds out about Ma on the Honda Fifty. There'll be blue murder. He'll have ten canaries and it'll be the Irish earthquake.

"I'm tellin'," Franey says, "about the soshitey man and the moro bike."

"So am I," Anna says.

"No you're not. Youse'll keep your gobs shut if ya know what's good for yiz."

She points her fist at them, but they know she's only messing.

"Misdor soshitey man. Misdor soshitey man," they're all shouting after him and her Ma thinks that's real funny.

"Begod, that name suits him down to the ground all right," she says.

"Doesn't it," Goo Chaney says. "Doesn't it just."

76

THE SICKBED

She sees them first: Granda's black shiny hobnail boots under the bed. She's watching though a crack, between the door hinge and the frame. Granda looks different with his teeth out. They've given him water to wet his lips. They're trying to keep the glass steady at his mouth. They're all there, around the bed; they've been up since all hours with granda who's sleeping in the kitchen. With sleepy eyes, they move between the scullery and the kitchen; it's her granny and her Da, the aunties and Uncle Willie. They bring a clean towel and soap. Every morning they shave him from a white enamel basin. Then they wash him and tidy him up. Later on they buy him a newspaper and tobacco. He's wearing stripy blue pyjamas. He's getting thinner. His face shrunken, like the old men you see in coffins. Patti notices afterwards, when she sits on the side of the bed, the bones sticking through his pyjamas. His neck is scrawny and creased looking and his hand is shaky when he tries to hold the glass of water.

His eyes have yellowy bits where the whites should be. He talks real slow and slurred. They say he's breathing a bit easier now. They've been up all night, turning him over and listening for his breathing. They prop him up on high pillows. They smooth down the sheets. It's like a hospital ward out there. She heard them talking in the kitchen, her Da and her granny. Granda has to sleep out in the kitchen now. They dragged out a single bed. Granny says he won't take medicine or tablets for the pain he's in. Her Da lights his pipe for him and he has a little smoke. He's able to read a bit of his Western paperback with his glasses on, but he gets tired easily. All he can manage to eat is chicken soup with a bit of dry bread.

He had this big operation. They took out a piece of his stomach and it was after the operation that he got worse. From the back bedroom, they can hear him in the night when they turn

him over. He moans out loud: Ahhh! Auhhh! So the pain must
be very bad. They sort of half carry him to the toilet with his
arms round their necks. His feet drag along the floor in his carpet slippers. His head hangs low on his chest. They all pity him.
They hope he'll get better and go back to work soon. He works
for Dublin Corporation as a caretaker.

"He's very low," granny says and whispers something to Da
with her hand covering her mouth. The priest comes and gives
him a blessing. Granda's face is trembly and grey on the pillows.
Granny squirts soda water into a glass from the soda fountain
on the locker and puts it to his lips. Everyone is narky. Da keeps
shouting at them: "Shut them doors!" and "Stay quiet youse
pair!" He means Patty and her brother.

"His breathing is very shallow," the aunties say.

Uncle Willie looks sad. They take turns to stay with him all
night again. They roll him over. They hear him moan. In the
bedroom, they hear decades of the rosary being said. They're
not allowed out, except to the toilet. They're not supposed to
look, but they see them all around the bed, granny slumped in a
chair with her rosary beads through her fingers. Patti can hear
the men in the fish market, through the bedroom window, auc-
tioning fish in their singsongy voices. It's very early in the morning. The seagulls are squealing like crazy. In the kitchen, the
blinds are pulled and he's gone out of the sickbed into uncle's
bedroom. They say he died in the night. The bed is stripped,
all the bedclothes bunched in a heap on the floor, and a smell
of Dettol all over the place. They'll send the bedclothes to the
Swan laundry. They're not allowed to see him yet. He has to get
laid out first; the woman who lays out has to come and wash
his body and put on the habit. Everyone has the waterworks.
They're standing with their arms folded, or they're making tea,
or they're making out lists for the black mourning clothes.

Out in the street, people stare at them, but they keep their
heads bowed. People pity them. They say: Another death in the
family and so soon. Patti and one of the aunties have to cross
the bridge to the southside to see the habit woman. They bring
granda's measurements written on a card. In the habit house,

there's a smell of fried onions in the hall. In the parlour, there's habits hanging along a rail on the wall, blue habits and brown habits and a bunch of scapulars hanging from a nail with pictures of the Sacred Heart and Our Lady. The habit woman has pins between her teeth, a tape measure around her neck. She takes out the pins and takes the card with the measurements. Her Singer sewing machine is out in the middle of the room, with a blue habit under the needle. She takes a pole with hooks on one end and reaches up and picks out a brown habit, and then she measures the length with her tape. She tells them to sit down, she won't be long, and the habit only needs a bit off the hem. She measures it again, cuts a bit off the bottom. Then she makes a new hem, going a mile a minute on her Singer with her head down. It only takes her a few minutes and then she wraps the habit up real neat in brown paper and ties it with twine. She tells them to hurry across the bridge and not delay and to pass on her sympathies to granny and the family.

When they get back, there's a card with black edging and a black ribbon tied to the gate. It has granda's name and the date. They bless themselves and say Lorda Mercy. People are out on the balconies talking. Long Paddy is spreading the news, talking real fast to people in the courtyard with spits coming out of his mouth. The woman arrives to lay out the body. She's carrying a big brown messagebag full of stuff. Someone already went to Clery's, to buy the black clothes. Someone else got the loan of a chapel pew and extra chairs for the mourners. They had to get the sliced pans in Johnston Mooney's bakery and the ham in Steins and the crate of stout in Lavin's pub. They filled the Sacred Heart fount with holy water. It's hours before they have the room ready.

He's laid out in the bedroom the next time they see him. It's like a little chapel in there, with wax candles burning, a crucifix over the bed, crispy white linen sheets, everything scrubbed and immaculate. It's stone cold in there, as if the windows were left open all night. Granda looks taller lying down flat, like he's been stretched, with his feet sticking up at the end of the bed. His face looks yellow in the candlelight, and it's not like him at all, but more like a statue of him that some artist carved. They can smell the blessed oil of extreme unction and the melting candle wax and the floor polish all mixed together. His hands look bigger the way they're joined with the rosary beads through his fingers. There's a bowl of hot water for the priest to wash his hands and a spotless clean new white towel. The priest comes into the room with his purple stole over his shoulders. They have to wait in the hall until he's finished. All through the day there's neighbours coming and going.

"Lorda Mercy," they keep saying and blessing themselves.

"He was a good man," or, "He was a gentleman," they say.

"He's not himself," another one says on her way out.

There's strange jumping shadows on the wall in the candle-light. It's dead spooky. They're waiting for granda's soul to lift up to heaven. No one will leave him alone. Someone has to sit with him all the time. They make pots of tea and plates of sandwiches. They say oceans of rosaries. They wait outside the room, while granda is laid in the coffin. The men stand in the hall; they take tea or bottles of stout. The women sit along the side of the coffin. The coffin lid is at the wall; it's brown and shiny with a brass crucifix and handles. Da says it's pure mahogany, so it must've cost a small fortune. It feels smooth like dress satin, when Patti feels it. When it's time, the kids are put in a line to kiss him; the smaller ones are lifted up first. His forehead is stone cold when she kisses it. They wait outside the room again, while the lid is being put on the coffin and then they carry him out.

All the mirrors are covered until after the funeral. There'll be no radio or telly for weeks. No dances or picture houses for the other aunties.

She'll miss him. He always had this nice smell of tobacco. She used to love it on his lap beside the fire, when the pipe-smoke went up her nose. When granda was reading one of his cowboy books. She remembers his arm around her, his warm woolly jumper, the red ashes in the pipe, blinking on and off, like a lighthouse, his mouth opening and closing like a fish's, making a strange popping sound. Her Ma says he was a good skin. Her

Da files his wood figure and her Ma asks him, what'll it be, if it's ever finished. But he doesn't answer. Granny stares at the wall. She holds onto her 1916 elbow with her good arm and nurses it into her like a new baby. She says her head is bealing and that means she has a bad headache. Her face looks hard with no face powder, a bit reddish under the eyes. You can hear her chest in the room, like a breeze down the chimney. It's dead quiet with just the ticking clocks. It's sad with him gone, but at least he's not paining now, Patti thinks.

77

NOAHS ARK

Granda used to feed the pigeons in the courtyard with bits of bacon fat and stale bread. He always said that pigeons aren't as stupid as they look. A flock of them will suddenly appear out of nowhere. The flats are always full of pecking pigeons. People throw out the stale bread over the balconies. On the top balconies and the roof, they keep lofts where they train the pigeons for races. There's always snares out in the flats. Patti and her brother make snares out of thread or wool. They put the bread in the middle of the snare and hide somewhere. They might be there for hours waiting for a pigeon to land in the circle. They might go to the Ice Lane or the Four Courts or the handball alley; it doesn't matter, because there's pigeons all over the place. They have to keep dead quiet. Some of them are too cute and see the thread around the bread. Maybe some of them are lampy like Patti and all they see are the pieces of stale bread. In go the webbed feet into the circle. The pigeon pecks at the bread. It bobs its head. They're after the white pigeons or the pale brown ones and not the ordinary grey fat pigeons that the flats are full of. The feet have to be over the line and that's when they pull the thread. Everyone is after this whitey pigeon for months, but no one can catch it. It's creamy white, with spotty bits near its neck. It's very cute and it always knows when they're there, even when they hide. It usually stands outside the thread and pecks at the bread inside.

They follow it everywhere. One hot sunny day they saw it in the Four Courts yard. The caretaker said they could come in, as long as they had no cheeky companions with them. It's very quiet, with no one going by, except the court barristers that look like penguins with their wigs and gowns. They hide behind a low wall with the snare spread out on a footpath. The pigeon appears all of a sudden into their snare. It pecks the bread. It looks up. Then down again. They can't believe their eyes. It's the nice white pigeon. They'll train it to do tricks; they might even get it into the circus, Patti thinks. Her brother is shaking and biting his nails. Then, he gives the snare a good chuck upwards. The pigeon's feet get entangled in the thread. It flaps its wings. It makes a pigeon sound and struggles against the snare, but it's trapped. Then it shits loads. It tries to fly away, but they hold fast, the two of them now. Patti can't look. It's horrible. If you pull it wrong, you injure the feet or the wing. Between them they manage to hold onto the flapping pigeon. They reel it in then, slowly in case the line snaps. When it's near enough, Jimmy grabs the pigeon and frees its feet from the thread. They rub its head and it starts to relax. Its belly is silky and warm. Patti holds it against her, feels the feathery wings and a heart beat. Jimmy puts it up his jumper.

"It's our whitey," he goes, "the best pigeon in Dublin."

The caretaker doesn't see them; they can hear the lawnmower round the other side of the courtyard, so he's probably cutting grass. They sneak out the gate. They know they can't bring it home.

"What'll we do now?"

"How do I know?"

They could sell it, but they don't want to. They know this young fella who has a loft on the roof. They ask him to mind it for them, but he tells them he has a full house up there already. He says they could try Mary Bassett in Parnell Street and they think it's a good idea.

They saw her first at the Hallfpenny Bridge feeding the seagulls with handfuls of buttered bread. There she was with all the seagulls milling around her, one on her shoulder, another one on the pram handle. They watched her until all the bread was gone and the seagulls flew off. She gave them a little wave and let them have a look in the pram. There's the puppies all huddled together, wrapped up like babbies in knitted jumpers. Sometimes they see her pushing her doggy pram along the street. She wears a tweed coat and green Cossack boots in winter. In summer, it's a bright coloured two-piece costume. She has her hair knotted up into a baker's bun or pulled into a ponytail. Her face is friendly, but sometimes she looks sad and faraway. She talks posh and granny says she's refined, and comes from a very respectable family, but she only has time for animals and birds. They call her Mary Bassett, but maybe that's not her real name. She nurses sick animals and birds. People say it's like Noahs Ark up there where she lives.

Her flat is above the music shop in Parnell Street. Up one flight of hallway steps to a painted green door. There's no door knocker so Patti taps with her fist. No answer. They wait a while. They hear noises inside. Then after ages, she knocks again. Mary opens the door with her sleeves rolled up.

"Well hello, what can I help you with?"

"It's our pigeon." Patti says and digs her brother in the arm. He takes out the pigeon and holds the wings down tight in case it flies away.

Mary looks at the pigeon and rubs it's head.

"Come in," she says in her posh voice.

Inside everything is painted green; the walls, the doors, the skirting boards and the fireplace. Mary says she'll be with them in two ticks. Through an open window, birds fly in and out. Mary is up to her eyes washing a puppy in a basin of suds.

"If you'll sit on the bed a while," she says.

The bed is made up real neat with this flowery shiny quilt. They sit down on the side. They can hear animal voices and bird voices and there's a smell, like in Pete's pet shop.

"What's that?" Patti whispers.

There's this basket of fur near the fireplace that seems to be moving. They look closer and it looks like kittens, teeny-weeny ones. The mother is lying on her side, like she's asleep. Then they see something else on the other side of the fireplace. It's a bit like a dog but different.

"It's a Vixen," Mary says. "Don't be afraid."

The poor thing has a broken leg and she's treating it with splints and poultices, she tells them. The fox gives them a starey look with its glassy eyes, but Mary says it wouldn't harm a fly. Still an all, they keep well away from it.

"Have a look outside if youse want," she says, drying a puppy off with a towel.

Out on the balcony, there's a row of birdcages with injured sparrows and other birds. A swan with a bandage wrapped around it sits in one of the bigger cages. Mary tells them it's a pen, her name is Lucy and her wing got caught up in a rusty bicycle wheel in the Liffey. It makes a whooshing noise and tries to flap its wings. Mary says she'll release it as soon as the wing heals.

"Lucy has a boyfriend," she says. "Down the quays, near the bridge at Heuston Station."

She puts the puppy down and dries her hands.

"Now let me see your pigeon. Give it here."

She takes the pigeon and cuddles it into her cardigan. She rubs it gently and examines it for injuries. She lifts the wings and checks underneath. She looks at the feet.

"She's a little shaken. What's wrong with her?" she says, stroking the head.

"Nothin'," Patti says and Mary hands the pigeon back.

"I can't fix it, if there's nothing wrong with it, can I?"

"No, I s'pose not," she says and her brother digs her in the arm.

"Em . . . We can't bring it home. There's no room and our Ma won't allow us to keep pets. So could you keep it for us?"

"Well, I don't know . . ."

Mary bends to mop up spilt suds.

"It'd only be for a while, until we find her a real home."

"And where would that be?"

"Oh, we have a few ideas; we have this friend who owns a loft. It's just that it's full up now."

Mary thinks for a minute. She fixes loose hair from her bun.

"Well, I don't know. I'm very busy and . . ."

"We thought we might get it trained to do tricks and we'd go on messages for you if you like to pay for its keep."

"Well . . . well maybe just for a few days then. How's that?"

"That's dead brillo . . . I mean that's terrific."

The young fella in the flats wanted rent money to keep the pigeon and Mary said it takes time to train pigeons to come home and do tricks. So they decide to set her free. It's sad, but Mary says it's the right thing to do.

"Well give her a good send off," she says.

This day, she opens one of the cages and carefully lifts out the pigeon. Out on the balcony they say goodbye. The pigeon blinks. Her head bobs, like she knows what's happening. Mary opens her hands and sets her free. Up into the cloudy sky, she flaps her wings, over the chimneys, over past the library, over by the Four Courts and back to where she came from.

"It wasn't fair keeping her cooped up," Mary says.

"She'll find her friends again. She'll have babies. It's the way of nature. All the animals will be set free some day," she says. They stand out on the balcony until the pigeon is out of sight. Mary tells them Lucy's wing is healed and she's gone back to Heuston Station. She and her boyfriend are coming along nicely and she wouldn't be surprised if they have babies soon.

78

A BIG STRETCH

She took a big stretch. She'll be tall, everyone says and Patti hopes she's not too lanky like this girl Deirdre in her class who's taller than everyone else, and she has to lean over like a bendy pole all the time. They passed into sixth class. In sixth, it's supposed to be easy. You can do what you want. Nearly. Especially if you're not going on to secondary school. Some of the girls have left already, the ones who're already fourteen. She'll be leaving next year for deffo. She'll have to go to tech until she's fourteen. She might be able to leave tech and get a job. Some of the girls don't bother coming back for the last year, but they have to watch out for the school attendance inspector.

There's a secondary school for the girls who want to do exams and work in offices. She's glad she's leaving. She's counting the months and the weeks. No more nuns. No more long division. No more stupid needlework. No more crappy gymslip. She'd like to be out earning and give her Ma money every week. The others say that it's no use leaving school. Some of them want government jobs like the Civil Service. Imagine! Working in an office; tap tap taping on your typewriter. All day. This cranky boss telling you what to do. Piles of paperwork and files all around you. Years and years you'd be in school, like a big kid and no money coming in. All the books you'd have to get and the new uniforms and shoes. Tons of eccer every night. Bloody exams.

"Education system is right. A money making racket, more like," her granny says.

"And what would you do with all that education, only go off and get married and then what? A waste of good money I say. An extravagance!"

They started doing painting and drawing on Friday afternoons. She bought a few poster paints in Eason's and a drawing pencil and pad. Sister gives them things to paint. She places things on her desk, a vase in the shape of a fish, a plant or a plate of fruit. It's called still life. They do embroidery on white cotton doilies and a beige cushion cover she bought in Hickey's.

She's getting them. Horrible pointy little things. They're sticking out through her vest and they're like big pimples. She doesn't want them. Not yet in-anyway. She wishes they'd go back in. She'll have to wear a bra now. She can't go round floppy and all over the place like that, granny says, or she'll be a holy show. They give her one of Aunt Dinah's bra's from the tallboy drawer, a lovely lilac lace one that's size thirty- two. It's miles too big. It feels hard on her skin. At the back, it pinches where the hooks are. In the mirror she looks grown up. A bit. And you wouldn't know the bra cups were nearly empty.

"That's better," they say, but she thinks the bra looks dead pointy under her gymslip so she keeps on her school cardigan all the time.

"My God you look different," Vera says. "You're lucky you have diddies."

"I haven't really. This bra's too big, but granny says I'll grow into it."

Vera looks down at her own flat cardigan front. There's nothing really there yet, but she sticks out her chest anyway like she's wearing a bra.

***

Mini skirts are all the fashion. All the dummies in the shop windows have them on, all the fashion models in London and Paris are showing them off on the catwalks. There's skirts that barely cover your bum; there's skirts with belts at the hip and zips up the front. Everything is denim and corduroy and crochet. There's hipster dresses and hipster trousers and skinny-ribbed tops. It's all Mary Quant and Twiggy in the fashion magazines. It's white pearl lipstick and black Twiggy lines; it's deep blue eye shadow and tons of mascara. She wishes school was over. That bloody long gymslip granny gave her is a hand-me-down from one of the aunties. It's below her knees and it's dead hickey look-ing. It makes her look like a little culchie. She's not the only one.

Vera and the others are sick of their gymslips too. There's this deadly new girl called Jackie in her class. Jackie is nearly fifteen. She wears a stiff bra and little high heels on her shoes. She says gymslips are gone out with the button boots. She says gymslips are gross. Jackie's gymslip has a shorter hem, so you can see well over her knees. That's where she got the idea. That's where the others got the idea. Why didn't they think of it before? Jackie said it was no bother to make a shorter hem. All it needs is a scissors or a blade and a few stitches. At home in the bedroom, Patti rips out the hemstitching, turns the cloth up further and makes a deeper hem. She uses the zigzag hemming stitches she learned in needlework class. When it's finished the hem looks a bit wonky, but it's well better than before. She looks in the mirror. It's nice, a good bit up over her knees and her knees look dead funny, now that you can see them. Her Ma thinks short skirts are nice and modern, but she knows Da won't.

"Ya know him, he'll have a canary, so keep your coat on and don't let him see that hem," she says. What if he has a canary? She wants to say. What if he has ten canaries?

In class there's trouble.

"A dis greace! " Stani says, looking down at all the pairs of legs. There's five of them with the short gymslips. There's five pairs of legs. Five pairs of white knocky knees. She pulls them, one by one by the cardigan sleeve, up to the front of the class. She points at their legs with her slapper. She turns and asks the class to have a look. The class look down at all their knees. She asks the class what type of girl would wear a hem like that to a decent respectable catholic school. The class don't answer. There's muttering and sniggering. She asks again. Still no answer. Her face goes dark red, like a boiled beetroot. Her eyes peer out from over her glasses. Then she bends down and grabs like mad at one of the hems, then another one, then another one, but it's no use. She tries to rip out the stitches but she can't. Instead, she grabs a scissors out of her drawer. She holds it up, like a doctor at an operation. She walks back over, snipping the air with the scissors. She tells them they have to rip the hems out themselves. They have to stand out along the wall and let down their hems one at a time in front of the class. Dead slow, Patti rips out the stitches. Dead slow Jackie. Dead slow the others, until all the hems are down over their knees. They're all standing there with jaggedy hanging down hems, with bits of loose thread sticking out.

"The cheek of them nuns," her Ma says, when she sees the hem all sloppy and messy. When she has time, she'll go over there and give them a piece of her mind. When she has time she'll swing for that cranky staniclaws. For the time being, she fixes the hem back, but this time it's shorter than it was the first time, but not too short so they can't complain.

"Give them nothin' ta complain about," she says.

All of a sudden, they're all trying to mould her into shape. First her granny with the bra, now Ma is on about roll-ons. She says she'll have to get a roll-on to keep her stomach from going out of shape. She says if she doesn't wear a roll-on, all her muscles will go slack. She doesn't like all that stretchy elastic, so she won't wear one, she says.

79

A SILENT PROTEST

On the telly, people were protesting in America. They were holding up banners and marching for civil rights. They were singing: *We Shall Overcome*. They were moving forward, like no one could stop them, their arms linked together like a human chain. They broke through barriers and they chained themselves to railings. It started in one state and spread like wildfire to other states. They sat down in the middle of roads and the police used water canon and tear gas to shift them. Some were dragged away kicking and shouting. There were students and black people and women's libbers. The black people wanted equal rights, same as the white people, and the women wanted equal rights, same as the men. The women from the universities hung up their bras on sticks and marched through the streets. Then they lit fires and burned them in rubbish bins. No one can understand why they would want to burn their bras.

Granny says: "Them women's libbers have more money than sense. It's disgraceful burning good bras and the price of them in Arnotts."

Granny Connor had to laugh. It was one of her sneery laughs, like she can't believe it. She said: education brings it's own problems.

Aunt Jinny said, "Don't be mindin' them Americans. Sure they'd do anthin' for attention."

Her Ma didn't get the point. All she said was: "Women's rights is right."

Da said: "It's a sign of the times, but the world is in a state of chassis and the end might be nearer than we think." Then he starts on about the man with his finger on the button again.

All of a sudden people were protesting all over the place, in France and London and Northern Ireland. It's on the news every night. Ma says it'd drive you melancholy. The marchers held rallies and gave fiery speeches about civil rights. In Derry, there's rioting between the police and the marchers. They want better houses and jobs. They want, one man one vote, whatever that is. It's like the whole place is gone nuts. Granny says: "Leave it to them northern ones to start a fight," but Patti thought maybe it was time to get back the six counties we were done out of. Maybe it was time for everyone to march forward and fight. It was no use sitting down in the middle of a street, she thought. No use walking around with a bra on a stick either. When she thinks of all the stuff she should protest against. She'd like civil rights for her Ma, for all the kids. She'd like to make all the Da's take the pledge to the Sacred Heart. She'd like to free all the babies, who weren't baptised and got stuck in Limbo.

She was thinking she might do a silent protest; instead of talking, she'll write everything down. No one ever listens to her anyway. From now on, she won't talk. In the mirror, she pretends to zip her mouth.

"What're ya doin'?" Anna says.

"It's a protest."

"What's a p'otest?"

"Oh nothin'. You wouldn't understand."

"This is a silent protest," Patti says into the mirror. In the mirror, she looks back at herself looking at herself.

"You're a nut case," Jimmy says.

"I don't care. From now on, I won't talk inside this flat, or any other flat."

"If it was silent, how come your talking into the mirror?" he says.

"Because."

"Because wha'?" Anna says.

"Because the mirror can't hear can it? The mirror hasn't got ears."

Bernie just keeps staring with her arms folded. Anna zips her mouth with her thumb. Then she bursts out laughing. Patti takes an oath of silence in front of the mirror.

"This is my silent protest," she tells the mirror. Then she takes a vow of silence. She promises not to speak. She'll only write everything down. The four of them are in front of the mirror looking at themselves when Ma comes in like a mad woman and catches them.

"Get away quick," she says, dragging them by the arms. "Youse'll see Nick the Devil in that mirror."

"It's a silent p'otest," Anna says.

"It's only for civil rights," Patti says.

"Civil wha'?"

"It's a kind of protest. Like the black people and the girls in the universities on telly."

She'll give her mirrors, she says, and silent protests; so she throws a sheet over the mirror and pushes them all out of the bedroom. She says it's all Patti's fault. She has them all gone mad, looking in mirrors and taking oaths. She'll have them like herself.

That's typical! Patti thinks, but it's no use explaining, because her Ma wouldn't understand. All she sees in mirrors are devils. She writes everything down. She nods for yes and shakes her head sideways for no. Her Ma says she'll swing for her, but she doesn't care. Granny Connor says she'll grow out of it, like all her other peculiar habits. Aunt Jinny says she has to catch herself on, or she might end up in the Gormon. Uncle Willie says: "Go ahead, get it off your chest. Write it all down in your jotter." Uncle Fran says it might be her age. No one tells her Da. He doesn't seem to notice she's not talking, so he says nothing. If the protest comes on telly, he scratches his head and sigh's like he's fed up. Then he rattles his newspaper and starts to read.

80

FACTS OF LIFE

On Friday afternoons, they usually have hygiene lessons, but it's nothing to do with hygiene really. It's all stuff about modesty and chastity, about Adam and Eve and the forbidden fruit, about the evils of short skirts and crossed legs. Then they hear a rumour about this new subject on the facts of life. At first, they thought it was a joke. Then Sister makes this announcement. This day, she tells them, they are about to have a very important lesson on the facts of life. It's a new subject that's being tried out on sixth class by the Department of Education. She calls it a pilot scheme.

It's not long before the end of primary school. A very warm day and they're all baked in the classroom. Everyone has their cardigans off. Sister tries to open the windows, but they're stuck shut. As usual there's this awful smell of cauliflower and cabbage wafting under the door from the convent kitchen. It seems stronger today and Patti feels queasy. Sister looks nervy. She keeps opening and closing drawers and turning the geranium pot on her desk. She starts to walk up and down the aisles, in between the desks, so you can hear her heels on the boards and all the stuff hanging from her belt: a silver scissors, a bunch of keys, black rosary beads with a huge wood crucifix.

Jackie gives Patti a dig in the arm.

"Don't start," Patti says under her breath. She knows if she starts, she won't be able to stop laughing. Then they'll be streeled up to Reverend Mother's office. There'll be her red wingy face and her big wood slapper, hot on their hands. Jackie always makes her laugh, when she looks kind of sideways or whispers something rude or funny in her ear. Sister stands at the top of the class and blesses herself, with a big showy sign of the cross. They all stand for the prayers. She starts with an Our Father. After five Hail Marys, a Glory Be and a Hail Holy Queen, they sit down again. They start to dig each other as Sister drags the blackboard out to the middle of the classroom. Someone behind them is chewing a sweet. She mustn't know they can hear the chewy sound. Sister must hear it too, because suddenly she stops and listens. She puts her hand to her ear like she's listening for a note. She walks down the aisle again. She does spot checks. She watches mouths for any movement. Whoever it was, must've swallowed it quick. Patti takes a sneaky look behind her. Down at the back, the slow girl rocks back and forth like a babby in her desk, Gita sits up dead straight with her arms folded in front of her. Deirdre the tall girl is hunched over the desk like she always is. Vera and the others are spread out around the far side of the classroom. At the top desk, Patti and Jackie sit with crossed legs. On the way back up, Sister stops and taps their knees under the desk with her slapper. She makes them uncross their legs and sit with their knees together. She has a book open in her left hand. She starts to copy stuff onto the blackboard. She chalks fast and the chalk makes a squeaky sound that gives Patti the shivers.

"Jesus Mary, what's she writing?" Jackie whispers, with her hand over her mouth.

Patti shrugs her shoulders. It's not clear yet. She's drawing these peculiar diagrams.

"Holy God! Do you see what I see?"

They can't believe it. It's a long shape with a pointy edge like a carrot.

"It's supposed to be a you-know-what?" Jackie whispers.

"It can't be."

She keeps writing. She makes two small circles at one end. Then she makes spikes sticking out of the circles, so it looks a bit like two hedgehogs. Then she makes millions of dots in the circles. There's snorts and sniggers from behind, but Sister doesn't turn around, even though she must be able to hear them. Patti takes off her glasses, polishes them with her school sash and puts them back on.

"What next?" Jackie goes.

Then she starts on the other side of the blackboard. She draws a shape like a small pear, with two curly bits growing out of the sides. Under the pear, three smaller rougher shapes that don't look like anything much.

"What's that?" Someone behind them whispers. Some of the girls have red faces, some have raised eyebrows, but everyone looks puzzled. Then Sister starts to write labels near the diagrams: Uterus. Ovary. Anus. Urethra. Vagina. On the other side of the blackboard: Penis. Scrotum. Semen.

Jackie whispers something rude in Patti's ear.

"No it's not! It couldn't be!"

Jackie crosses her heart with her thumb and points down at her lap. Sister turns around, puts the book on the desk and picks up her slapper. She looks down at the class. Raises her eyes, like she's looking past them at the back wall. Then she starts on about family life and the sanctity of marriage and the importance of being blessed with children in a good catholic home. She says the miracle of conception is a gift from God. It all begins with a seed, a seed so small it cannot be seen by the human eye. She turns and points over at the dots in the circle. The seeds are made here, she says. Then she points at the pear shape with the curly things at the side, and the word ovary. The ovary makes an egg, she says. Seeds escape from the male and join up with the egg and that's called conception. After conception, a baby grows for nine months in the uterus. Sister keeps looking at the blackboard, like she's trying to figure it out herself.

There's something not right about it. It's like there's something missing. Patti understands, but she doesn't understand. She has questions that she can't ask. Maybe everyone has questions. How do the seeds escape? She thinks of the seeds in a pear if you cut the pear down the middle. She thinks of the big seeds in a melon and the tiny seeds in a cucumber. And the strange seeds stuck to the outside of a strawberry. You could grow anything from seed if you had a garden, her granny Connor told her that. They have to copy the diagrams and the labels into their jotters. They have ten minutes. It goes real quiet in the class while everyone is working. They all have their heads down drawing the facts of life. Then they hear a snorty laugh and that makes everyone else laugh. Patti sucks in her jaws to try to stop it. It's a laugh that starts deep down, like a belly pain, a laugh that you can't keep in. Jackie holds her stomach. Behind them they can hear the other girls tittering.

Sister has on her vexed face, but she says nothing. Instead, she grabs a duster and starts to clean the blackboard real fast. She rubs out the facts of life; she rubs and rubs until the board is squeaky clean. The part of her face that you can see under her veil is shiny with sweat. She straightens her shoulders. She tidies her desk. It's not home time yet, but she allows them to go early, because she's not feeling very well, she says. Outside, they look at the diagrams again. They turn them around and upside down. Jackie thinks the spikes are not in the right place. Neither are the circles. Jackie knows about all those things. Jackie is going steady with her fella. She's a bit mental but she's nice. Brainybox says that she was right all along about the seeds. Good job it's their last few day's at school, so they won't be punished for laughing. It's not like she cares or anything. Patti couldn't care less.

****

It's their last day in primary school, so they didn't have to bring their schoolbags. They're all yapping in the class. Sister claps her hands to get their attention, but no one is listening. It's like they can't be bothered now, especially the ones who're leaving for good. Sister's face goes deep red. She bashes her slapper down on the desk with a CRASH! And it nearly breaks.

"Those girls who don't wish to listen, may leave the room now!" she goes, but no one leaves, even though they want to.

It must be one of her speeches. She claps her hands again. Holds her head up high. "Girls girls, you must pay attention on this, the last day of your primary education. Especially those of you who'll be leaving us. I hope you'll take with you the lessons you've learned here with the Presentation Sisters. Lessons to take with you through life. Be vigilant at all times, never let go the values of our school and our foundress Maria Teresa Mulally and her successor, Nano Nagle. Christian values of chastity and modesty. Keep these values close to your hearts. Keep a tight reign on your emotions, steer clear of temptation and the sins of the flesh, keep away from bad company, cigarettes and alcohol. Don't fall into idleness or trouble. Beware of those who might lead you astray: remember the Garden of Eden. Never lose the faith of the Holy Catholic Church, pray often and frequent the blessed sacraments."

Her eyes go to the front desk. She gives Patti and Jackie a long look. She drops her eyes and looks under the desk. Jackie gives her a long look back, and crosses her legs on purpose. Her head goes up again and she turns back to the class. Jackie opens her mouth and lets out a long loud yawn. So does Patti. She can't help it; it's like it's contagious. Then there's' a row of yawns, across the three rows of desks. Sister doesn't seem to notice. She continues on and on, like the priest in the pulpit on Sunday. There's more about their foundress, more about chastity and modesty, heaps about Nano Nagle and tons about Adam and Eve and the Garden of Eden. No one is listening; they're fiddling with inkwells and pencils, like they can't be bothered. They heard all this stuff before loads of times. They know all about Nano Nagle and Teresa Mulally. You can only learn a thing once and then you know it for good. You can't learn it all over again. Every day, they pass the framed picture in the convent hall of the old woman with the scrunched up face and her bonnet tied under her chin. You could never forget a face like that. After forever, Sister finishes her speech. Then it's time for questions. When it's Patti's turn, she goes:

"And what about yourself, Padrigín. Have you work for the summer?"

As if she was interested. As if.

"Yes sister, I think so. A tailoring factory."

"A factory is it? Very well, your Mother must be pleased."

She must mean about the wages.

It's a bit sad. After the speech, the girls who're going on to secondary school stay sitting in their desks. The one's like Patti who are leaving have to stand out along the wall. Some of them are fourteen, so they can start full-time work in the factories. The others are supposed to be going on to tech. She know's she probably won't see some of them again, especially the ones from out far in Finglas or Cabra.

They get a half day and there's a big scatter to the door. Forty pairs of feet hurry through the hall. Then the lovely sound of the convent door banging behind them.

Such a feeling! It's what it must feel like to escape from Daingean or Letterfrack or Artane. She'll never forget that day and the last smell of the convent in her nose, and the smell of the convent leaving her nose. Outside, the apple and orangey smell of the fruit market, then the chicken smell of Cartons and then the fishy smell. And somewhere in there, the smell of ordinary clean air. She won't forget the light feathery feel of her feet, as they walk through the gate. She stands and looks back at the high grey walls, the crucifix behind the railings, Jesus on the cross with his chipped white face hanging down on his chest, the convent windows where the nuns sleep in their cells. She pities them in a way now, locked up and all in black, like so many lonely widows. She knows she could never be a nun, not even for God. She knows now what it feels like to be free. Near the gate, they take off their neck ties and bunch them into their gymslip pockets. They check up the hill and down the hill. They wait until the coast is clear. They do a quick over tumble on the safety bar outside the convent gate. It's the last time she'll do that. Jackie buys two Players and a club milk in Stephen's Cafe. The fat lorry driver from Cartons is at the counter munching a big fry-up. He has a chicken smell all around him, so they have to hold their noses.

Around the corner, near Cartons chicken factory, behind a trailer with crates of chickens looking out at them, they have a last smoke between them. There's three of them: Patti and Vera and Jackie.

"Could a chicken smoke?" Vera says.

Jackie lets on to give the chicken a smoke; she puts the Player up, than pulls it away. The chicken makes a clucking sound.

"Cluck off yourself," Vera says.

"You're a nutcase," Patti says.

They hang around for a while and tell a few jokes. The chickens stare out of the steel cages, their beaks stuck up against the bars. The cages are stacked on top of one another, like the balconies in the flats. There's a heap of feathers piled on the ground like a dirty carpet. The chickens make sad clucking sounds into the air; it's like they know they're for the chop. There's rows of these horrible smelly trailers parked near the convent wall. There's this close, sickly smell of chicken shit. Vera takes out a jellybaby and tries to feed it to a chicken. The chicken pecks at the jellybaby, then pulls it's head back in.

"Stupid fuckin' chicken," she says.

They cross over to Cartons where the green gate is wide open. The noise of motors and machinery makes them cover their ears. They can see the rows of factory girls with their white smocks and turbans. The chickens are hanging upside down. They start out at the bottom, go round and round on this pully thing, like a huge corkscrew up to a higher level near the roof. There's the live chickens at the bottom with flapping wings, then headless chickens in the middle, then plucked chickens near the top and then they disappear out of sight. They stand and watch for a while. A man in rubber wellies is shovelling waste into a big steel bin. There's chicken heads and feet and feathers in a big messy pile.

"Imagine, working in there all day," Patti says.

"You'd want your head examined," Jackie says.

"If we could open those horrible cages and let the chickens out."

"No way, them cages are locked. You'd never get them open."

"I had this chicken dream once," Patti says.

"Fuck off you dreamer," Vera says.

"I did. Someone let the chickens out. The sky was full of chickens. They were all over the place, the fish market and the flats, flocks of them flapping their wings like seagulls."

"That's tick."

They turn the corner and say goodbye outside Stephen's Cafe.

"I'll see yeah." Patti says.

"Yeah, see yeah's around," Jackie says.

They say maybe they'll meet up in town. They might go to the pictures or the Ierne Ballroom one Sunday. They'll have a bit of gas and hang around like. They see the back of Jackie, walking down Mary's Lane, with her navy knee socks loose down her legs, and her sash blowing sideways in the breeze. She walks with her hair bouncing from side to side, like she couldn't care less about anything in the world and it must be dead brill to be nearly fifteen, Patti thinks. The other girls, she'll see around town. Probably. The brainyboxes who stayed on at the convent might say hello or they mightn't. They might go all posh because they're in secondary school and she'll be just a tech girl.

In her Ma's back bedroom, she takes off the gymslip. She lays it out on the bed. It looks stupid and thick, she thinks. With the big scissors, she cuts straight up through the boxy pleats, five big cuts on each side. She gathers the long pieces of gymslip together. She bunches it all up into a navy blue ball. All of a sudden, her Ma is there in the bedroom.

"What d'ya think you're doin' with that good gymslip?"

"What d'ya think?"

"Here show me. What've ya done? It's in ribbons!"

"It's ancient Ma and I won't need it anymore."

The gymslip falls asunder in her Ma's hands.

"It's destroyed, but I s'pose it's had it's day, but gimme that sash and tie. They'll do for Anna or Bernie."

"This is for the chute," Patti says. "Bye bye gymslip! Bye bye convent on the hill!"

Outside, she opens the rubbish chute wide, throws in the balled up gymslip and closes it again with a BING! GOOD RIDDANCE! That's the end of that. She wipes her hands. She always wanted to do that.

81

A TROUSER FACTORY

Her Ma says she needn't think she can lie in bed all day, just because school is finished. Granny says she needn't think she can gallivant down town either. She needn't think it's a permanent holiday she's on. As if. It's always the same in the school holidays. It's dead boring running for granny's messages and working on her market stall in the Daisy, lifting heavy boxes of fruit and serving cranky customers. She wants a summer job. She wants her own money, like picture house money and dancehall money and money for clothes and makeup. You're supposed to be fourteen, but the factory owners will take you on if you're big for your age. In the meantime a few of them from the flats go around the factories.

"Have you any vacancies?" they say. It's the same at every factory. There's supposed to be plenty of work at the sewing. There's all kinds of factories. They make clothes, underwear, hosiery, handbags, umbrellas, and shoes. There's the match factory and the soap factory in King Street. There's William's and Wood's in Parnell Street; they make jam and beetroot and vinegar and sweets.

They try everywhere. There's no summer vacancies anywhere, but they leave their names and addresses in a hosiery factory called Glen Abbey. Then her granny has an idea. One of her best customers is a Jewman tailor called Mister Harris. Mister Harris owns a clothing factory in Smithfield. He'll give her a job no problem.

"He's a dacent skin," she says. "And you couldn't work for a nicer man."

Granny says he pays good wages and there'll be plenty of overtime. First she gets out her baptism certificate. She does a thing called doctoring. Where her birth date is, she does a thing with a magic white pen; she paints over the five and makes it into a four, so now she's fourteen instead of thirteen. She wishes she really was fourteen.

"Mister Harris'll barely look at it. He's a bit lampy like yourself," granny says.

She has to go to Smithfield for the interview. Granny gives her directions.

"You pass the Bridewell station, you cross over Church Street and turn right at the match factory. Up the top of that street you take a left turn. You can't miss it, a small brown brick place in the corner. Ask for Mister Harris. He's a proper gentleman."

It's a Monday morning. She has on her new shoes, the shell pink patent sling backs, with the little blocky heel and the button at the front. She's carrying her brown shoulder bag with her glasses and birth certificate inside. She feels very grown up since she left school. She's wearing one of Aunt Dinah's green plaid figured-in dresses with the crochet collar. It's a little bit big for her, but it's nice. There's road works in Church Street. Someone whistles at her when she crosses; it's one of those stupid wolf-whistles. There's heads sticking up out of a hole in the road and a spade throwing out dirt. She's mortified. She pulls down her dress. It's at her knee and it's a good job it's not a real miniskirt. She hurries past and pretends not to hear. The bloody eejit! He does it again, louder this time so everyone looks around. She turns right at the corner, passes the match factory and keeps going up the long cobbled street. The smell of matches goes up her nose. Outside, she can hear the noise of the machines, clankity clank a clank! Clinkity clink a clink, and the girls singing while they make the matches. Left into Smithfield. A car place across the road, called Linders, has shiny new cars for sale in the big showroom window. Smithfield is busy. There's bales of hay stacked up in the middle of the street, countrymen with caps loading up trailers and carts. Men are selling potatoes and vegetables from boxes on the ground. Up here the smell is strong; it's the match factory and Jameson's distillery and the hay all mixed up.

She sees it then. A dark brown brick place with dirty windows. She waits outside. She can see faces at the windows upstairs. What has she to say to Mister Harris? He's expecting her. She's looking for a summer job. She's gone fourteen if he asks. There's a glass door with a Venetian blind. She can't stand here all day. She presses the buzzer. A woman with glasses on a string around her neck opens the front door. Patti tells her she has an appointment to see Mister Harris. The woman asks her for her birth certificate. Patti opens her bag. She takes out the white piece of paper. The woman puts on her glasses and looks it over.

"Wait in here," she says and closes the door. The hall is full of cardboard boxes; they're piled to the ceiling along one wall. There' s a smell of something like scorching. The woman comes back and shows her into the office. The office is small with more boxes stacked up; there's a man sitting behind a desk with black horn rimmed glasses. He's wearing a brown check jacket. She saw him before in the market, buying fruit from granny's stall.

"This is Mister Harris," the woman says and closes the door.

There's receipts and loose papers all over his desk.

"Come in. Take a seat," Mister Harris says.

Patti sits down on the chair in front of the desk. This must be the interview. She feels a bit nervous all of a sudden and she wishes she wasn't in knee socks. She wishes she had the new pantyhose tights that are all the fashion. He might guess she's not fourteen. Granny said he was a gentleman. She knows it's a tailoring place, but Mister Harris tells her in- anyway. He says they make uniforms for the guards and the army. They export to England as well. They have a reputation in high quality tai- loring, that goes back a couple of generations in their family. He says they're very busy at present with a very big order, so there's a job for her if she wants it and a bit of overtime too.

"Oh yes, I need the job," she says.

He has the birth certificate on the desk in front of him. He picks it up and hands it back to her. He says nothing so it must be ok. Granny was right about him being lampy. His lenses are as thick as her own. He mustn't have noticed the five that was turned into a four.

Is she finished school? He wants to know. She tells him yes, she's finished primary and now she wants to learn a trade. Some day she might be a dress designer. Her Ma worked at the tailoring before she got married and her aunties are dressmakers.

"That's very good," he says, "but you'd start off here first as a clipper, then maybe you'd train as a machinist later on if you like it here."

He tells her the wages are three pounds ten flat rate and there's overtime if she wants it, and she can earn a bonus doing piecework when she's fully trained in. Three pounds ten! It's a fortune. She never had that much money in her life.

"That's ok," she says.

Then Mister Harris shows her around. Up a dark narrow staircase, into a long noisy room with rows of sewing machines, and girls in white smocks bent over them. Stacks of navy-blue and green cloth everywhere. There's loud noise from the sewing–machines and the radio is blaring. Over by the window, there's a long wood bench with girls sitting on stools clipping threads from jackets and trousers. They look up when they see Mister Harris. A long row of heads with hair tied back in ponytails. They look down and start clipping again. Would she like to start right away? He asks. She'd be able to go home for her dinner break. She nods. He leads her past the rows of machines to the end of the bench near the window. There's piles and piles of navy blue trousers covering the window so you can barely see out. Mister Harris lifts up a pair of trousers, holds them up and points out the loose threads.

"The girls will show you the ropes. This is Mrs Clarke, our steam-presser."

He points out a stout red- headed woman behind a pressing machine in the corner. The woman is wearing a flowery smock with the sleeves rolled up. There's steam everywhere. She smiles through the wall of steam and says hello to Patti. She's working real fast, like she's part of the steam- presser machine. She puts the trousers under lengthways; she bangs down the lid real fast with a Bhhump, so her arms kind of wobble. Then she lifts it up again and the steam makes a hissing sound. Her face is shiny

421

and pink from the sweat. She does the same thing over and over, like a wind up toy, and it looks like very hard work. She wipes her face with a hankie. Mister Harris leans over and opens a window.

"This is where you'll sit for the time being," he says. "If you need to know anything you can ask one of the girls."

The stool is one of those roundy ones you can make high or low. You twist it clockwise to raise it and anticlockwise to lower it. Patti hires it one notch, but she still can't see out the window. They're all clipping threads like crazy and the clipping sound mixes with the machine sound. Mister Harris walks back through the room and down the stairs. Someone puts a pile of navy- blue trousers in front of her on the bench and hands her a scissors. Patti takes out her glasses and puts them on. The weight of the trousers, when she lifts up a pair. She's not holding the scissors right, one of the girl's says. You're not supposed to hold it by the handles, you're supposed to hold it by the middle part where the screws are, but it doesn't feel right. She does it her own way first, until she gets used to it. She's a bit slow, but it's easy enough. You start on the inside. You clip along the seams, then the hems, the pockets, the waistbands, and the fly. A babby could do it. The same on the outside. There's tons of threads on one pair of trousers. She's raging about having to wear her glasses, but she'd never manage without them. She'd only cut the fingers off herself. After a good while her hand is sore. In the soft part between her thumb and first finger, there's a red dent from holding the scissors. She can see the girls watching her and giving her sideways looks. They start to dig one another and whisper to each other with their hands over their mouths.

"Hey slowcoach, you'd want ta hurry up, you'll never be kept on at this rate," one of them says, real smart-alecky, so she tries to go faster without cutting herself. She tries to get all the threads in a line along the seam. She can hear the others tittering. They don't like her. She doesn't like them either. They're rough girls from the southside, the kind of girls who always want to pick fights. She'll have to avoid them. She'll have to keep her head down. After tons of clipping, a siren sounds and there's a big scatter. They grab their bags and rush down the stairs. It's break time. Misses Clark the steam-presser tells her there's a canteen downstairs, with a kettle and cups, where she can have lunch if she wants. She tells her she'd better go home, because she wasn't supposed to start today. She thought it was just an interview.

Her back is sore from the stool. She's jaded. It's not as easy as she thought. She takes off her glasses. She walks the long way home up through King Street where there's no roadworks. She only has three quarters of an hour lunch break, so she better hurry. Granny wants to hear all about it. How much wages will she get? Is there any overtime? Will she be on piecework?

"It's three pounds ten flat rate. There's overtime and you can earn more on piecework after you're trained in."

She's delighted.

"I told ya Mister Harris'd take ya on. Now isn't that grand and better than hangin' round the streets and gettin' inta fights. You can dress yourself and your Ma'll be delighted with the few bob and you'll have money for the picture houses too."

"Here's the Baptism cert."

"Did he look at it?"

"Yeah, he saw it, but he said nothin'."

"Sure aren't ya big enough for your age and anyone'd take ya for well more than fo'teen."

She supposes she is big enough to be out working. It's true what granny says, it's better than hanging around, but she wishes the factory girls were nicer. Every morning, she starts at half eight. In the factory hall, there's a clocking machine you put a card into that reads the time you started. It's called clocking in. If you clock in late it's stopped from your wages. There's two tea breaks and a lunch break and she finishes at six, except when there's overtime and then she works until half eight or nine. You get time and a half for overtime so it's well worth it.

She's able to buy makeup and talcum powder and toothpaste and Mum deodorant. She hides them in the wardrobe with her Ma's rouge. She has to watch the kids, because they'd rob the eye out of your head. She bought eyeliner and white lipstick and a tweezers. She plucks her eyebrows into an arch shape. She makes a Twiggy line in the eye socket. She puts talcum powder on her face to make it paler. She buys white lacey stockings that go up high over the knee. In the factory, the days are very long. On sunny days, the sun blares in through the dirty windows. It's hot from the steam-presser and it's noisy from the sewing machines. Outside the factory at lunchtime, the rough girls call her names. Specky specky specky, Pippi pippy long stockin'. She wants to bash them and brain them, but she heard they're in a rough gang from Oliver Bond Flats. What her Ma calls: Targers. In her head, she tells them to shurrup. In her head, she hears her Ma saying: Shoulders back, head up, no slouchin'. So she does, she walks past them with her shoulders back. She puts the invisible cone of silence over her head, so she doesn't hear them.

Her granny thinks she's doing great, and so does her Ma, but she doesn't really like the factory. It's crap. All she does is clip bloody threads off piles and piles of trousers and jackets. Her hand goes numb from all the clipping and sometimes she just wants to get up and walk out the door, but the money is grand. She likes having her own money and she likes giving her Ma money. The only thing is, that she's starting to have this horrible dream every night. In the dream, she sees the piles of trousers in front of her, the navy-blue and the army-green. Gillions and trillions of trousers, clipityclipclip goes her shears, Bhhump! goes the Hoffman steam-presser beside her. She sees the guards with their baton's raised and the soldiers with their rifles. They're after her, with the unclipped threads, hanging off their uniforms. Mister Harris is there too in his brown check suit. It's because she didn't clip them properly. The bloody trousers. A gang of factory girls from Oliver Bond Flats are behind the soldiers. She's running as fast as she can. She gallops past the match factory and legs it around the corner. She stops to catch her breath at Saint Michan's protestant chapel. That's when she sees them, all the mummies out of their coffins and coming towards her. All the mummies dressed as guards and soldiers, wearing the navy-blue and army-green trousers.

There's nowhere to run. Her heart races. She tries to tell them. She can't say it, the words won't come out. She has to stop clipping threads. She hates the smell of scorching cloth in her nose. She hates the heat and the steam! That's when she wakes in a sweat. It's always the same dream, like when she used to have the dream about the man who was following her.

Vera got a job in some factory, so she hardly ever sees her. But this night, they get pissed. They're in the Ice Lane. They have Pepsi Cola and Misses Cullen's powders. Patti sneaked some of Alfredo's wine out of the cupboard. Vera got some of her Da's stout. They mix it all up.

Vera says you have to drink it while it sizzles.

They drink it.

It tastes crap, but they don't care.

They feel dizzy.

They're pissed. Patti is on her ear. Vera walks in zigs and zags. They're in the Ice Lane and it's lashing out. They're under the tin shed where no one will find them and that's grand because they can hold out here for hours.

82

SINK OR SWIM

She joined the youth club to meet new friends. They said she has to mix more outside the flats. It's across the road in the boy's school, next to the church. A leader takes your money at the door. It might be a woman or it might be a priest. It's not much inside, a long cold hall with long windows, a low stage at the top with childish scenery in the background, a table-tennis table, a high bar across a steel frame for gymnastics, and a rope frame to climb into like a monkey-puzzle. They do concerts and singing and stuff. She knows some of the girls from around. After the club, they hang around up at Kevin Barry flats and Constitution Hill. They go on walks to Arbour Hill. They sit on walls or just walk around. They talk. They sing songs. The FCA boys hang out in their green uniforms. They're not as rough as the flats boys. They live in cottages with parlours at the front. They have Ma's who wear twin sets and invite you in for tea.

This Sunday they went to Blackrock baths. There were a few of them from the club. Patti bought a new flowery bikini in Todco's sale. It fits her to a T, but she feels a bit bare in it. It's not like the Iveagh baths and the water is cold seawater, with bits of floating seaweed. It has a dirty brownish colour and it tastes salty. She can't swim properly yet. It's freezing cold. She's shivering. There's two swimming pools. A small one for kids with a slide and a big one for good swimmers. She feels like a right nincompoop going down the slide in her new flowery bikini. There they all are, out there in the deep part of the big pool, like a gang of girly fishes and there she is at the side and she wants to jump. They wave at her to jump. It's the girls from the club who can swim underwater and do back flips and swanky dives and everything.

"C'mon it's lovely," they shout and she wants to jump. She does. Really. She knows it's deep. Over six foot. Your feet wouldn't reach the bottom. There's little kids out there bobbing around like beach balls and she should be able to swim by now for Godsake. She's bloody big enough. Her Uncle Willie, the sea scout, says you always come up three times before you drown, but the third time you'd probably swim on your own. Sink or swim, it's called. She's like a frozen bloody fish, shivering there at the side of the big square pool.

"Go on for Godsake," one says out in the middle. She stands back and holds her nose. She closes her eyes. Ready steady go. She jumps in with a big splash. Cold water slaps her in the face. Then her body. She goes under. Water gushing up her nose and in her mouth. She sinks. Down deep. She stays like that. Still. It's all quiet. She sees legs when she opens her eyes. Feet and arms wriggling along in a doggy paddle. It's like she's in a watery cage with no bars. She comes up and she hears the roars and squeals of them up there. Down again. She chokes. She's choking. She's drowning. She grabs at the top of the water. It's no use. The water goes through her fingers. She tries to swim to the bar, but her hands only grab water. Maybe no one saw her jumping. Seaweed floats by, long yellow stringy things with eggs attached. A bit sticks to her leg. She can feel it twining round her. A jellyfish with light going through it passes. A hand then. Someone's hand reaches out for her. She grips it. It moves her along a bit. It's ok. It's a man's hand. Then another one; one of the youth club girls. She puts up her face. She takes a big breath. It rushes down her throat. It nearly smothers her. She can feel a bar now. She spits out water and pulls herself up at the bar. She stares into the man's face. She feels stupid and happy at the same time.

"Thanks." she says, when she catches her breath. "Thanks very much." The man says nothing and goes back to his seat. She looks at the girl from the youth club, who's standing there with her hands on her hips.

"Ya bloody eejit ya," the young one says and skips off and does a showoffy dive into the pool.

Ya bloody eejit, she says to herself. Ya stupid bloody eejit!

83

PARNELL ONE

Then the brown letter came to say she got a place in Parnell One. Big deal!! Her granny thinks it's a pity about her job at the factory, but Mister Harris might take her back on if she doesn't like the tech. Her Ma says she'll miss the money, but maybe it's for the best, because that school attendance inspector might track her down. Uncle Willie says she might do better than tech, but what good are brains in girls when they only go off and get married? Uncle Fran says he thinks she'd make it into the Civil Service no bother for a pensionable job, but she'd have to go back to school first. She's not going back to school for deffo and she couldn't care less about a crappy pension, but she likes Uncle Fran, so she says nothing.

Patti doesn't really care herself where she goes. She'll leave the tech when she's fourteen or maybe even before that, so it doesn't matter. She'll get another job then. She did an entrance test for Parnell One tech. She didn't really care if she failed. A bit of her wanted to fail and another bit of her didn't. She thought it'd be better to get a low mark. The ones who get a low mark can get away with murder, she heard, because they think you're dead stupid and they don't expect you to do any work. They put you down at the end of the class, like the slow girls in her school. Everyone says it's a right doss down there. The teachers sit around smoking and chatting all day, and you can come in late if you want, or not come in at all. It's a doddle. You don't have to wear a stupid gymslip; you can smoke in the toilets, wear miniskirts and have fella's. As soon as you're fourteen you do a runner pronto and get a job. Fourteen is the legal age for leaving school. It's handy enough because the tech is in town, so Patti can hang around and maybe meet her pals and doss. Everyone dosses now:

"Are ya goin' for a doss?" they say.

You don't even have to bring a school bag, just a couple of books and a jotter and pen. It's her first day. The tech is near the Parnell monument, up a bit on the left, facing the Gardens of Remembrance. It looks like a posh private school from the outside. There's long square paned windows and black railings around the front. On her way, she stops into Roche's Stores ladies toilet to do up her eyes. She does a black Twiggy line and puts blue eye shadow on her lids. She has it dead neat, the same as the mannequin's in the window. She has on her beige corduroy miniskirt and her bottle-green polo neck jumper. There's bunches of girls standing around smoking outside the railings. There's a queue in the hall. Girls are filling out forms at a desk. A woman is checking the names. The queue moves up and after ages Patti gets signed in. The woman ticks her name off a list and says there's a meeting starting in the gym-hall soon. She has a look around. It's all black and white tiles on the floor, a big staircase and steps down to where the gym hall is. It's nothing like the convent; and it doesn't smell of anything much except paint.

After the meeting, they're allowed to go home early. Patti sees a couple of the girls from the youth club and she's delighted she knows someone. Outside, they hang around for a while near the railings. There's a few young fellas in school uniforms talking to young ones near the corner.

"They're from that posh school around the corner, called Belvedere," one of the girls says. They walk to the Ierne Ballroom up the street. There's a picture of a showband in dark blue shiny suits on a billboard outside. There's another notice about the bands that play there on Friday night. Next Friday it's The Vampires. The other girls know all about The Vampires.

"It's great gas on Friday night," they say. "Especially when The Vampires are on."

They doss for a while in the Gardens of Remembrance. They hang around the benches, where a few oulfellas with walking sticks are nodding off. They walk along the edge of the ornamental pool with their hands out. There's coloured mosaic tiles on the bottom in a cross pattern. Out in the middle, there's loads of coins that people threw in. It'd be dead easy to fish them out. It's only about a foot deep and you could wade in easily. A gardener with a rake comes out of nowhere. He tells them to give over the messing or he'll bar them. One of the girls gives him the two fingers behind his back. They leg it then, out the gate, down to Moore Street. They chat to a few dealers and one of them gives them a Granny Smith apple each.

In Parnell One, there's different rooms for each subject. The sewing room is on the first floor. It looks a bit like the Trouser factory in Smithfield, with two rows of sewing machines up the middle. There's bobbins and spools of thread rigged up along the side. Mister Levins, their new sewing teacher, introduces himself to the class. Mister Levins is lanky looking with a caved-in chest. He seems very fidgety and edgy. He says he'll take them twice a week for the first year. They'll learn the skills of the rag trade, how to work a sewing machine and cut a pattern. By the time they leave Parnell One, they should be able to get jobs as machinists in the tailoring business. He's tells them he's from a tailoring background himself but he prefers teaching. He has oily brownish hair and wears a pale lemon nylon shirt and brown trousers. His fingers are yellow stained from smoke, like her Ma's. His voice is hoarse, like he always has a sore throat. He keeps raking his fingers through his hair, like a comb. He's a bit odd, Patty thinks. He puts on this creepy smile and he must have falsers because his teeth are way too big for his mouth.

There's two girls to every sewing machine. First they have to learn the basics, Mister Levins says. For the first few days all they have to do is watch. The first week, he teaches them how to thread up the machine; the next week, it's how to wind the bobbin. By the end of the first month, they're supposed to be able to sew two pieces of cloth together in a straight line to make a proper seam. Then it's on to cutting out. Then lo and behold, before they know where they are, they're making this pair of men's trousers. Mister Levins says they have to watch at every step and follow his instructions. This day, he has a pair of half made trousers laid out on the workbench. He marks them out with tailor's chalk. Then he holds up a small piece of grey cloth.

"Now no talking girls and pay attention," he goes.

"This here in my hand is a trouser fly."

Someone starts to laugh. Then they're all laughing so they can't stop. It's like that in Parnell One. No one cares.

"Girls, if youse want to work in tailoring, you must learn how to cut out and sew in trouser flies. It's a bit tricky at first, but once you can get the hang of that, everything else is plain sailing."

Then he makes the fly from start to finish. They have to group around him to watch. Up this close, he has a hair oil smell. It looks easy enough. He does a demonstration on his own sewing machine. Inside out, he places the fly into the trousers, he stitches up both sides, and then he puts the zip in. This is the tricky bit, he tells them. It's all about getting the zip to sit right. He fiddles it around until it's just right. He stitches real fast with the zip open. He makes it look dead easy. He clips the loose threads and holds up the trousers. He pulls the zip up and down to make sure it works properly. He turns the trousers right side out. He holds them up. He sends them around so everyone can see. He wants every girl to check it very carefully, because any day now, they'll be doing the same thing. One by one, they examine the fly. When it's Patti's turn she tries to keep in the laughing, but she has to admit, it's dead neat. The zip goes up and down no bother and she knows she could never make one so neat. Mister Levins says they should take note of how neat the stitching is, the way it's not dragged or puckered. Then he has them all making their own trouser flies on the workbench.

Later on they'll do zips as well. They all get a chance to be tailors. Patti can barely thread the sewing machine, never mind make trouser flies. She's afraid of the needle even with her glasses on. If you put your finger too close to the needle, it would rip right through your finger. She saw it happen in the factory in Smithfield, a girl had to go to hospital and get stitched when the needle stabbed her little finger.

The trouser stuff goes on for weeks. It's trousers, trousers, trousers, flies, flies, flies. All they do is make stupid flies. Even though it looks easy, no one can get the hang of it, but they have to keep trying. Her Ma always says, that God loves a trier. But it's no use. They all have crooked yokes with bokety zips, but that's ok, Mister Levins says, practice makes perfect and before they leave this class they'll be making a whole suit. And by the time they're finished they could be working for Louis Copeland himself. But Patti can't be bothered with flies or trousers or suits and she doesn't want to work for Louis Copeland either. Tech is dead boring. Mister Levins is a big sap. Mister Levins is gross. One of the girls says he's a big sicko.

It's true what they said about Parnell One. It's like the teachers can't be bothered whether you're there or not. There's no roll call, like in the school on the hill and the girls give backcheek all the time. They don't care if they get expelled, because that means they have more time to doss. They're even allowed to wear makeup. Patti does her face up every day in the jacks, but she has to rub it off before she goes home. Her Ma says her Da'll streel her if he catches her with makeup on.

During lunchtime, the teachers smoke in the hall and around the door. The different girl gangs gather beside the Parnell monument. There's some from Hardwick Street and some from Sheriff Street. They're awful jeerers, especially with the teachers. If a teacher passes they shout out things like:

"Miss, your slip is showin'," or "Miss, is that a perm or a mop up there on your head?"

The teachers pretend they don't hear and just keep walking with their heads in the air. They jeer people passing too, people on walking sticks or people with humps or limps.

"Hey, you, hopalong," or "Hey you humpty dumpty!"

They ask people for cigarettes and sometimes they ask the teachers.

"Giz a smoke Miss."

There's fellas from Belvedere College, around the corner and younger fellas from another school beside them. It might be an Irish school, because they hear them talking Irish to one another. They wear uniforms and caps and sometimes they carry hurley sticks. The girls jeer the young fellas with the caps. They chat up the Belvedere fellas and ask them for smokes. Some of them have fellas already. They stand in doorways kissing on the lunch break. You see the back of the fella, with his arms around a girl, and it reminds her of the kissin in the Ice Lane.

There's plenty of gang girls on the look out for fights. Patti heard some of them carry penknives up their sleeves, so she has to be careful. Everyone goes to the Ierne Ballroom on Fridays. This Friday, they have to queue up for ages because The Vampires are playing. All the tech girls are there in their miniskirts and knee-boots. Aunt Jinny made her this fab denim dress, with a hipster belt and front buttons. They saw it in Moran and Flynn's window and Jinny copied it exactly with the same material. Inside, there's a lemonade bar that sells orange and club milks and a cloakroom to put your bag and coat. You buy a ticket first. There's strange violet lights that make you look suntanned, a twirling silvery ball that sends out lighted yellow circles across the ceiling and floor. The boys are hunched together in groups at the end of the ballroom. They're wearing tweed parallel trousers and short jumpers. Some of the older ones are wearing dark shiny suits. The modish ones have their hair cropped on top and long at the bottom. They eye the girls up and down, and then they nudge one another like oulones. Under the violet lights, they have brown faces and pearly white teeth; outside, in the lemonade bar; they have pimply white faces and brown teeth. Some of them have underarm and bad breath.

The Vampires start a bit late. Everyone cheers when the lead singer comes onto the stage with a big smile. He has dark curly hair with a dimple in his chin. The youth- club girls say he's gorgeous and everyone is chasing him. His name is Tony. In the jacks, the gang girls send around warnings. If they're chasing some fella, no one can dance with him, even if he asks them up. They pass around his name and give a description of what he's wearing. They keep looking them up and down in the jacks and staring at them in the mirror. They wear pointy bras they stuff with cotton wool under skinny-rib polo necks. They think they're great, with their big falsers, but everyone knows they're not real. They're too pointy and lumpy and sometimes the cotton wool falls out on the dance floor. They're dead vulgar; they spit and curse and blow enormous bubble gum bubbles. One of them keeps practicing in front of the mirror. She makes the biggest bubble, then bursts it on purpose and gathers it all up again like a parachute with her fingers. She keeps giving Patti the dagger eyes in the jacks mirror.

She says: "Just wait!" and points at her with her long fingernails.

84

BLACK BABIES

"We don't know how lucky we are," granny says, hiring the telly up. "Look at them poor people with not a crust of bread to eat."

It's on the six o'clock news, a big story about the famine in Africa. There's thousands starving with the hunger out there, maybe millions. It's a famine, like the Great Irish Famine, but it's happening in a place called Biafra. It's the first time they ever saw so many black babies on telly. This field is crowded with them, and there's millions of flies all stuck to their faces. They have tents set up, so it's like a big campsite. They look out of the telly with their big sad eyes. The babies have big heads and black eyes, and huge swollen bellies like balloons. A nurse holds up a little boy to the camera; you can see his ribcage, like a sheet of ribs in Steins window, and the bony arms and legs like a skeleton. He's lovely looking but he's covered in flies. His eyes are half closed. His Mother has tears and flies in her eyes. She doesn't even bother to push them away. It's like a desert they're in. There's this English reporter with a white shirt; he says this boy will probably die soon, and thousands more will die of famine. He sees them dying every day, he says. There's volunteers and Red Cross people doing their best, but it's not enough.

It must be where they sent the black baby money. In school, they used to give money for the black babies; one of the nuns had a box with a picture of a black baby stuck to the top. She was always shaking it around the class, every Monday morning and especially after the communions and confirmations and during Lent. She always shook the box in your face.

"Help the black babies, help the black babies."

They collected silver chocolate wrappers and sweet wrappers and the nun sent them away and they were supposed to be worth money.

Granny Connor shakes her head from side to side like she can't believe it. She says: "Blessus and save us all."

Her Ma says: "You think you're bad. It just goes to show, there's always someone worse off than yourself."

85

A BLACK MARIA

She's in big trouble this time. The works. She's up in court. She doesn't want to go, but she has to. At two o'clock sharp. A stupid summons her Ma got a few weeks ago. A policeman from the Bridewell read it out at the hall door. It said Patti's name and her date of birth; it said she had to attend the children's court at Dublin Castle for a hearing, with a parent or guardian. Her Ma was deck-scrubbing the steps when she saw him standing there in his navy blue uniform like a big statue. She nearly died. She said he nearly put the heart crossways in her. It was the first time a policeman ever came to their door and she thought someone was dead. She knew they were all gawking over the balconies and at the doors. She knew they'd be all talking about her.

"Do you understand Mam?" he goes, so Ma tells him of course she understands, she's not stupid.

It's because she never went back to the tech. Her granny wasn't well and neither was her Ma and she hated the bloody tech in-anyway, so she never went back. It wasn't like she was learning anything there; she couldn't even make the stupid trouser flies, never mind a whole suit. It was just a big doss down there. She wasn't the only one not to go back, loads of girls never returned after the holidays. They thought the school inspector wouldn't chase them, but they were wrong.

After the policeman left, her Ma hid the summons in her pocket. Like a mad woman she was.

"That's oul Ryan," she says. "The nosey aul so an so. Bloody Dublin Castle. You'd think you were after committin' a murder."

That's the way she feels, like she's in big trouble, like she's done something terrible.

Granny Connor is minding some of the kids. It's showery; that spitty light rain that starts and stops. The court is between

437

Lord Edward Street and Dame Street. They start walking up the quays, they cross Capel Street Bridge, and go up Parliament Street. Her Ma stops at Sloan's Loans window. A sign says they have lovely new stuff just in. A man is fixing things in the window. He waves out at them. They wave back.

"C'mon, we'll be late if we don't hurry," her Ma says.

They cross through the slow traffic at the corner. She zigs and zags with the pram, around and in-between cars. Someone beeps her, but she keeps going.

"Cheek of them drivers, won't give an inch!" she says.

They're there at the big posh building with the flags flying on the roof. Patti looks up. There's two flights of steps at each side. Her legs feel wobbly and she has the bloody waterworks. Stupid bloody girly tears. A man tells them the children's court is around to the left.

Outside the court, her Ma tells her to put on her glasses.

"Take them out of your pocket."

"No."

"Put them on I said."

"Why?"

"Just put them on, that's the why."

She takes them out of her pocket. She puts them on. She feels like a big gink.

"Here gimme them glasses." Her Ma grabs the glasses. She breathes on them first; she shines them with her coat hem and shoves them back on her nose.

Outside on the cobblestones a big crowd is gathered; it's mostly women with kids, like themselves.

"Wait, it's not two o'clock yet. I've time for a smoke."

A woman beside them holds out her cigarette.

"Thanks very much."

She bends her head in close to get a light.

"Your own young one is it?" The woman asks.

"Yis."

"God bless her."

"And yours, that young fella?"

A young fella in short trousers with a very pale face. He's biting his nails down to the quick, and one of his legs is shaking.

"Yeah."

"Grand big young fella, Go' bless him," her Ma says.

"It's his second time up, so say a prayer."

"I will misses. Course I will."

"Thanks. Her first time is it?"

"Yis. That humpy oul school inspector it was. That Daddy Ryan. Daddy is right. The baldy article."

"You're tellin' me? An aul Get."

"Think butter wouldn't melt in his own mouth."

"That's a grand young one. Out working for yeah is she?"

"Well, she had a good job, in a tailorin' factory. Then she was in the tech. She's lookin' after her granny's stall until she's better."

"Nearly fo'teen is she?"

"Next year, please God."

"She's big for her age. Plenty of work she'd get, a grand big young one like her."

The courtyard is packed.

"Ma."

"What."

"C'mon, that policeman over there, he's lookin' over at us."

"Let him look all he wants."

They're in the porch then, under a big cloud of smoke. They're all smoking and yapping. The kids are charging around the courtyard. The young fella with the woman has on his confirmation suit; it's dark grey with a red V-neck jumper and a white shirt. He's very thin with knocky knees and a runny nose. He looks like he has the shivers. He's probably afraid to cry, Patti thinks.

Her Ma pulls hard on her Player, smokes down to the very end, until it nearly burns her finger. They're opening doors then behind them. The woman stamps her butt out with her foot. Patti wants to run out that castle gate, all the way to Alexander Basin, then all the way to England. The crowd starts to move forward. A cranky looking policeman packs them in with his arms out. He goes behind then to shoo them in.

"D'ya mind? You'd think we were Brown's cows. "

Her Ma wipes her shoulder, like there was dust there. The policeman gives her a look.

"Shurrup Ma," Patti whispers.

They wait in the porch, until most of the crowd are gone in. On the ground, there's tons of stamped-out butts.

Her legs are wobbly now; her bloody knees are chattering. Hail Holy Queen, Mother of Mercy, hail our life our sweetness and our . . .

"You'll have to leave that pram outside," the policeman shouts, real snotty like.

"It'll be robbed," Ma tells him, but he doesn't care.

"Do you know that's a genuine Silvercross model?"

He doesn't answer.

"The weight of that child,"

Her Ma lifts Doris up. She tries to hide the go-car in under the stairs, but there's loads of prams already there in a line. She parks it at the end of the line and puts on the brake. Inside, the place is a bit like a protestant chapel with a high ceiling and rows of wooden seats. There's some kind of a desk at the top, with a chair behind it. There's more policemen with their hats off, walking up and down. Her Ma has the summons creased up in her purse. She takes it out. One of the policemen is taking them and checking names. He looks at the creased summons and takes it up to the desk. They're all squashed into this seat down the back. Packed, the place is. Some of them are standing around the wall. Her Ma whispers into her ear that some of them are up for robbing. It goes quiet then. A policeman bangs the door shut behind them and stands with his back against it.

Patti says a quick prayer to the Virgin Mary. At the end of the Memorare, she says: Oh mother of the word incarnate, do not reject my petition, but graciously hear and answer me. Amen. Please Our Lady; please don't let me get sent to Daingean or Letterfrack or Artane. I promise I'll go back to the stupid tech until I'm fourteen. I promise not to mitch. She looks up the aisle. There's the school inspector in his long overcoat and hobnail boots, a big red face on him. He has the school attendance book under his arm. He walks down the aisle, looks into the rows of seats. Every so often, he opens the book as if he's checking the names. When he gets to their row, Patti tries not to look at his face. She stares straight ahead, like she doesn't notice him. When he turns she makes a face at him behind his back. Her Ma gives her a dig in the arm.

"You'll get sent away if ya keep that up," she whispers.

And then Patti has the waterworks again. What if she does get put away; some culchie place up a mountain and she won't see any of them for years. The kids'll be all grown up. They won't let her out maybe until she's seventeen or eighteen.

"Baldy ornament," her Ma says to the woman beside them.

"Wants lockin' up himself, that fella. Thinks I've nothing better to be doin' than sittin' all day in courts and a bath of washin' waitin', up to the ceilin' at 'ome!"

What if they ask her questions, Patti thinks? What is her excuse for leaving tech before the legal age? She tries to think of something. They won't believe the sick granny story, even though it's true. She can't tell them she worked on her stall while she was sick. They won't believe the polio story, either; she was thinking she might say she had a touch of polio, that's why she's so sallow in the face. Or maybe she has fits like a girl in the school on the hill. After she gets the fits she goes into a trance and she can't concentrate. They all got this horrible contagious disease in her family and they had to stay indoors. Maybe her Ma wasn't well. Now, that's not telling lies. Her Ma lies down when she's not well. Patti helps out with the kids. She could tell the truth and shame the devil. She could say she was allergic to convents and Parnell tech, to margarine on bread, to bloody stitching and to Mister Levins, with his bloody trouser flies. She could say she used to like hiding in the wardrobe, it was well better than school. And only the once, she mitched and got caught, by Maloney Baloney the big fat Moany.

In front of them, someone starts to cough, then someone else, then everyone is coughing and sneezing. Then it's noses being blown into hankies.

"All stand," a clerk in a black suit says.

Everyone stands.

Up the top of the court, a door opens and a woman comes out.

"Surely she's not the judge," her Ma whispers.

The woman sits down in the seat behind the desk.

The clerk says," all sit," so they all sit down again.

Patti can make out a pale powdery face, a jet black perm, and a black gown with big batwing sleeves like the penguins in the Four Courts.

"She has on oceans of makeup," her Ma whispers.

"Sacred Heart and his blessed mother. We're in for it," the woman beside them whispers.

"That one's a hard oul bitch, sent one'a mine to the Artane already. I think she's called a magistrate or somethin'."

Oh God! Patti has this floaty feeling all of a sudden. Everyone is floating: her Ma, the sleeping babby in her arms, all the heads, the policemen and the judge. A crow is cawing at one of the big open windows. The clerk is talking to the judge. He has some kind of a book they're reading from. It must be their names. First, the clerk reads out the names on the list. He says to stand up when your name is called. There's loads standing in different rows, then she hears her name; it's her surname first, then one of her first names that she hates; it's Patricia, her poshy woshy name. Ma digs her arm. Patti stands up. She nearly dies. She has the shakes, but she tries not to show it. All of a sudden, she's bursting. She crosses her ankles. She can't see any toilets. After ages, the clerk says they can sit down again, but the next time they call out their names, they have to come up to the front with a parent or guardian. There's more talking then. The attendance inspector joins in with his roll book. There's shuffling and coughing and the cranky policeman starts to walk up and down the aisle. He has a fat neck and a grey face with hard lines at his mouth and all of a sudden Patti pities his wife and kids.

Why is she here in this horrible place? It's not like a castle at all, more like a big swanky house that rich people live in. It's not just the tech she supposes. It's all the marked absent days in the roll book. All the days she was hiding in the wardrobe, maybe the big mitch. If they send her away, she might be a big dunce when she comes back. She hopes she won't be. She heard it's mostly dunces that go to the Artane. Or else, they're dunces when they come out years later, fit for nothing only Mountjoy. It wouldn't be that bad if they let her join the Artane band, but she thinks that's only for the boys. Maybe the other culchie places are not that bad, you'd have your own bed with a scratchy bedspread. Maybe they'd put on plays; maybe there might be a library and a garden. She'd love a bit of grass and trees. They'll teach her how to play the piano. She'll have friends from East Wall and Sheriff Street. They'll form a secret society. There'll be this nice modish leader with a miniskirt and a long jumper who'll take a liking to her. She'll let them smoke and drink on the sly. She'll miss the kids, but she'll write letters home to see how they are. Ma will just have to manage without her; so will granny. She won't turn into a little culchie. Maybe they'll send her to one of them places out in the middle of no-where. A mountainy cold place on the edge of Ireland, where it's always raining. It's a square grey building called Saint some-thing, with a high barbed wire fence so you can't escape. It has a crucifix in the front garden. A girl in tech told her all about it. Her big sister got sent to a place like that for mitching. It's not that bad, she told her. The food in-anyway. They get cornflakes for breakfast; mince meat and mashed potatoes for their dinner and boiled eggs for their tea. Yes, it's not that bad. Patti's bed is at the wall, there's six beds in a row with the grey blankets. The dayroom has a red shiny floor and pissy green walls. The leader gives them soap and smelly stuff to wash their hair in case they have nits. Hanging off the wall, there's a geezer that makes a farting sound and squirts out warm water and then it stops, like it's jaded tired. There's water in the bath from the girl before her and it looks a bit greyish, but at least it's warm. She hopes there's no hoppers there. She hates hoppers. They drink your blood like vampires. They'll make rosary beads and Saint Brigid's crosses. They'll . . .

Her Ma digs her arm.

"What?"

"Listen, will ya and stop bloody daydreamin' and open your ears in case you're name is called."

"Gerup the yard!" a redheaded young fella in front of them shouts and everyone looks around. The judge bangs down her hammer. Everyone jumps. The babby wakes up and wants to climb down. Her Ma shivers and Patti shivers and it's a line of shivers in the seat.

The policeman looks along the seat.

"Who said that?"

No answer.

"Who said that? Speak up, I said."

"Oh Jeysus!" her Ma says under her breath.

Now he has his baton out and it's dead quiet in the row. There's titters and laughs from somewhere. A baby starts to cry, then another one. The young fella in front stays dead still. His hair is shaved halfway up his head into a crew cut. His ears are those pointy ones, that stick out too far, like mug handles. There's more talking. The policeman marches up to the front and there's this horrible echo of his hobnail boots. Muttering voices then. More talking between the clerk, the judge and the policeman. The next name that's called out is the redhead's.

"Step forward please," the clerk says. The woman beside him grabs him by the arm, pulls him up out of the seat and up the aisle. The judge says his name again and reads stuff from her notes. "Are you the boy's mother," she asks. The woman nods. She tries to tell her he's a good boy really but he has bits missing. She points at her own head. She says he can't learn anything, so there's no use sending him to school is there? The judge says he got chances before. The last time was his last chance. Then she opens a book on her desk and reads out the sentence. She gives him two years in Artane. She says he might be moved from Artane after a few months as it might be closing down. Then she bangs down her hammer thing.

"I told ya, didn't I," the woman beside them says.

"God love him, he's for the boys band," her Ma says.

The policeman takes him by the shoulders, to a side seat, like a church pew. The young fella tries to make a run for it, but another policeman catches him by the collar. Then it's like this tug of war, between his Ma and the policeman, her with one of his arms and him with the other. She won't let them take him, she shouts.

"That young fella's arms'll come out of their sockets," her Ma says.

Then it's all over. They're brought out through side doors at the top, with the woman shouting something at the judge. The doors close and the place goes quiet again. Then they start reading out again, like nothing happened. Here comes loads of names from the list. There's a few more for Artane and a couple for another place they never heard of. Patti thinks she'll fly out that big open window, she'll magic up wings. She looks back, at the black door at the back of the court. The big policeman is standing to the side of the door, like a statue. If she was fast enough, she might make it. She'll do a runner; she'll jump on a banana boat and go to the Canary Islands, or she'll get the cattle boat to Liverpool; she'll go to the Isle of Man and never come back. When her name is called, she jumps. They walk to the front row, and it's further than it looks. Up closer, Patti can see the judge is wearing bright pink lipstick.

"Sweet Jesus have mercy," her Ma goes under her breath, but Patti thinks it's too late for praying now. The judge reads out her name again.

"Are you the girl's mother?" she says.

"Yes your honour," she says.

"Speak up!" The policeman says.

The judge reads more notes. Says her attendance record is very bad, says she's under the legal age for leaving school. She looks at her Ma. Has she anything to say? Yes she has. Her Ma asks the judge to go easy. It's her first time ever up in court and she's no mitcher and she'll make sure she finishes school, even if she has to drag her there herself. She's on about her sick granny who's destroyed with the asthma, she's on about colds and flues and bad kidneys and bad throats. She might make things worse if she doesn't shut up. Patti wants to say loads of stuff, but she can't open her mouth. It's like it's stuck shut. The judge looks like she's thinking it through. She looks up real slow from her notes. She looks first at Patti, then at her Ma. She says she hopes she won't see her again in the children's court. Then she reads out a fine to be paid within one calendar month. Ma says: "Thanks your honour," even though she's mortified about the fine.

The judge bangs her hammer down. Hard. They walk back down the aisle and it feels like she's floating.

"Snotty aul bitch, but still an all, I suppose she's not too bad, if she let ya off with a fine."

They're outside in the porch. They wheel out the go-car.

"Lucky it wasn't robbed and lucky that babby is a good child and slept through most of it."

She straps Doris in.

Outside, they see the Black Maria parked near the side door. A few women standing around the courtyard, sniffling into hankies. There's a brown van, like a small minibus.

"Must be for the ones who got sentenced," her Ma says.

Outside the gates. It's stopped raining. A nice clear sky up there now, over Christ Church. A little bit in-anyway. She's glad she said that Memorare back there. Yes. And her Guardian Angel prayer too. She might've got a year or two years. Probably more.

"We were steeped in there. Had someone's prayer."

"Yeah. And mine."

"Did ya say a prayer?"

"Course I did Ma. I said loads."

"We'll have to give thanks. I thought you were for the Black Maria."

Across the busy road. Lorries and cars; a horse and cart. Ma makes a go for it in front of the horse. In Sloan's Loans side window round the corner, there's this dead brill record player in a beige leather case.

"Isn't that lovely, "Patti says. "Vera says they're getting one from Cavendishes."

"Oh it's nice all right."

"Be lovely to play the records on. Wouldn't it. If we had records?"

Her Ma's head stuck to the window.

"Your Da. He'd have a fit."

"We could always hide it."

"Ha ha. No we couldn't."

"We could. Behind the bed or behind the coalhole lid.

"Did ya hear that? Down there."

"Where?"

There's this commotion. A parade or something. It's coming towards them; people holding up banners and placards. The banners are spread out across the road like big sheets.

"Bloody Trinity students, always on about something or other. Nothin' better to do."

"Maybe it's a protest. Look."

The protesters march down Dame Street. They stop in the middle of the road, a bit up from the Castle. There's roars and chants, but they can't really hear what they're saying. A Black Maria speeds up Parliament Street. The crowd gets nearer. They can hear drumbeats. The fellas have long hair and the girls have long jumpers and miniskirts. Are they Mods or Rockers, Patti wonders, but she thinks they're probably a mixture. Her Ma says there might be arrests, so they shouldn't dilly-dally. They cross the road. The Black Maria stops in the middle of the road and a policeman jumps out and shouts through a loudspeaker. He warns the protestors to move back.

"It must be a rally, can we stay?" Patti says.

"No we can't. Are we not in enough trouble without rallies?"

They cut through a side street onto the quays. Her Ma blesses herself and tells them to bless themselves at the church.

"Thank God and his holy blessed mother you got off," she says passing Saint Michael's and John's church. She went to school in there, she tells them in that little stone schoolhouse beside the church. Loved school she did, never missed a day. Her and her twin brother Michael.

"Good day's them were, very good days."

"Ma."

"Wha'?"

"Can we get Russian slices?"

"I haven't a smoke, never mind Russian slices. I'd love a cuppa tea."

"Crumpets then?"

"We'll see what your granny has."

Ikey, the newspaper man passes and winks with his one eye, shouts HERALOPRESS and sticks out a Herald at them, but Ma smiles and says: "No thanks."

Granny is up to her eyes with the kids. They have her place smashed up in atoms!

"Did she get off?"

"Course she did. She's here isn't she?" Granny nods her head.

"Thanks be to God and his holy blessed mother. Thanks to the mother of good council."

Has she any cakes?

She's no cakes, but plenty of bread fresh from Catherin's bakery. And she has tae. And would she hurry up and take them kids home for Godsake. They have her heart scalded and her head is splittin' and she has to lie down.

It's getting dark early, a few lights starting in the Liffey. A gusty wind blowing up the quays. The babby is gone asleep in the go-car.

It was probably because it was her first offence that she got off with a fine. Patti knows she could've been sent away like the others. Parnell One is gross, but she'll have to go back. She'll have to do the crappy stitching: trouser flies and seams and hems. The whole suit! If only she was fourteen.

"It won't be that long. You've only a few months to go," her Ma says.

That's like forever and ever, she thinks.

"Count yourself lucky. It could be worse. You might've gone for a long stretch with them other poor divils. You might've been joining the Artane boy's band."

Dear Diary,

Sometimes you think you're drowning. It's like you can't breath. Your lungs and your head are full up with stuff, good stuff and bad stuff, about babbies and hell and heaven, stuff about the nuns and the Atom bomb and the Russians and the six counties. I know I was lucky, to get off. The aul bitch could easily have sent me away with the others. The fine Ma has to pay will have to wait until Children's Allowance day. All I want, is to be free, to have my own life with my own money. I don't want to end up like Ma. I can't stop thinking about them, the poor kids on their way to Artane and Letterfrack and Daingean. I can't stop wondering what it's like there and is it as bad as they say. Imagine it! The hidings with leather straps every day, the brothers beating the daylights out of them and them homesick an all. Their bums and eyes all red-raw from the hidings. How they must miss their sisters and brothers. I have to go back to tech, or I'll be sent away.

Night diary. I'll have to hide you now somewhere safe away from them bloody kids.